TECHNOLOGY, INDUSTRY, AND MAN
the age of acceleration

TECHNOLOGY, INDUSTRY, AND MAN
the age of acceleration

Charles R. Walker
Yale University

Assisted by
Adelaide G. Walker

A revision of
Modern technology and civilization

McGraw-Hill Book Company
New York
St. Louis
San Francisco
Toronto
London
Sydney

preface

OST of us are both disturbed and exhilarated by such technological revolutions as nuclear energy, space travel, and automation. This book, like the first edition, is designed for all people who want to explore both the human problems and the promises of the machine age in which we live.

Each chapter theme has an introductory discussion by the author. The book is intended to provide the general reader with an overall view of the impact of the massive technological revolutions of recent years on the life and work of Man. For college classes the book is designed as a text for courses on modern technology and society. When so used, sections may be assigned and the theme of each supplemented by lectures and by collateral reading. Or this book may be used as a supplementary text or source book for courses in the history of technology or the history of science and also for certain courses in the social sciences. It may also be used to supplement other texts in the study of the individual firm and for courses in industrial sociology and industrial psychology.

For students in business and engineering schools it is suitable for a short—or a long—orientation course designed to show, through detailed case material and discussion, the relation between the student's future profession and the kind of society in which he will live. For such students the book provides material for both the analysis of practical problems and the discussion of larger social issues in the field of machine-man relationships.

Charles R. Walker

acknowledgments

fOR the ideas which have gone into this book, the author is indebted to a very large number of persons. To the scholars who have permitted selections to be printed here from their work, he is most grateful, and also for the helpful suggestions from many of them which went into the overall shaping of the book. For direct assistance and encouragement he is heavily indebted to his colleagues on the Technology Project of Yale University and to the Project staff. For ideas and criticisms over the years he is grateful especially to E. Wight Bakke, Franklin Baumer, Lloyd Reynolds, John Dollard, Neil Chamberlain, and Chris Argyris of Yale University; to George Homans of Harvard University and to Fritz Roethlisberger of the Harvard University Business School; to Charles Myers, the late Douglas McGregor, and Warren Bennis of MIT; and to Rensis Likert and Floyd Mann of the University of Michigan.

My wife, whose name appears modestly on the title page as my "assistant," is responsible for launching me on the predecessor of this book and for much of the research which has gone into the preparation of the present volume.

bibliographical note

THE selections and bibliographical references in this book are drawn largely from books or journals published in the United States or in the United Kingdom. References have also been made to the work of a group of French scholars who, for many years, have concentrated in this field. Scholarly research into the social effects of technology has been growing in other countries, and it was the author's original intention to include translations from the most important publications in this field for all countries, as well as bibliographical references. Lack of both time and space has compelled the postponement of this enterprise.

Besides the bibliographies that accompany each chapter the reader's attention is called to a useful "Selected Bibliography" published by the U.S. Department of Labor in the volume entitled *Technological Trends in Major American Industries,* Bulletin No. 1474, February, 1966, pp. 260–269. It is divided into four subject areas: "Technological Change and Forecasts," "Manpower Trends and Outlook," "Adjustments to Technological Change," and "Bibliographies on Technological Change."

contents

TECHNOLOGY, INDUSTRY, AND MAN
the age of acceleration

prologue to an age of acceleration

The gulf separating 1965 from 1943 is as deep as the gulf that separated the men who became the builders of cities from Stone Age men.   Margaret Mead

a N age of acceleration in nearly every department of man's life on earth was well under way in 1962 when the precursor of this book was first published. The eloquent words of J. Robert Oppenheimer had already begun to be true: "In an important sense this world of ours is a new world. . . . One thing that is new is . . . the changing scale and scope of change itself, so that the world alters as we walk in it." Since the early sixties when the earlier book came into circulation, new velocities have been reached and new areas of men's lives accelerated.

There are, of course, many causes of rapid change in the modern world. Armed and bloody conflict is a major one as is the rapid spread of old and new ideologies, including religious ones, into many hitherto passive—or pacified—areas of the earth's surface. But it is the assumption of this book that the most dynamic and pervasive source of accelerating change is science and the multiple technologies that stem from it.

The historian of science Derek Price has put together some hard-core data, helpful toward realizing this major cause of acceleration. He tells us, for example, that the multiplication of scientists has followed an exponential law, doubling in the United States every fifteen years so that we now have a population of about a million persons with scientific and technical degrees. A large proportion of everything scientific that has ever occurred has happened within the memory of men now living. "Using any reasonable definition of a scientist, we can say that 80 to 90 percent of all the scientists that have ever lived are alive. . . . Any young scientist, starting now and looking back at the end of his career upon a normal life span, will find that 80 to 90 percent of all scientific work achieved by the end of the period will have taken place before his very eyes, and that only 10 to 20 percent will antedate his experience."

A hundred approaches might be taken in writing a prologue to this age of acceleration. But inasmuch as our time, more than any other in human history, is an age of organization whose forms grow daily in complexity and vital impact, we shall study mainly organizations, as transformed by technology, and their increasing power to influence human lives. As this theme is still too broad to be enclosed, even in summary form, within the covers of one book, we shall focus largely on *organizations in industry* together with the men and women whose lives are directly affected by them.

This book is called *Technology, Industry, and Man,* instead of *Modern Technology and Civilization,* which was the title of its predecessor, for two reasons. The first is to underscore industry, which is still the major model for organizational structures employing modern technology, and the second, to put a new emphasis on Man as race or species. For it is not to be forgotten that he is the prime creator of all the sciences and all the technologies, and certainly the most important recipient of their effects, whether they enhance his personality and his powers, diminish them, or extinguish life itself.

In a suggestive volume on accelerations, entitled *The Great Leap,*[1] John Brooks uses 1939 as the "watershed year" between the past and the present period. The major changes reported have their root origins in the sciences and technology. Here are some down-to-earth ones, dealing with very personal matters such as a man's income, TV sets, and washing machines. Obviously, many more people look at TV today than go to the movies; a rapid and revolutionary change has taken place in communications media. The number of TV sets rose from virtually none in 1945 to over 56 million in 1963. Likewise TV programs have increased in scope and depth.

A quick way to grasp what the age of acceleration has meant to millions of American homes is to thumb through a 1939 Sears Roebuck, catalog. That encyclopedic volume contained in 1939 no items on long-playing records, no turntables with changers, no dishwashing machines, no drip-dry clothes, no tape recorders, no riding lawn mowers other than tractors, no geiger counters, and no TV sets or accessories.

Or consider travel. There was no overseas airplane service, either for passengers or for mail, until May, 1939, when the Yankee Clipper, a four-engine flying boat, started carrying mail from Port Washington, Long Island, to Lisbon, Portugal. It took 26½ hours with a stopover at the Azores. Passenger service began in June of that year with one weekly Pan American flight.

A useful summary of accelerations since 1939 may be given in dollar

[1] Harper & Row, Publishers, Incorporated, New York, 1966.

terms. Note first that population doubled since that year to about 195 million, and then observe these items. Disposable personal income rose from approximately 76 billion dollars in 1939, or under $600 per capita, to 435 billion dollars in 1964, well over $2,000 per capita. The average weekly wage for production work in 1960 was about $100, over four times what it had been twenty years earlier, but because the price index had gone from 42 to 100, real wages had about doubled, not quadrupled, between 1935 and 1960.

General Motors, largest of American corporations, reported net earnings in 1939 of 183 million dollars; in 1964, 1.75 billion dollars. During the Second World War, as we shall see in more detail in a later chapter, the government began to revolutionize its role in the American economy. It began giving massive support to scientific and technological research in universities and in industries. And it soon became for many corporations their largest customer. As a result it upset the old balance of power between public and private enterprise. These multiple revolutions are vividly reflected in the Federal budget, which rose from 9 billion dollars in 1939 to over 100 billion dollars in the next twenty-five years.

The sociologist Daniel Bell considers the "root fact" which enables us to comprehend the many bewildering changes marking off our time from the past the "change of scale in our lives." Using this concept, he compares the year 1789 in the United States, when the Constitution was signed, with the present:

> The real change of scale between 1789 and today, has to do with the number of persons each of us knows and the number each of us knows of —in short, the way in which we experience the world.

This is obviously a strategic phenomenon for this book, which is designed to study the impact of technology on man. Bell continues:

> An individual today, on the job, in the school, in a neighborhood, in a profession or social milieu, knows immediately hundreds of persons, and if one considers the extraordinary mobility of our lives—geographical, occupational, and social—over a lifetime one comes to know, as acquaintances and friends, several thousand. And through the windows of the mass media—because of the enlargement of the political world and the multiplication of the dimensions of culture—the number of persons (and places) that one knows of accelerates at a steeply exponential rate.[2]

The use of scientific breakthroughs to make possible worldwide communications, pointing now to a planetary human culture, will be fully discussed in the last two chapters of this book.

[2] From the original manuscript by Daniel Bell by permission. Parts of this manuscript were published in *Life,* May 12, 1967, under the title "Toward a Communal Society."

An equally dramatic but thoroughly threatening fact is the multiplication of people living on the planet—the "population explosion," due in large measure to scientific and technological breakthroughs, especially in biology and medicine. Here is a problem in social control as urgent and as threatening in its own terms as the obverse threat of a destruction of all life on earth through nuclear war. In 1850, after thousands of years of life on earth, the planet achieved a population of one billion. The second billion was reached in only seventy-five years—from 1850 to 1925; and the third billion was added only thirty-five years later, in 1960.

It is obvious that our age of acceleration brings new assets but also new debits to our way of living. Many of the positive gains are reported daily in every conceivable medium from the printed word to oral declamations at meetings of the Chamber of Commerce and many times a day in TV and radio broadcasts. Negative aspects as well are being broadcast by the same media: pollution, the population explosion, the growth of violence and crime in our cities, and of course the threatening peril of nuclear war.

The themes of this book, both positive and negative, as suggested earlier, are simpler but basic to our way of life. They are confined more directly to technology and industry and to the quality of living, both in the time spent at work and in that lived apart from the job. We shall find ourselves continually talking about yesterday, today, and tomorrow, for it is no longer possible to think of the "condition of man" in industrial or other organizations without being aware of the past which produced what we are today, or of the future, and of how rapidly the organizations and technologies of today are creating those of tomorrow. Major themes or threads which tie together the varied readings and the author's comments upon them may then be summarized as follows:

1. The theme of rapid change in the dimensions of work and leisure for nearly all participants in nearly all organizations, but especially industrial ones, is central to the book.

2. The overarching phenomenon, still too little realized, of what might be called the "new technological environment" in which we live changes not only man's work at all levels—and in all organizations—but the way individuals think about themselves and others. Put in different words, science and technology have created an all-embracing field of force out of which have come new evaluations of man's nature and his place in the universe.

3. As repeatedly suggested in this prologue, the speed of change creates in its own right, so to speak, new problems and indeed a fundamentally new approach to solving them. These include the basic prob-

lems of growth and survival which exist today at a new and higher level of urgency than in the past. Some time ago the author wrote:

Rapid change has now left most Americans a little breathless. So complex are effects of changing technology that they have overtaken mankind as problems rather than as opportunities. If men are to utilize technology for the good life, they will have to find a substitute for time, which in the past permitted the human organism, and the community, to adjust to the pace of history.

This book will suggest at least two substitutes for time: (1) systematic knowledge of human behavior under the impact of technological change, and (2) an assumption of responsibility by all parties at interest for the problems as well as the benefits of industrial progress.

4. Throughout, the choice of selections and what the author says about them illustrate another theme and approach. The selections for the most part are accounts of actual encounters between men and women and the technological environments within which they live and work. Nearly all of them describe and analyze the impact of that environment upon real organizations and real people within them. Much emphasis is also given to practical solutions, or therapies for human problems caused by technology. The authors of most of the selections draw their descriptions, analyses, and solutions from actual field work or from personal experience. There are selected references to writers of pure social theory, but few of their theoretical discussions are in this book. This is not to depreciate theory, model building, or speculative thinking in the social sciences. Rather the selections are mainly designed to encourage the reader to meet substantial aspects of the concrete world in which he lives and then move on to more general and theoretical reasoning about them.

5. The book emphasizes the meshing of old and new. It assumes that we do indeed live in a new world but that many of the building blocks were made yesterday and the day before, and that even the newest concepts stem from a long evolutionary development.

6. By pointing in each case to man, and yet dealing always with the technological component in his life and work, the book by implication continually asks three questions: What for today and for tomorrow can best be done by human organisms of hand, nerve, and brain? What best or better can be done by the Machine (the capital "M" signifies all non-human hardware and techniques)? And finally, what is the most productive and satisfying relation between the two?

There have been many statements, analyses, and exclamations of optimism or terror about the "condition of man" in the present era when the rivers of change have become torrents, but the fundamental appraisal of Oppenheimer still remains one of the most basic and challenging:

> *In an important sense this world of ours is a new world, in which the unity of knowledge, the nature of human communities, the order of society, the order of ideas, the very notions of society and culture have changed and will not return to what they have been in the past. What is new is new not because it has never been there before, but because it has changed in quality. One thing that is new is the prevalence of newness, the changing scale and scope of change itself, so that the world alters as we walk in it, so that the years of man's life measure not some small growth or rearrangement or moderation of what he learned in childhood, but a great upheaval. What is new is that in one generation our knowledge of the natural world engulfs, upsets, and complements all knowledge of the natural world before. The techniques, among which and by which we live, multiply and ramify, so that the whole world is bound together by communication, blocked here and there by the immense synapses of political tyranny. The global quality of the world is new: our knowledge of and sympathy with remote and diverse peoples, our involvement with them in practical terms, and our commitment to them in terms of brotherhood. What is new in the world is the massive character of the dissolution and corruption of authority, in belief, in ritual, and in temporal order. Yet this is the world that we have come to live in. The very difficulties which it presents derive from growth in understanding, in skill, in power. To assail the changes that have unmoored us from the past is futile, and in a deep sense, I think, it is wicked. We need to recognize the change and learn what resources we have.*[3]

[3] J. Robert Oppenheimer, *The Open Mind,* Simon and Schuster, Inc., New York, 1955, pp. 140–141.

CHAPTER TWO
perspectives: time, space, and history

INTRODUCTION

aS the relatively new sciences of anthropology and archeology have developed, the great importance of technology has been demonstrated not only for modern man but for man throughout the whole period of his life on the planet. To begin with one example: Of the discovery and use of fire, the first great technological revolution, Carleton Coon, the anthropologist, writes: [1]

> The use of fire is the only open-and-shut difference between man and all other animals. Fire was the first source of power which man found out how to use which did not come from the conversion of food and air into energy inside his own body. In Early Pleistocene times he made beautiful tools and brought up his children without it. In the Middle Pleistocene he used it only to warm his knuckles in the mouth of a cave. In Late Pleistocene times it made him a more efficient animal, and during the last eight thousand years he has found increasing uses for it, and burned ever greater quantities of fuel. Fire has been the key to his rapid rise in mastering the forces of nature, his conquest and partial destruction of the earth, and his current problems.

Of nonliterate man who possessed our earth for many thousands of years before the coming of civilization, Melville Herskovits comments: [2]

> By means of their technology, men wrest from their habitat the foodstuffs, the shelter, the clothing, and the implements, they must have if they are to survive. . . . The picture of non-literate man we draw from studying his technology and

[1] Carleton S. Coon, *The Story of Man*, Alfred A. Knopf, Inc., New York, 1954, p. 63.
[2] Melville J. Herskovits, *Cultural Anthropology*, rev. ed., Alfred A. Knopf, Inc., New York, 1955, pp. 119, 123.

material culture is of a hard-working individual who effectively calls on the skills he has learned, and that are adequate to gain him the living he desires.

The evidence suggests that technology has always been essential to human existence and progress, both before and after the dawn of history. But the time dimension emphasizes another fact of great significance, the incredible slowness in technological progress in all the early stages of man's development, and the astonishing acceleration in the rate of that development in later stages.

Sir Julian Huxley clearly had this point in mind when he wrote: [3]

The psychosocial phase of evolution is thus in its infancy: man, as dominant evolutionary type is absurdly young. I may adapt a simile of Sir James Jeans: If you represent the biological past by the height of St. Paul's cathedral, then the time since the beginning of agriculture and settled life equals one postage stamp flat on its top. And, unless man destroys himself by nuclear war or other follies, he can look forward to evolving through at the least the time equivalent of another St. Paul's.

Of equal importance with time for giving perspective to technologies past and present is the dimension of space. Prehistoric Man with his technologies possessed, it is to be inferred, only a few favored spots on the earth's surface. Today, although the situation is altering rapidly, Industrial Man still has not fully possessed the habitable globe. The dimension space, then, is suggestive, indeed indispensable, for any study of modern technology and its influences. In the field of astrophysics, the spatial dimensions of the universe have been expanding at a staggering pace. Space technology has now enabled men to enter interplanetary space for the first time. But even taking an earth-bound look, the dimension of global space has been vastly expanded by the modern technologies of communication and transportation and also by the rapid spread of every variety of industrial technology to more and more areas of the earth's surface. The incredibly rapid industrialization of the Soviet Union by the aid of technology is one of the miracles of the twentieth century. Perhaps it is only necessary to mention India, the Middle East, Red China, and Africa to suggest the growing importance of spatial expansion of industrial technology to the modern world.

Time and Space and their relation to the development of Industrial Man are given particular illustration by the selections in this part. (But they are very useful dimensions to keep in mind throughout the book and especially in the concluding chapters.)

[3] Julian Huxley, "The Future of Man," *Bulletin of the Atomic Scientists,* vol. 15, no. 10, December, 1959.

There are, of course, elements other than science and technology which make up a society or a civilization, and the relative influence of each is not easy to weigh or measure. The political system is one of these elements, religious beliefs are another, and the "mores" which relate marriage, sex, and family are a third. In attempting to classify such components of the major culture systems in Man's history, the Human Relations Area Files [4] have arrived at a number of basic categories. But from age to age, and between one nation or one culture system and another, it is obvious that there have been immense variations. First one culture component like war, or religion, appears preeminent in influence, then another or a combination of components. We shall argue in this book that in our own time, Science and its lusty offspring Technology are more vigorous and dynamic than in any previous age or culture system. Put another way and perhaps more accurately, Science and Technology have given our age more of its unique characteristics and coloring than they have any other age. They have done so by altering nearly all the basic components which make up the life of modern man, and altering them in important ways. It might also be said that our civilization is unique in that compared with others, technology offers a greater potential for either progress or annihilation.

We have discussed briefly Time and Space in broad perspective, and suggested that the reader keep them in mind in reading this book. Two new disciplines are flourishing which have begun to put both of these dimensions into a firm historical setting. They are the history of science and the history of technology. The literature in both of these fields is recommended to the interested reader, but since this volume is limited to contemporary technology and its effects, we can only illustrate briefly a few of the important ways in which the technological and scientific past lives on in the present. Out of a large and growing historical literature, selected references are given at the beginning of the section. Among them it is important to emphasize the pioneer work of Lewis Mumford in *Technics and Civilization, The Culture of Cities,* and other volumes, and the new and monumental series edited by Charles Singer and his associates, entitled *A History of Technology.* The several ways of evaluating the importance of technology to civilization are well set forth in the Epilogue to Volume II of this series, which we are reprinting as the first selection in this chapter.

This selection is followed by the composite of selections by Lewis Mumford to which we have given the title "Historical Origins of the Ma-

---

[4] The Human Relations Area Files is a system for organizing materials and for information retrieval for the use of scholars in sciences related to the study of man. It is sponsored by twenty-two universities. Central office is at 755 Prospect Street, New Haven, Connecticut.

chine Age." It is accompanied by illustrative excerpts from Singer. Although some recent historians have added new approaches and material to the subject of machine-age origins, Mumford's work in *Technics and Civilization* remains the best general introduction to the subject.

That past technologies and past technological ideas live on in the present is strikingly true in the history of the machine. But there is another point—and point of view—of great importance to our inquiry which is discussed in the Mumford selections, and this is the interrelation between the cultural climate of any age and its technological achievements. Before men could turn their energies or their creative imagination to producing an "age of science" or an "age of technology," a long period of cultural preparation had to come first. "Behind all the great material inventions of the last century and a half," Mumford writes, "was not merely a long internal development of technics; there was also a *change of mind*." [Italic added.]

He then makes an even more provocative comment:

> *Technics and civilization as a whole are the result of human choices and aptitudes and strivings, deliberate as well as unconscious, often irrational when apparently they are most objective and scientific; but even when they are uncontrollable, they are not external. . . . No matter how completely technics relies on the objective procedures of the sciences, it does not form an independent system, like the universe. . . . The machine itself makes no demands and holds out no promises: it is the human spirit which makes demands and keeps promises. . . .*

The group of selections called "Historical Origins of the Machine Age" begins with an analytical discussion of the question "What is a machine?" and makes important distinctions between tools, machines, and utilities. The reader is reminded of the strategic role of many technologies *other* than tools and machines; for example, houses, temples, pottery, roads and bridges. He is also reminded that certain ages which possessed high technological skills may have devoted most of them to art or religion rather than to commerce. Aesthetic materials, techniques, and skills are also technology.

The theme of a cultural climate which favors the machine is given special attention in the selection called "Ideological Preparation: The Wish before the Fact." The other selections are self-explanatory: "Time and the Machine—Authority of the Clock," "Monasteries and Mechanization," and "Leonardo da Vinci—'Compleat Technician.' "

The selections also illustrate the two dimensions discussed earlier, Time and Space. Between 1400 and 1700 the swelling stream of scientific and technological development was profoundly influenced and accelerated by both dimensions. Time ceased to be associated with organic or natural changes such as waking and sleeping or, in nature, sunrise and sundown, and was transformed into a mathematical—and hence divisible—entity created by the clock. This point is elaborated in "Time and the Machine—Authority of the Clock," but its full significance for modern men cannot be understood without uniting the concept of mathematical time with the concept of mathematically measured space. Both grew in the fifteenth and sixteenth centuries and together produced wholly new ideas about motion and locomotion. "The new attitude toward time and space infected the workshop and the counting house, the army and the city," Mumford writes. "The tempo became faster; the magnitudes became greater; conceptually, modern culture launched itself into space and gave itself over to movement."

The last quotation suggests a question as we move closer to modern times: What is the relation between technology and modern industrialism? Did modern technology create modern industrialism, or was it the other way around? Data on these questions appear in "New Ideas of Space, Time, and Motion: 1400–1700," and in "Technics and the Growth of Capitalism."

For any historical study of modern technology, there is no more crucial theme than the relation between technology and science. Most historians and many scientists are agreed that in important respects, the relation is today reciprocal. Advances in "pure" science are rapidly reflected in new technological revolutions. The phrase "science-based corporation" is a popular acknowledgment of this fact.

The mounting debt of science to technology is not always as fully realized. Without the telescope, a technological invention, the science of modern astronomy would have been impossible. Without the microscope, the modern sciences of zoology, biology, and bacteriology would not have developed. But the cases are endless and to be found in nearly every department of modern science and modern technology. One of the latest and most striking debts of science to technology lies in the fields of mathematics and physics. Progress in both is now dependent in part on the high-speed automatic computer. The computer in turn owes its development to information theory, and the researches of the mathematician.

The systematic development of new technical inventions out of the expanding stores of scientific knowledge only became conspicuous in the nineteenth century, although from the time of the Renaissance there was a growing interdependence. The abstractions of science began from 1500 on to furnish ideas to inventors and craftsmen, and the latter paid back their debts with instruments and techniques useful to the scientist.

Alfred North Whitehead comments on the strategic change in the relationships between science and technology as follows: [5]

The greatest invention of the nineteenth century was the invention of the method of invention. A new method entered into life. In order to understand our epoch, we can neglect all the details of change, such as railways, telegraphs, radios, spinning machines, synthetic dyes. We must concentrate on the method in itself; that is the real novelty, which has broken up the foundations of the old civilization. . . . The whole change has arisen from the new scientific information. Science, conceived not so much in its principles as in its results, is an obvious storehouse of ideas for utilization. But, if we are to understand what happened during the century, the analogy of a mine is better than that of a storehouse. Also, it is a great mistake to think that the bare scientific idea is the required invention, so that it has only to be picked up and used. An intense period of imaginative design lies between. One element in the new method is just the discovery of how to set about bridging the gap between the scientific ideas, and the ultimate product. It is a process of disciplined attack upon one difficulty after another.

The possibilities of modern technology were first in practice realized in England, by the energy of a prosperous middle class. Accordingly, the industrial revolution started there. But the Germans explicitly realized the methods by which the deeper veins in the mine of science could be reached. They abolished haphazard methods of scholarship. In their technological schools and universities progress did not have to wait for the occasional genius, or the occasional lucky thought. Their feats of scholarship during the nineteenth century were the admiration of the world. This discipline of knowledge applies beyond technology to pure science, and beyond science to general scholarship. It represents the change from amateurs to professionals.

There have always been people who devoted their lives to definite regions of thought. In particular, lawyers and the clergy of the Christian churches form obvious examples of such specialism. But the full self-conscious realisation of the power of professionalism in knowledge in all its departments, and of the way to produce the professionals, and of the importance of knowledge to the advance of technology, and of the methods by which abstract knowledge can be connected with technology, and of the boundless possibilities of technological advance—the realisation of all these things was first, completely attained in the nineteenth century; and among the various countries, chiefly in Germany.

In the past human life was lived in a bullock cart; in the future it will be lived in an aeroplane; and the change of speed amounts to a difference in quality.

[5] A. N. Whitehead, *Science and the Modern World*, The Macmillan Company, New York, 1925, pp. 137–292.

BIBLIOGRAPHY

Ashton, Thomas Southcliffe: *The Industrial Revolution, 1760–1830,* Oxford University Press, Fair Lawn, N.J., 1948.
Butterfield, Herbert, et al.: *A Short History of Science,* Doubleday & Company, Inc., Garden City, N.Y., 1959.
Cohen, B., and F. G. Watson (eds.): *General Education in Science,* Harvard University Press, Cambridge, Mass., 1952.
Coon, Carleton S.: *A Reader in General Anthropology,* Holt, Rinehart and Winston, Inc., New York, 1948.
————: *The Story of Man,* Alfred A. Knopf, Inc., New York, 1954.
Gille, B.: *Les Origines de la grande industrie métallurgique en France,* Domat, Paris, 1947.
Glotz, Gustave: *Le Travail dans la Grèce ancienne,* Librairie Felix Alcan, Paris, 1920.
Herskovits, Melville J.: *Cultural Anthropology,* rev. ed., Alfred A. Knopf, Inc., New York, 1955.
Horblit Lecture on the History of Science, *Harvard Library Bulletin,* vol. 13, p. 330, 1959.
Kranzberg, Melvin, and Carroll Pursell (eds.): *Technology in Western Civilization,* 2 vols., Oxford University Press, Fair Lawn, N.J., 1967.
Mumford, Lewis: *Technics and Civilization,* Harcourt, Brace and Company, New York, 1934.
————: *The City in History,* Harcourt, Brace & World, Inc., New York, 1961.
————: *The Myth of the Machine: Technics and Human Development,* Harcourt, Brace & World, Inc., New York, 1967.
Oliver, J. W.: *History of American Technology,* The Ronald Press Company, New York, 1956.
Oppenheimer, J. Robert: *The Open Mind,* Simon and Schuster, Inc., New York, 1955.
Parias, Louis-Henri (ed.): *Histoire générale du travail,* Nouvelle Librairie de France, Paris, 1960.
Price, Derek J. de Solla: *On the Origin of Clockwork, Perpetual Motion Devices, and the Compass,* The Smithsonian Institution, Washington, D.C., 1959.
————: *Science since Babylon,* Yale University Press, New Haven, Conn., 1961.
————: *Little Science, Big Science,* Columbia University Press, New York, 1963.
Sarton, G.: *The History of Science and the New Humanism,* Holt, Rinehart and Winston, Inc., New York, 1956.
Selected Readings in the Study of Technology and Society, 2d ed., Carnegie Institute of Technology, Pittsburgh, Pa., September, 1941.
Singer, Charles: *A Short History of Scientific Ideas,* Oxford University Press, Fair Lawn, N.J., 1959.
Singer, Charles, E. J. Holmyard, A. R. Hall, and Trevor I. Williams (eds.): *A History of Technology,* vol. 2, *The Mediterranean Civilizations and the Middle Ages,* Oxford University Press, Fair Lawn, N.J., 1956.
Sociologie du travail (Journal published by l'Association pour le Développement de la Sociologie du Travail), Editions du Sevil, 27 Rue Jacob, Paris, France.
Stover, Carl F. (ed.): *The Technological Order,* Wayne State University Press,

Detroit, Mich., 1962. (See especially, Aldous Huxley, "Achieving a Perspective on the Technological Order," p. 252 passim.)

"Technology and Culture," *The International Quarterly of the Society for the History of Technology,* Wayne State University Press, Detroit, Mich.

Usher, A. P.: *History of Mechanical Inventions,* rev. ed., Harvard University Press, Cambridge, Mass., 1965.

Weber, Max (trans. by Henderson and Parsons): *The Theory of Social and Economic Organization,* The Free Press, New York, 1947.

———— (trans. by Knight): *General Economic History,* The Free Press, New York, 1950.

Whitehead, Alfred North: *Science and the Modern World,* The Macmillan Company, New York, 1925.

1. ON EVALUATING TECHNOLOGY IN HISTORY

From Charles Singer et al. (eds.), A History of Technology, *vol. 2, The Mediterranean Civilizations and the Middle Ages, Oxford University Press, Fair Lawn, N.J., 1956, pp. 774–776.*

In our time technology has become almost synonymous with the application of scientific knowledge to practical ends. To us it seems that science is the source, the parent, of technology. Up to . . . about 1500, and perhaps much later, it would be more accurate to say that technology was the parent of science. But from the rather indeterminate period usually called the Renaissance, natural phenomena came to be more and more systematically observed. Moreover, knowledge of nature was ever-increasingly elicited by experiment, which is another word for controlled observation— a far more rapid and reliable way of extending knowledge. The rise of the use of experiment and the recession of empiricism from technology will become increasingly evident as these volumes proceed. In parting from this one, it may be well to glance back at the main technological achievements, almost wholly empirical, of the two millennia [500 B.C.–1500 A.D.] under consideration. Many different selections are possible, for each of which much is to be said, and perhaps no two persons would choose precisely the same set of examples.

Some would give first place to the process by which the forces of nature have been made to do the work previously performed by the muscles of men and animals. Thus regarded, primacy would be given to the mill, first the horizontal water-mill, then the vertical mill, then the windmill. It is to be remembered, however, that the development of such machines owes much to a growing mastery of the principles of rotary motion, introduced long before and especially to their application in the construction of gearing. The fabrication and smooth working of mills was facilitated by the introduction of several tools—the screw, the plane, the lathe, the brace, the pulley, and the haulage-tongs—the arrival of all of which comes within our period. The exploitation of new sources of power with the aid of such simple tools may be held to represent the first step in the passage from antiquity to modernity.

Or it might be said that man's prime need is for food and that therefore improvement of crops and stocks must take first place. On this view the change from the dry-farming of the Mediterranean area and the irrigation-methods of the Near East to the drainage-farming and deep ploughing of the heavy soils of the west and north made possible the development of the higher forms of technology in the north-west. A very important place would then be accorded to the improvement of farming-instruments and especially the development of the plough, which opened up northern and western Europe to the possibilities of civilization.

Yet again, since techniques can have no permanent frontiers, every-thing that increased means of communication, and especially of trans-port, must have hastened the spread of local devices into wider cultural areas. This line of thought would stress many of the ideas and inventions that have spread from east Asia to west Europe, such as the wheelbarrow, deep drilling, cast iron, lock gates, gimbals, paper, printing, and so on. It would emphasize the importance of the mechanisms of the intercom-munication of peoples, such as made roads, passenger-vehicles, the in-troduction of horses and camels, draught with the horse-collar, advances in the wheelwright's craft, and perhaps above all improvements in ship-building and navigation.

There is surely a case for judging a civilization by its use of such social surplus as is at the disposal of the favoured few for the lofty purposes of art and literature. This, in a history of technology, would lead to stress on the techniques of the fine arts, such as those of the golden age of Greece with its architecture and sculpture, and of fifteenth-century Italy with its pictorial art and its beginnings of modern science. It would emphasize too the amenities of life introduced by glazing and by blown glass, by paper, parchment, printing, and the luxury of figured weaves. Such a judgement would give less attention to the mechanical advances of the Middle Ages and make the change to modernity rather later than is im-plied in these volumes.

Others, thinking backward from our time, would see in the period we have here considered the beginnings of types of manufacture character-istic of modern industry. They would attach great importance to metal-lurgy, specially to the introduction of case-hardened steel and to the newer alloys of copper, notably brass. They would also lay emphasis on the preparation on an industrial scale of substances that include many of those nowadays of prime industrial importance, such as alkalis, pig-ments and dyes, nitre, alum, soap, and alcohol.

Yet others would claim the prevalence of the scientific mood as the test of modern civilization, since its diffusion has determined the course of our lives today. They would therefore give much attention to instruments of precision in antiquity, to the variety of ingenious and skilfully made measures of time, and notably to the astrolabe. For them the rise of modern science, and, following it, of scientific technology, would be a continuation, *longo intervallo*, of the science of the ancients. On this view, modernity would perhaps begin in the seventeenth century. . . .

All these, and many other, ways of contemplating the technology of the past have had their advocates. On each of these ways many books have been written. But the work now before the reader has been put together in a spirit that takes none of these views. It seeks to present what seem to the authors and editors the salient facts arranged in the best sequence that they have been able to devise, and with that very high degree of condensation of a vast mass of material that is demanded even by these portly volumes. When their task is complete there may emerge a clearer interrelationship of the techniques to each other and to the cultures in which they have arisen. Until that broad view can be taken we must be content to know that techniques, like those who practise them, are all parts one of another, and that we live in a world the unity of which can emerge only very slowly. This may be a hard saying, but it is the way and method of science.

2. HISTORICAL ORIGINS OF THE MACHINE AGE

a. What is a machine?: tools, machines, and utilities defined

From Lewis Mumford, Technics and Civilization, *Harcourt, Brace and Company, New York, 1934, pp. 9–12.*

During the last century the automatic or semi-automatic machine has come to occupy a large place in our daily routine; and we have tended to attribute to the physical instrument itself the whole complex of habits and methods that created it and accompanied it. Almost every discussion of technology from Marx onward has tended to overemphasize the part played by the more mobile and active parts of our industrial equipment, and has slighted other equally critical elements in our technical heritage. . . .

The essential distinction between a machine and a tool lies in the degree of independence in the operation from the skill and motive power of the operator; the tool lends itself to manipulation, the machine to automatic action. The degree of complexity is unimportant: for, using the tool, the human hand and eye perform complicated actions which are the equivalent, in function, of a well developed machine; while, on the other hand, there are highly effective machines, like the drop hammer, which do very simple tasks, with the aid of a relatively simple mechanism. The difference between tools and machines lies primarily in the degree of automatism they have reached: the skilled tool-user becomes more accurate and more automatic; in short, more mechanical, as his originally voluntary motions settle down into reflexes, and on the other hand, even in the most completely automatic machine, there must intervene somewhere, at the beginning and the end of the process, first in the original design, and finally in the ability to overcome defects and to make repairs, the conscious participation of a human agent.

Moreover, between the tool and the machine there stands another class of objects, the machine-tool: here, in the lathe or the drill, one has the accuracy of the finest machine coupled with the skilled attendance of the workman. When one adds to this mechanical complex an external source of power, the line of division becomes even more difficult to establish. In general, the machine emphasizes specialization of function, whereas the tool indicates flexibility: a planing machine performs only one operation, whereas a knife can be used to smooth wood, to carve it, to split it, or to pry open a lock, or to drive in a screw. The automatic machine, then, is a very specialized kind of adaptation; it involves the notion of an external source of power, a more or less complicated interrelation of parts, and a limited kind of activity. From the beginning the machine was a sort of minor organism, designed to perform a single set of functions.

Along with these dynamic elements in technology there is another set, more static in character, but equally important in function. While the growth of machines is the most patent technical fact of the last thousand years, the machine, in the form of the fire-drill or the potter's wheel, has been in existence since at least neolithic times. During the earlier period, some of the most effective adaptations of the environment came, not from the invention of machines, but from the equally admirable invention of utensils, apparatus, and utilities. The basket and the pot stand for the first, the dye vat and the brick kiln stand for the second, and reservoirs and aqueducts and roads and buildings belong to the third class. The modern period has finally given us the power utility, like the railroad track or the electric transmission line, which functions only through the operation of power machinery. While tools and machines transform the environment by changing the shape and location of objects, utensils and apparatus have been used to effect equally necessary chemical transformations. Tanning, brewing, distilling, dyeing have been as important in man's technical development as smithing or weaving. But most of these processes remained in their traditional state till the middle of the nineteenth century, and it is only since then that they have been influenced in any large degree by the same set of scientific forces and human interests that were developing the modern power-machine.

In the series of objects from utensils to utilities there is the same relation between the workman and the process that one notes in the series between tools and automatic machines: differences in the degree of specialization, the degree of impersonality. But since people's attention is directed most easily to the noisier and more active parts of the environment, the role of the utility and the apparatus has been neglected in most discussions of the machine, or, what is almost as bad, these technical instruments have all been clumsily grouped as machines. The point to remember is that both have played an enormous part in the development of the modern environment; and at no stage in history can the two means of adaptation be split apart. Every technological complex includes both: not least our modern one.

When I use the word machines hereafter I shall refer to specific objects like the printing press or the power loom. When I use the term "the machine" I shall employ it as a shorthand reference to the entire technological complex. This will embrace the knowledge and skills and arts derived from industry or implicated in the new technics, and will include various forms of tool, instrument, apparatus, and utility as well as machine proper.

b. Ideological preparation: the wish before the fact

From Lewis Mumford, op. cit., pp. 3–7.

During the last thousand years the material basis and the cultural forms of Western Civilization have been profoundly modified by the development of the machine. How did this come about? Where did it take place? What were the chief motives that encouraged this radical transformation of the environment and the routine of life: what were the ends in view; what were the means and methods: what unexpected values have arisen in the process? These are some of the questions that the present study seeks to answer.

While people often call our period the "Machine Age," very few have any perspective on modern technics or any clear notion as to its origins. Popular historians usually date the great transformation in modern industry from Watt's supposed invention of the steam engine; and in the conventional economics textbook the application of automatic machinery to spinning and weaving is often treated as an equally critical turning point. But the fact is that in Western Europe the machine had been developing steadily for at least seven centuries before the dramatic changes that accompanied the "industrial revolution" took place. Men had become mechanical before they perfected complicated machines to express their new bent and interest; and the will-to-order had appeared once more in the monastery and the army and the counting-house before it finally manifested itself in the factory. Behind all the great material inventions of the last century and a half was not merely a long internal development of technics; there was also a change of mind. Before the new industrial processes could take hold on a great scale, a reorientation of wishes, habits, ideas, goals was necessary.

To understand the dominating role played by technics in modern civilization, one must explore in detail the preliminary period of ideological and social preparation. Not merely must one explain the existence of the new mechanical instruments: one must explain the culture that was ready to use them and profit by them so extensively. For note this: mechanization and regimentation are not new phenomena in history: what is new is the fact that these functions have been projected and embodied in organized forms which dominate every aspect of our existence. Other civilizations reached a high degree of technical proficiency without, apparently, being profoundly influenced by the methods and aims of technics. All the critical instruments of modern technology—the clock, the printing press, the water-mill, the magnetic compass, the loom, the lathe, gunpowder, paper, to say nothing of mathematics and chemistry and mechanics—existed in other cultures. The Chinese, the Arabs, the Greeks, long before the Northern European had taken most of the first steps toward the machine. And although the great engineering works of the Cretans, the Egyptians, and the Romans were carried out mainly on an empirical basis, these peoples plainly had an abundance of technical skill at their command. They had machines; but they did not develop "the machine." It remained for the peoples of Western Europe to carry the physical sciences and the exact arts to a point no other culture had reached, and to adapt the whole mode of life to the pace and the capacities of the machine. How did this happen? How in fact could the machine take possession of European society until that society had, by an inner accommodation, surrendered to the machine?

Plainly, what is usually called *the* industrial revolution, the series of industrial changes that began in the eighteenth century, was a transformation that took place in the course of a much longer march.

Technics and civilization as a whole are the result of human choices and aptitudes and strivings, deliberate as well as unconscious, often irrational when apparently they are most objective and scientific: but even when they are uncontrollable they are not external. Choice manifests itself in society in small increments and moment-to-moment decisions as well as loud dramatic struggles; and he who does not see his choice in the development of the machine merely betrays his incapacity to observe cumulative effects until they are bunched together so closely that they seem completely external and impersonal. No matter how completely technics relies upon the objective procedures of the sciences, it does not form an independent system, like the universe: it exists as an element in human culture and it promises well or ill as the social groups that exploit it promise well or ill. The machine itself makes no demands and holds out no promises: it is the human spirit that makes demands and keeps promises. In order to reconquer the machine and subdue it to human purposes, one must first understand it and assimilate it. So far, we have embraced the machine without fully understanding it, or, like the weaker romantics, we have rejected the machine without first seeing how much of it we could intelligently assimilate.

c. Time and the machine: authority of the clock
From Lewis Mumford, op. cit., pp. 12–18.

Where did the machine first take form in modern civilization? There was plainly more than one point of origin. Our mechanical civilization represents the convergence of numerous habits, ideas, and modes of living, as well as technical instruments; and some of these were, in the beginning, directly opposed to the civilization they helped to create. But the first manifestation of the new order took place in the general picture of the world: during the first seven centuries of the machine's existence the categories of time and space underwent an extraordinary change, and no aspect of life was left untouched by this transformation. The application of quantitative methods of thought to the study of nature had its first manifestation in the regular measurement of time; and the new mechanical conception of time arose in part out of the routine of the monastery. Alfred Whitehead has emphasized the importance of the scholastic belief in a universe ordered by God as one of the foundations of modern physics; but behind that belief was the presence of order in the institutions of the Church itself.

The technics of the ancient world were still carried on from Constantinople and Baghdad to Sicily and Cordova: hence the early lead taken by Salerno in the scientific and medical advances of the Middle Ages. It was, however, in the monasteries of the West that the desire for order and power, other than that expressed in the military domination of weaker men, first manifested itself after the long uncertainty and bloody confusion that attended the breakdown of the Roman Empire. Within the walls of the monastery was sanctuary: under the rule of the order surprise and doubt and caprice and irregularity were put at bay. Opposed to the erratic fluctuations and pulsations of the worldly life was the iron discipline of the rule. Benedict added a seventh period to the devotions of the day, and in the seventh century, by a bull of Pope Sabinianus, it was decreed that the bells of the monastery be rung seven times in the twenty-four hours. These punctuation marks in the day were known as the canonical hours, and some means of keeping count of them and ensuring their regular repetition became necessary.

According to a now discredited legend, the first modern mechanical clock, worked by falling weights, was invented by the monk named Gilbert who afterwards became Pope Sylvester II near the close of the tenth century. This clock was probably only a water clock, one of those bequests of the ancient world either left over directly from the days of the Romans like the water-wheel itself, or coming back again into the West through the Arabs. But the legend, as so often happens, is accurate in its implications if not in its facts. The monastery was the seat of a regular life, and an instrument for striking the hours at intervals or for reminding the bell-ringer that it was time to strike the bells, was an almost inevitable product of this life. If the mechanical clock did not appear until the cities of the thirteenth century demanded an orderly routine, the habit of order itself and the earnest regulation of time-sequences had become almost second nature in the monastery. Coulton agrees with Sombart in looking upon the Benedictines, the great working order, as perhaps the original founders of modern capitalism: their rule certainly took the curse off work and their vigorous engineering enterprises may even have robbed warfare of some of its glamor. So one is not straining the facts when one suggests that the monasteries—at one time there were 40,000 under the Benedictine rule—helped to give human enterprise the regular collective beat and rhythm of the machine; for the clock is not merely a means of keeping track of the hours, but of synchronizing the actions of men.

Was it by reason of the collective Christian desire to provide for the welfare of souls in eternity by regular prayers and devotions that time-keeping and the habits of temporal order took hold of men's minds: habits that capitalist civilization presently turned to good account? One must perhaps accept the irony of this paradox. At all events, by the thirteenth century there are definite records of mechanical clocks, and by 1370 a well-designed "modern" clock had been built by Heinrich von Wyck at Paris. Meanwhile, bell towers had come into existence, and the new clocks, if they did not have, till the fourteenth century, a dial and a hand that translated the movement of time into a movement through space, at all events struck the hours. The clouds that could paralyze the sundial, the freezing that could stop the water clock on a winter night, were no longer obstacles to time-keeping: summer or winter, day or night, one was aware of the measured clank of the clock. The instrument presently spread outside the monastery; and the regular striking of the bells brought a new regularity into the life of the workman and the merchant. The bells of the clock tower almost defined urban existence. Time-keeping passed into time-serving and time-accounting and time-rationing. As this took place, Eternity ceased gradually to serve as the measure and focus of human actions.

The clock, not the steam-engine, is the key-machine of the modern industrial age. For every phase of its development the clock is both the outstanding fact and the typical symbol of the machine: even today no other machine is so ubiquitous. Here, at the very beginning of modern technics, appeared prophetically the accurate automatic machine which, only after centuries of further effort, was also to prove the final consummation of this technics in every department of industrial activity. There had been power-machines, such as the water-mill, before the clock; and there had also been various kinds of automata, to awaken the wonder of the populace in the temple, or to please the idle fancy of some Moslem caliph: machines one finds illustrated in Hero and Al-Jazari. But here was a new kind of power-machine, in which the source of power and the transmission were of such a nature as to ensure the even flow of energy throughout the works and to make possible regular production and a standardized product. In its relationship to determinable quantities of energy, to standardization, to automatic action, and finally to its own special product, accurate timing, the clock has been the foremost machine in modern technics: and at each period it has remained in the lead: it marks a perfection toward which other machines aspire. The clock, moreover, served as a model for many other kinds of mechanical works, and the analysis of motion that accompanied the perfection of the clock, with the various types of gearing and transmission that were elaborated, contributed to the success of quite different kinds of machine. Smiths could have hammered thousands of suits of armor or thousands of iron cannon, wheelwrights could have shaped thousands of great water-wheels or crude gears, without inventing any of the special types of movement developed in clockwork, and without any of the accuracy of measurement and fineness of articulation that finally produced the accurate eighteenth century chronometer.

The clock, moreover, is a piece of power-machinery whose "product" is seconds and minutes: by its essential nature it dissociated time from human events and helped create the belief in an independent world of mathematically measurable sequences: the special world of science. There is relatively little foundation for this belief in common human experience: throughout the year the days are of uneven duration, and not merely does the relation between day and night steadily change, but a slight journey from East to West alters astronomical time by a certain number of minutes. In terms of the human organism itself, mechanical time is even more foreign: while human life has regularities of its own, the beat of the pulse, the breathing of the lungs, these change from hour to hour with mood and action, and in the longer span of days, time is measured not by the calendar but by the events that occupy it. The shepherd measures from the time the ewes lambed; the farmer measures back to the day of sowing or forward to the harvest; if growth has its own duration and regularities, behind it are not simply matter and motion but the facts of development: in short, history. And while mechanical time is strung out in a succession of mathematically isolated instants, organic time—what Bergson calls duration—is cumulative in its effects. Though mechanical time can, in a sense, be speeded up or run backward, like the hands of a clock or the images of a moving picture, organic time moves in only one direction—through the cycle of birth, growth, development, decay, and death—and the past that is already dead remains present in the future that has still to be born.

Around 1345, according to Thorndike, the division of hours into sixty minutes and of minutes into sixty seconds became common: it was this abstract framework of divided time that became more and more the point of reference for both action and thought, and in the effort to arrive at accuracy in this department, the astronomical exploration of the sky focussed attention further upon the regular, implacable movements of the heavenly bodies through space. Early in the sixteenth century a young Nuremberg mechanic, Peter Henlein, is supposed to have created "many-wheeled watches out of small bits of iron" and by the end of the century the small domestic clock had been introduced in England and Holland. As with the motor car and the airplane, the richer classes first took over the new mechanism and popularized it: partly because they alone could afford it, partly because the new bourgeoisie were the first to discover that, as Franklin later put it, "time is money." To become "as regular as clockwork" was the bourgeois ideal, and to own a watch was for long a definite symbol of success. The increasing tempo of civilization led to a demand for greater power: and in turn power quickened the tempo.

Now, the orderly punctual life that first took shape in the monasteries is not native to mankind, although by now Western peoples are so thoroughly regimented by the clock that it is "second nature" and they look upon its observance as a fact of nature. Many Eastern civilizations have flourished on a loose basis in time: the Hindus have in fact been so indifferent to time that they lack even an authentic chronology of the years. Only yesterday, in the midst of the industrializations of Soviet Russia, did a society come into existence to further the carrying of watches there and to propagandize the benefits of punctuality. The popularization of time-keeping, which followed the production of the cheap standardized watch, first in Geneva, then in America around the middle of the last century, was essential to a well-articulated system of transportation and production.

To keep time was once a peculiar attribute of music: it gave industrial value to the workshop song or the tattoo or the chantey of the sailors tugging at a rope. But the effect of the mechanical clock is more pervasive and strict: it presides over the day from the hour of rising to the hour of rest. When one thinks of the day as an abstract span of time, one does not go to bed with the chickens on a winter's night: one invents wicks, chimneys, lamps, gaslights, electric lamps, so as to use all the hours belonging to the day. When one thinks of time, not as a sequence of experiences, but as a collection of hours, minutes, and seconds, the habits of adding time and saving time come into existence. Time took on the character of an enclosed space: it could be divided, it could be filled up, it could even be expanded by the invention of labor-saving instruments.

Abstract time became the new medium of existence. Organic functions themselves were regulated by it: one ate, not upon feeling hungry, but when prompted by the clock; one slept, not when one was tired, but when the clock sanctioned it. A generalized time-consciousness accompanied the wider use of clocks: dissociating time from organic sequences, it became easier for the men of the Renascence to indulge the fantasy of reviving the classic past or of reliving the splendors of antique Roman civilization: the cult of history, appearing first in daily ritual, finally abstracted itself as a special discipline. In the seventeenth century journalism and periodic literature made their appearance: even in dress, following the lead of Venice as fashion-center, people altered styles every year rather than every generation.

The gain in mechanical efficiency through co-ordination and through the closer articulation of the day's events cannot be overestimated: while this increase cannot be measured in mere horsepower, one has only to imagine its absence today to foresee the speedy disruption and eventual collapse of our entire society. The modern industrial regime could do without coal and iron and steam easier than it could do without the clock.

d. Monasteries and mechanization

*From Bertrand Gille, "Machines," in Charles Singer et al. (eds.), A History of
Technology, vol. 2, The Mediterranean Civilizations and the Middle Ages,
Oxford University Press, New York, 1956, pp. 650–651.*

There was . . . one important type of concentration of manufacture that favoured mechanization. This is exemplified by the monasteries, particularly those of the Cistercian order, which formed the sole economic autarkies of the Middle Ages. They played a major part in the development of machinery and in particular of the various applications of the water-mill.

In principle, and generally in practice, each monastery had itself to meet all its own needs. To avoid unnecessary labour, which reduced the time available for meditation and prayer, all manufactures in monastic hands were mechanized as far as possible. For this reason the Cistercian regulations recommend that monasteries should be built near rivers that could supply power. A description of Clairvaux Abbey in France gives some idea of this mechanization:

> The river enters the abbey as much as the wall acting as a check allows. It gushes first into the corn-mill where it is very actively employed in grinding the grain under the weight of the wheels and in shaking the fine sieve which separates flour from bran. Thence it flows into the next building, and fills the boiler in which it is heated to prepare beer for the monks' drinking, should the vine's fruitfulness not reward the vintner's labour. But the river has not yet finished its work, for it is now drawn into the fulling-machines following the corn-mill. In the mill it has prepared the brothers' food and its duty is now to serve in making their clothing. This the river does not withhold, nor does it refuse any task asked of it. Thus it raises and lowers alternately the heavy hammers and mallets, or to be more exact, the wooden feet of the fulling-machines. When by swirling at great speed it has made all these wheels revolve swiftly it issues foaming and looking as if it had ground itself. Now the river enters the tannery where it devotes much care and labour to preparing the necessary materials for the monks' footwear; then it divides into many small branches and, in its busy course, passes through the various departments, seeking everywhere for those who require its services for any purpose whatsoever, whether for cooking, rotating, crushing, watering, washing, or grinding, always offering its help and never refusing. At last, to earn full thanks and to leave nothing undone, it carries away the refuse and leaves all clean.

Most early abbeys had an extensive water-system of this type. In some of them the various hydraulic workshops were concentrated in a single factory, as, for example, at the French abbey of Royaumont, near Paris. There the "works" was built over the river itself, which passed along the axis of the building through a high and narrow tunnel 32 m long and 2.35 m wide. The workshops supplying the material needs of the abbey, such as the grain-, tanning-, fulling-, and iron-mills, were situated on each side of this tunnel. At the abbey of Vaux de Cernay, also near Paris, there was a similar works. The abbey of Fontenay in Burgundy still has its factory, a huge structure with four rooms built at the end of the twelfth century and measuring 53 m long by 13.50 m wide. The forge was in the second room. The river passed alongside the building and the grain-mill was at the end and built over the river.

Many other Cistercian abbeys had similar buildings where all the equipment used for their work was concentrated. In the twelfth-century Fountains Abbey, Yorkshire, an underground river passes through a series of tunnels feeding a brewery, a corn-mill, and various workshops. There were also private factories in the Limousin district in France; the Materre mills included those for corn, hemp, and tanning. In the same district there was a single mill which dealt with flour-grinding, cloth-fulling, and tanning.

e. Leonardo da Vinci: "compleat technician"

From Bertrand Gille, op cit., pp. 651, 652.

The first medieval technical revolution occurred in the twelfth and thirteenth centuries. The fourteenth century was a period of adaptation, when the disastrous Hundred Years' War (1338–1453) between England and France, and the Black Death (1348–50), contributed not a little to a slackening of progress. This was to reappear with added vigour in the second half of the fifteenth century.

The new phase of technical advancement occurred in a region distant from the protracted war. Northern Italy, southern Germany, and the Rhine valley enjoyed a very rapid cultural evolution—the beginnings of a renaissance in art, literature, science, and technology. Now appeared the first of the long line of engineers who were later to form or to train the various groups of technicians—men who were at the same time architects, mechanical engineers, and military engineers.

Leonardo da Vinci's description of himself when writing to the Duke of Milan corresponds perfectly to this new definition of the "compleat technician." He says that he has a process for the construction of very light bridges, capable of easy transport. He knows how to drain moats and make scaling-ladders. He knows how to make light cannon easy of transport, capable of ejecting inflammable matter. By narrow and tortuous subterranean tunnels, he can create a passage to inaccessible places, even under rivers. He can make cannon, mortars, and engines of fire different from those now in use, and can replace them by catapults and other projectile weapons at present unknown. He can compete with anyone in architecture, and in the building of canals.

This superbly gifted technician had of course progressed far beyond his predecessors. He had a better knowledge of science than they, and was more given to conscious thought on the development of the means at his disposal. The development of machinery now required comprehensive solutions of problems. Interposed between prime-mover and operative tools there must be mechanisms that do not belong specifically to any one of the five simple machines. There are also such general problems as friction, the transformation of motion, and the reduction and augmentation of power. Moreover, there are problems of stresses and strains in materials, problems of mechanization in a multitude of machines, and, above all, strictly scientific problems that became soluble only when science had adopted the experimental method. On all of these Leonardo touches in his notebooks.

3. NEW IDEAS OF SPACE, TIME, AND MOTION: 1400–1700

From Lewis Mumford, op. cit., pp. 20–22.

Between the fourteenth and the seventeenth century a revolutionary change in the conception of space took place in Western Europe. Space as a hierarchy of values was replaced by space as a system of magnitudes. One of the indications of this new orientation was the closer study of the relations of objects in space and the discovery of the laws of perspective and the systematic organization of pictures within the new frame fixed by the foreground, the horizon and the vanishing point. Perspective turned the symbolic relation of objects into a visual relation: the visual in turn became a quantitative relation. In the new picture of the world, size meant not human or divine importance, but distance. Bodies did not exist separately as absolute magnitudes: they were co-ordinated with other bodies within the same frame of vision and must be in scale. To achieve this scale, there must be an accurate representation of the object itself, a point for point correspondence between the picture and the image: hence a fresh interest in external nature and in questions of fact. The division of the canvas into squares and the accurate observation of the world through this abstract checkerboard marked the new technique of the painter, from Paolo Uccello onward.

The new interest in perspective brought depth into the picture and distance into the mind. In the older pictures, one's eye jumped from one part to another, picking up symbolic crumbs as taste and fancy dictated: in the new pictures, one's eye followed the lines of linear perspective along streets, buildings, tessellated pavements whose parallel lines the painter purposely introduced in order to make the eye itself travel. Even the objects in the foreground were sometimes grotesquely placed and foreshortened in order to create the same illusion. Movement became a new source of value: movement for its own sake. The measured space of the picture re-enforced the measured time of the clock.

Within this new ideal network of space and time all events now took place; and the most satisfactory event within this system was uniform motion in a straight line, for such motion lent itself to accurate representation within the system of spatial and temporal co-ordinates. One further consequence of this spatial order must be noted: to place a thing and to time it became essential to one's understanding of it. In Renascence space, the existence of objects must be accounted for: their passage through time and space is a clue to their appearance at any particular moment in any particular place. The unknown is therefore no less determinate than the known: given the roundness of the globe, the position of the Indies could be assumed and the time-distance calculated. The very existence of such an order was an incentive to explore it and to fill up the parts that were unknown.

What the painters demonstrated in their application of perspective, the cartographers established in the same century in their new maps. The Hereford Map of 1314 might have been done by a child: it was practically worthless for navigation. That of Uccello's contemporary, Andrea Banco, 1436, was conceived on rational lines, and represented a gain in conception as well as in practical accuracy. By laying down the invisible lines of latitude and longitude, the cartographers paved the way for later explorers, like Columbus: as with the later scientific method, the abstract system gave rational expectations, even if on the basis of inaccurate knowledge. No longer was it necessary for the navigator to hug the shore line: he could launch out into the unknown, set his course toward an arbitrary point, and return approximately to the place of departure. Both Eden and Heaven were outside the new space; and though they lingered on as the ostensible subjects of painting, the real subjects were Time and Space and Nature and Man.

Presently, on the basis laid down by the painter and the cartographer, an interest in space as such, in movement as such, in locomotion as such, arose. In back of this interest were of course more concrete alterations: roads had become more secure, vessels were being built more soundly, above all, new inventions—the magnetic needle, the astrolabe, the rudder—had made it possible to chart and to hold a more accurate course at sea. The gold of the Indies and the fabled fountains of youth and the happy isles of endless sensual delight doubtless beckoned too: but the presence of these tangible goals does not lessen the importance of the new schemata. The categories of time and space, once practically dissociated, had become united: and the abstractions of measured time and measured space undermined the earlier conceptions of infinity and eternity, since measurement must begin with an arbitrary here and now even if space and time be empty. The itch to *use* space and time had broken out: and once they were co-ordinated with movement, they could be contracted or expanded: the conquest of space and time had begun. (It is interesting, however, to note that the very concept of acceleration, which is part of our daily mechanical experience, was not formulated till the seventeenth century.)

The signs of this conquest are many: they came forth in rapid succession. In military arts the cross-bow and the ballista were revived and extended, and on their heels came more powerful weapons for annihilating distance—the cannon and later the musket. Leonardo conceived an airplane and built one. Fantastic projects for flight were canvassed. In 1420 Fontana described a velocipede: in 1589 Gilles de Bom of Antwerp apparently built a man-propelled wagon: restless preludes to the vast efforts and initiatives of the nineteenth century. As with so many elements in our culture, the original impulse was imparted to this movement by the Arabs: as early as 880 Abû l-Qâsim had attempted flight, and in 1065 Oliver of Malmesbury had killed himself in an attempt to soar from a high place: but from the fifteenth century on the desire to conquer the air became a recurrent preoccupation of inventive minds; and it was close enough to popular thought to make the report of a flight from Portugal to Vienna serve as a news hoax in 1709.

The new attitude toward time and space infected the workshop and the counting house, the army and the city. The tempo became faster: the magnitudes became greater: conceptually, modern culture launched itself into space and gave itself over to movement.

4. TECHNICS AND THE GROWTH OF CAPITALISM

From Lewis Mumford, op. cit., pp. 26–27.

While the feudal families, with their command over the land, often had a monopoly over such natural resources as were found in the earth, and often retained an interest in glass-making, coal-mining, and iron-works right down to modern times, the new mechanical inventions lent themselves to exploitation by the merchant classes. The incentive to mechanization lay in the greater profits that could be extracted through the multiplied power and efficiency of the machine.

Thus, although capitalism and technics must be clearly distinguished at every stage, one conditioned the other and reacted upon it. The merchant accumulated capital by widening the scale of his operations, quickening his turnover, and discovering new territories for exploitation: the inventor carried on a parallel process by exploiting new methods of production and devising new things to be produced. Sometimes trade appeared as a rival to the machine by offering greater opportunities for profit: sometimes it curbed further developments in order to increase the profit of a particular monopoly: both motives are still operative in capitalist society. From the first, there were disparities and conflicts between these two forms of exploitation: but trade was the older partner and exercised a higher authority. It was trade that gathered up new materials from the Indies and from the Americas, new foods, new cereals, tobacco, furs: it was trade that found a new market for the trash that was turned out by eighteenth century mass-production: it was trade—abetted by war —that developed the large-scale enterprises and the administrative capacity and method that made it possible to create the industrial system as a whole and weld together its various parts.

Whether machines would have been invented so rapidly and pushed so zealously without the extra incentive of commercial profit is extremely doubtful: for all the more skilled handicraft occupations were deeply entrenched, and the introduction of printing, for example, was delayed as much as twenty years in Paris by the bitter opposition of the guild of scribes and copyists. But while technics undoubtedly owes an honest debt to capitalism, as it does likewise to war, it was nevertheless unfortunate that the machine was conditioned, at the outset, by these foreign institutions and took on characteristics that had nothing essentially to do with the technical processes or the forms of work. Capitalism utilized the machine, not to further social welfare, but to increase private profit: mechanical instruments were used for the aggrandizement of the ruling classes. It was because of capitalism that the handicraft industries in both Europe and other parts of the world were recklessly destroyed by machine products, even when the latter were inferior to the thing they replaced: for the prestige of improvement and success and power was with the machine, even when it improved nothing, even when technically speaking it was a failure. It was because of the possibilities of profit that the place of the machine was overemphasized and the degree of regimentation pushed beyond what was necessary to harmony or efficiency. It was because of certain traits in private capitalism that the machine—which was a neutral agent—has often seemed, and in fact has sometimes been, a malicious element in society, careless of human life, indifferent to human interests. The machine has suffered for the sins of capitalism; contrariwise, capitalism has often taken credit for the virtues of the machine.

By supporting the machine, capitalism quickened its pace, and gave a special incentive to preoccupation with mechanical improvements: though it often failed to reward the inventor, it succeeded by blandishments and promises in stimulating him to further effort. In many departments the pace was over-accelerated, and the stimulus was over-applied: indeed, the necessity to promote continual changes and improvements, which has been characteristic of capitalism, introduced an element of instability into technics and kept society from assimilating its mechanical improvements and integrating them in an appropriate social pattern. As capitalism itself has developed and expanded, these vices have in fact grown more enormous, and the dangers to society as a whole have likewise grown proportionately. Enough here to notice the close historical association of modern technics and modern capitalism, and to point out that, for all this historical development, there is no necessary connection between them.

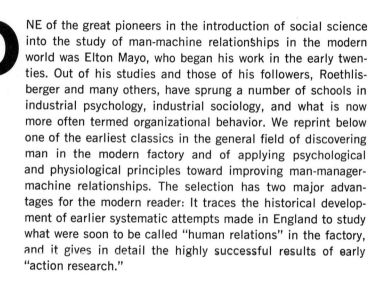

discovery of man in the factory

INTRODUCTION

O NE of the great pioneers in the introduction of social science into the study of man-machine relationships in the modern world was Elton Mayo, who began his work in the early twenties. Out of his studies and those of his followers, Roethlisberger and many others, have sprung a number of schools in industrial psychology, industrial sociology, and what is now more often termed organizational behavior. We reprint below one of the earliest classics in the general field of discovering man in the modern factory and of applying psychological and physiological principles toward improving man-manager-machine relationships. The selection has two major advantages for the modern reader: It traces the historical development of earlier systematic attempts made in England to study what were soon to be called "human relations" in the factory, and it gives in detail the highly successful results of early "action research."

1. WHAT IS MONOTONY?
From Elton Mayo, The Human Problems of an Industrial Civilization, *The Macmillan Company, New York, 1933, pp. 28–54.*

Industrial investigation has from the beginning been compelled to recognize that the interferences which operate to prevent sustained work in industry are not merely or mainly organic. An early report, 1924, of the Fatigue Board in discussing the effect of systematically arranged rest-pauses says: "Rest-pauses must clearly be treated from two points of view according to the nature of the work. In muscular work they must be regarded mainly as rests in the literal sense; that is, they serve as recovery periods from the effects of physiological fatigue. On the other hand, in work of which the main feature is repetition rather than effort, boredom and monotony are the factors to be taken into account rather than fatigue, and here the action of the rest-pauses probably depends on change from the main occupation rather than on complete cessation from work. The two problems, therefore, are quite distinct and ought to be studied independently." [1] The problem of monotony as clearly distinct from fatigue owes its definition chiefly to Dr. H. M. Vernon, one of the senior investigators of the original Health of Munition Workers Committee and of the Board. In the year 1924 he published two monographs, one a study of rest-pauses in industry, the other some observations on the effects of variety in repetitive work.[2] Mr. S. Wyatt, who has since developed the study further, was associated with both inquiries. The former of these monographs consists of two studies, the first by Vernon and Bedford, industrial; the second by Wyatt, experimental. The industrial study is thus summarized: "Estimation of the effect of introducing rest-pauses (five to ten minutes) during the work spells is very difficult, because other influences cannot be excluded. . . . However, the rests were followed by a slight but genuine improvement of output in most of the instances investigated, even after making a full allowance for the effect of practice. . . . The rest-pause effect takes several months to reach its full extent."

"Apart from regularized rest-pauses, the workers always get a certain amount of change (a) by taking voluntary rests from work, and (b) owing to the fact that they have to fetch and carry material, and do other jobs which afford relief from the monotony of their chief occupation." [3] Wyatt, as a result of his experimental study uncomplicated by industrial conditions, is more specific. "The objective conditions of modern industry show an increasing tendency to give rise to monotony. This is due to the increased sub-division of labor and amount of repetition work. . . . Although such objective conditions are conducive to increased monotony, the amount of monotony experienced probably depends more on the attitude of the operative towards his work. It is well known that the same industrial task has different subjective effects upon different individuals, and while some may find the work extremely monotonous and at times even intolerable, others find it comparatively pleasant, and prefer it to more varied occupations. Where, however, the work has a subjective sameness and gives rise to monotony, it has an inhibiting effect upon activity." [4] Both Vernon and Wyatt are observing output curves; both find that fatigue is not the only "interference" that diminishes production,

[1] Industrial Fatigue Research Board, Fourth Annual Report, p. 697.
[2] Industrial Fatigue Research Board, No. 25, H. M. Vernon, T. Bedford, S. Wyatt; No. 26, H. M. Vernon, S. Wyatt, A. D. Ogden.
[3] Industrial Fatigue Research Board, No. 25, p. 19.
[4] *Ibid.*, p. 23.

monotony is equally effective. "The results of the experiment described in this report suggest that monotonous activities of the type under consideration cause a considerable reduction in output, which is most apparent about the middle of the spell of work. This reduction can be avoided to a certain extent by the introduction of a rest-pause of fifteen minutes' duration half-way through the spell. . . . There is an increase in output not only after the rest, but also before the rest takes place. . . ." [5]

Four years later, in 1928, the two Vernons in the course of a study of the effect of hours of work say, "The psychological effects of a rest-pause may be even greater than the physiological, especially for operatives engaged on monotonous repetition work. . . . It is impossible to measure the psychological effect of a rest-pause directly, but indirect evidence was obtained from a study of the labor turnover at three factories where somewhat similar work was performed at similar rates of pay." All the factories were large and well-appointed modern buildings; the weekly hours of work were nearly the same. At Factory B the labor turnover between 1923 and 1925 averaged 25 per cent on the average number of women employed, 42 per cent at Factory A, and 94 per cent at Factory C. "Labor turnover depends on such a number of different factors that it is impossible to argue closely, but it is a suggestive fact that at the factory with the lowest labor turnover the workers were given a fifteen-minute rest-pause in each work spell, during which they went to the canteen, and a free tea was provided for them in the afternoon. In the factory with the intermediate turnover the workers did not leave their places, but had a three-minute pause in which to drink the tea provided by the management, whilst in the factory with the highest turnover no rests at all were allowed, and the workers were discouraged from surreptitious feeding." [6]

Vernon summarizes thus: "The adoption of a rest-pause—with opportunity for refreshment—during work spells of five hours' duration is desirable:

a. for physiological reasons, dependent on the fact that there is often a period of six hours between breakfast and dinner.

b. for psychological reasons, dependent on the relief from monotory." [7]

In 1929 Wyatt published the results of a study done in collaboration with J. A. Fraser of "the effects of monotony." The work reported is in part laboratory experiment and partly also direct industrial inquiry. The industrial study includes a number of different operations, all of them

---

[5] *Ibid.*, p. 34.
[6] Two Studies on Hours of Work, No. 47, Industrial Fatigue Research Board, pp. 3–5.
[7] *Ibid.*, p. 16.

repetitive—winding, tobacco weighing, chocolate packing, soap wrapping. The industrial workers studied differ widely in intelligence. Wyatt's conclusions, briefly put, are that "the experience of boredom is fairly prevalent among operatives employed on repetitive processes," that "boredom causes a reduced rate of working which is particularly noticeable about the middle of the spell," that "boredom also causes a more variable rate of working" and "is responsible for an overestimation of time-intervals," which tends to be associated with a slower rate of working. Once again he finds that "the experience of boredom is largely dependent on individual characteristics and tendencies." Workers of superior intelligence are more easily bored, but are nevertheless "usually above the average in productive efficiency." "Temperamental tendencies are important determinants and need special investigation."

In addition to all this, however, he makes two comments of high interest: "The amount of boredom bears some relation to the degree of mechanization of the task. It is less liable to occur when (a) the work is entirely automatic. In such cases thought can be detached from work and directed to more interesting subjects, or utilized in conversation with other workers. If, however, the mind is not distracted in this manner, boredom can be very intense." Boredom is also less likely (b) "when attention is entirely concentrated on the task. In such cases unexpected and varied situations frequently arise. . . . It (boredom) is most marked in semi-automatic processes which require enough attention to prevent mind-wandering but not enough for the complete absorption of mental activity." These observations can, I think, be extensively confirmed by the experiences of industry in the United States. O. S. Lovekin . . . was interested to discover that some of the lowest and steadiest pulse-products—work with least effort—he encountered were those of young women working on conveyors. His opinion was that in such instances the work was at its automatic maximum and the group cheerfully social.

Wyatt's second interesting conclusion is expressed thus: "The amount of boredom experienced bears some relation to the conditions of work. It is less liable to arise (a) when the form of activity is changed at suitable times within the spell of work, (b) when the operatives are paid according to output produced instead of time worked, (c) when the work is conceived as a series of self-contained tasks rather than as an indefinite and apparently interminable activity, (d) when the operatives are allowed to work in compact social groups rather than as isolated units, and (e) when suitable rests are introduced within the spell of work." [8]

At this point it is wise to pause for a moment in order to make certain that we do not misunderstand the observations of Vernon and Wyatt. The

[8] Industrial Fatigue Research Board, No. 56, "The Effects of Monotony in Work," S. Wyatt and J. A. Fraser assisted by F. B. L. Stock, pp. 42, 43.

word "monotony," no less than the word "fatigue" arouses reminiscences in all of us which make it easy for us to assume that there must be a simple fact that corresponds with the word. Because we have ourselves known what it is to be "tired" and "bored," we tend to assume an identity of personal attitude in all the industrial situations where a fall in output is recorded in the middle of a working spell, or a high labor turnover over a period of time. Yet the fall in output and the labor turnover are facts of record; the experience of "boredom" is a highly hypothetical explanation. I say highly hypothetical because it is clear that just as "fatigue" is used to describe a variety of organic incapacities all externally conditioned in a different manner, so also monotony is used to describe a variety of personal situations, differently conditioned. Everything that Vernon and Wyatt say is designed to drive home this caution. Cathcart, writing in 1928, echoes this claim: "Closely allied to fatigue is another phenomenon as obscure and difficult, viz., monotony. What do we really understand by monotony? . . . Who decides what is monotonous? The old adage that 'one man's meat is another man's poison' is true here. There is a large element of the personal equation. An occupation may be perfectly monotonous to one man, arousing only hatred and disgust, whereas another may find it soothing and suitable. And again, what may be found monotonous one day may not be so the next. It varies from individual to individual, and even from time to time in the same individual." [9]

From the observations of Vernon and Wyatt, quoted above, two interesting considerations emerge. First, the capacity to be unfavorably influenced by repetitive work differs between individuals in respect of, for example, what can be tentatively called intelligent endowment and temperament. Second, the social or personal aspect of the particular industrial group affects the situation in some way, and profoundly. Fortunately these two aspects of the study have received capable attention from two investigators of the Fatigue Board; I refer to the work of May Smith and Millais Culpin.

Miss Smith makes her first contribution to the inquiry into the social determinants of individual activity in a far too little-known essay upon "General Psychological Problems Confronting an Investigator" published as early as 1924.[10] Her statement is so excellent that I quote it at some length. "It is more than probable," she says, that a student of industrial conditions "will be confronted with the problems of the general sameness of the work and the effect of this on individual workers. The word most commonly used to describe this sameness is monotony; this is often un-

[9] "The Human Factor in Industry," E. P. Cathcart, Oxford University Press, pp. 31, 32.
[10] Industrial Fatigue Research Board, Fourth Annual Report, pp. 26 ff.

critically assumed to be synonymous with 'repetition of movement' and the reason is not far to seek. The person usually employed in criticizing or describing industrial processes belongs to a class which is unaccustomed to remain long hours at purely repetitive work. When observing workers so employed, he therefore tends to imagine what he would feel like in such a position, to project his own feelings on to the worker, and to stigmatize the process as monotonous. His verdict may or may not be true; its truth or falsity depends on the worker.

"Literally, 'monotonous' means 'one tone'; it suggests absence of change, a flat wash, a dead level, a situation which fails to provide for the person any intellectual stimulus or emotional change. For the realization of change two factors are necessary: (a) an actual objective change; (b) a person who can be affected by it. The most exciting situations would fail to be appreciated as such by certain melancholic individuals. Repetitive processes, therefore, must either be studied as such, or else put in their complete setting, which setting would include, at least, the repetitive work, the varying amount done as the hours go on, the opinion of fellow-workers and the authorities with regard to that work, physiological changes with regard to meals, fatigue, etc., emotional changes . . . and the collective life of the factory. *The total reaction at any given moment will be a reaction to a composite situation which does not remain unchanged. The consciousness of one or other factor of the composite situation varies from person to person and even from time to time in the same person.*" [11]

Miss Smith develops the theme of individual differences with respect to monotony, then returns to her main topic: "The writer had recently to spend some time in two factories doing the same repetitive work; in the one there were many complaints of dullness, in the other none; in the one the majority of faces expressed a dull acquiescence in existence, in the other, the general joy and happiness in the work was obvious. If a study of repetitive work done in these two factories had followed the same lines, the result would have been different. In the one, no one apparently took any interest in the workers, there was no esprit de corps and a general slackness prevailed; to get the week's money was the only interest and that is bound to be a fitful interest. In the other there was not only a real interest in the work, in the accumulation of it as the day wore on, but also a desire to win the approval of the authorities and interest in many social activities binding one to another. *The repetitive work is a thread of the total pattern, but is not the total pattern.*[12]

"Another point of view sometimes overlooked is that there are compensations in many processes, if one studies the worker as a human being and not only as a performer of a repetition process. . . . The

[11] *Loc. cit.*, p. 29; italics mine, E. M.
[12] Italics mine, E. M.

adoption of particular machines by particular workers and their dislike of a temporary removal reveal an interest in the machines as such, which an observer when judging the work might easily overlook, but which cannot, without falsifying the account, be omitted.

"The worker on repetitive processes may be repeating a very limited number of movements, but his emotional life may be quite varied; he has to adjust to superiors, to equals, to subordinates; if he fails to please the first he may find sympathy and support from the others; he has an audience so that even a tyrannical foreman does not exert an unmodified influence. It is difficult to assess a situation which comprises from the point of view of a worker, at least, the sense of injustice resulting from the careless criticisms of a superior, the feeling of support from one's fellow workers' sympathy, the *esprit de corps* in allying with them against the superior, while to certain characters the joy of having a grievance is incalculable. When such situations arise—and they are not rare—the focus of interest would go from the monotony of the work to the emotion aroused." Miss Smith then describes how praise from a superior while arousing another type of emotion may nevertheless similarly move the focus of interest from the repetitive work to the social situation. She continues: "Days vary in length, as every worker knows, and ten hours of one day are shorter than eight or nine of another. *The work remains the same; it is the general situation and the individual emotional changes that vary.*[13] So many descriptions of factory conditions are like skeleton outlines, or those wire reproductions of the correct movements for motion study; they are quite true, but they lack humanity.

"It is not intended to suggest that repetitive work is good in itself; the point is that an investigator of repetitive work will find himself constantly faced with these personal problems which ought not to be neglected. The mechanical point of view is the result of this neglect."

"The point of view which looks upon a person as a kind of extension to a machine is sometimes implicit, even in discussions on intelligence. Those responsible for selecting people sometimes talk as if the problem of selection were merely that of finding out: (a) the degree of intelligence required for a particular job; (b) the person with that degree. While it is probably true that such an adaptation might bring about a more harmonious relationship than where the two did not fit, yet a problem of equal importance is the study of emotional differences. . . . Where the activity concerned involves highly developed attention or a limited set of delicate adjustments, mental conflicts, conscious or unconscious, will be more likely to interfere with the success of the work than where the movements are cruder and the registration of changes less refined. Doubtless, the best thing to do would be to cure the sufferer, but while this is a counsel

[13] Italics mine, E. M.

of perfection it is at least desirable and more possible to direct his activities into channels where a feeling of inefficiency with its attendant depression is not added to the original weakness. Intelligence alone is not the only criterion of success."

Finally Miss Smith returns to the very important question as to the assumptions an industrial investigator should make, the method he should use. "Dr. Cyril Burt has described very aptly in discussing juvenile delinquency what he calls 'multiple determination,' *i.e.* that a particular result is not caused by some one factor operating equally on all people, so that the presence of this factor invariably would produce the same result. Rather is it that there are several factors which together, operating on a particular temperament, will produce the result." [14] It is clear that before we can profitably assess the part played in industrial determinations by something termed "monotony," we need to be accurately informed with respect to (a) external working conditions, (b) the social-personal situation in its relation to the individuals concerned, and (c) individual differences of capacity and temperament.

Millais Culpin and May Smith demonstrated the importance of their method in an inquiry into the incidence of telegraphists' cramp, a report of which was published by the Board in 1927. Dr. Culpin is an authority upon the psychoneuroses and it is probable that the original intention of the study was, at least in part, to discover a simple means of excluding from telegraphic work persons liable to develop the disability. The issue of the investigation proved to have an interest far above this; in effect it illustrates a method by which the different individual "boredoms" may be further analyzed and in some instances resolved.

The method of inquiry is simply described. "To study a subject merely as the doer of a particular piece of work is of little value; the work to the worker is part of a whole, made up of his numerous reactions to situations, real and ideal, over and above his work. Sometimes it is the phantasy life that is of more importance to the individual than the apparent real life. It is clearly impossible to obtain a thorough knowledge of anyone, but *it has proved possible to get the point of view of a subject with sufficient clearness to yield an insight into the relation of the work he does to his general attitude to life.*" [15]

The investigators point out that, whereas it is now comparatively easy to assess by means of "tests" a subject's general intelligence, "there are no reliable objective methods" of determining other important qualities of his personal make-up. They, therefore, use the method of the clinical interview, "reliance has to be placed on the observation and interpreta-

[14] Industrial Fatigue Research Board, Fourth Annual Report, pp. 29–32.
[15] "A Study of Telegraphists' Cramp," Smith, Culpin, and Farmer, Industrial Fatigue Research Board, No. 43, p. 17. Italics mine, E. M.

tion of a doctor experienced in such work." "The method adopted was somewhat as follows:

i. General observation of the subject (*i.e.* the individual) such as we are all accustomed to make.

ii. Guided by the knowledge of many subjects (individuals), the external behavior and appearance were linked up to the mental state of which they were probably the expression.

iii. By questions framed so as to bring up different situations in life, it was possible to study the subject more fully and accurately, and thereby verify, disprove, or modify the earlier impression.

"It often happened that when once started the subject would give a very detailed personal account of himself, in which case the investigator would not interfere with questions." [16]

In presenting their conclusions, the investigators inquire "why telegraphy should have a 'cramp' when other occupations of an allied nature have not." We would suggest that the exacting nature of the work, the inevitable rigidity of the conditions, the isolation of this one symptom, with its disabling effects, have all operated to concentrate attention into this channel. The type likely to get cramp may have a nervous breakdown in other occupations, but it is also probable that many who break down in telegraphy might carry on more or less efficiently under conditions more amenable to individual requirements. In England telegraphy is a permanent occupation, which to some is one of its attractions; in America there is more mobility of labor and the disease is hardly recognized. As against the advantage of permanence one may have to put the disadvantages of relative immobility.[17]

Telegraphy, then, has a characteristic "cramp" while "other occupations of an allied nature have not." The work is "exacting in nature" and the conditions "rigid"; but while English telegraphists are numerously plagued with the disability, American operators hardly know it. Some difference in the general situation, and not in the nature of the work, serves to bring this about—perhaps the greater "mobility of labor" in the United States in 1926. This is strongly suggestive of (a) a difference in the social industrial situation, and (b) a personal attitude characterized by mental conflict—a desire to retain the permanent job at war with an increasing aversion from the exacting work and the rigid conditions. Perhaps this is a step towards the analysis of at least one type of boredom. . . .

In September, 1923, some of us were asked to undertake an inquiry into working conditions in the mule-spinning department of a textile mill near Philadelphia, with the object of devising methods of diminishing an

[16] *Loc. cit.,* p. 16; italics mine, E. M.
[17] *Loc. cit.,* p. 36.

exceedingly high labor turnover. This labor turnover was reported to us as being approximately 250 per cent; that is to say, the mill had to "take on" about one hundred piecers every year in order to keep approximately forty working. The difficulty tended to be most acute when the factory was most busily employed and most in need of men. The mill was very well organized; the management was unusually enlightened and humane. Four financial incentive schemes were in operation and were working well in departments other than mule-spinning. The morale and production elsewhere in the mill were satisfactory; the general labor turnover, excluding the mule-spinners, was estimated at five or six per cent. The investigation and its outcome have been fully reported elsewhere.[18] I propose here to recall a few salient features of the situation that disclosed themselves, and to add some exposition of the method of inquiry used, a method which was not fully described in previous reports.

On a first inspection, the conditions of work in the mule-spinning department did not seem noticeably inferior to the conditions of work elsewhere in the plant. The spinners, like the others, worked only five days in the week; on Saturday and Sunday the factory was closed down. The working day was ten hours in length, five hours in the morning and five in the afternoon, with an interval of forty-five minutes for lunch. The work was done in long "alleys" on either side of which a machine head was operating spinning frames. The number of spinning frames operated by each machine head varied from ten to fourteen; all these frames required close watching by the "head-tender" and the "piecers" in charge. The number of piecers in an alley varied according to the type of yarn that was being spun; as a general rule there were two or three. The distance between the terminal frames was approximately thirty-five yards. The work was repetitive; the piecer walked up and down the alley twisting together broken threads. When there was a "run" of inferior yarn the work demanded vigilance and constant movement. The only variation in work was that which occurred when the machine head was stopped in order to "doff" or to replace a spool. Machine "breakdowns" of a minor character were fairly frequent.

The observations of Wyatt and Fraser, quoted above, were published in London in 1929 and accordingly were not available in Philadelphia in 1923. It is interesting, however, even at this distance in time, to look back and see how the conditions of work which had evolved in mule-spinning implied an infraction of every principle these authors state. Mule-spinning was probably, for example, a "semi-automatic process" which required enough attention to be irritating and "not enough for the complete absorption of mental activity." Beyond this, Wyatt says that boredom (interpreted to mean a general down-grade rather than up-grade mental ac-

[18] "Revery and Industrial Fatigue," *Personnel Journal*, Vol. III, No. 8, Dec. 1924.

companiment to work, a "minus" rather than a "plus") is less liable to arise:

a. "When the form of activity is changed at suitable intervals within the spell of work." The twisting together of broken threads for hours at a time was only rarely interrupted by "doffing" or a machine breakdown. Neither of these interruptions was in any sense pleasant or a relief. The "carding" operation performed alongside the mules looked more "monotonous" to such external observers as those described by Miss Smith. The carding operative, however, was much better able to work in leisurely fashion, to break off and chat, to vary his day.

b. "When the operatives are paid according to output produced instead of time worked." The spinners were paid a flat-rate wage but were offered a group bonus which up to the time of the inquiry they had never earned. This was one of the incentive schemes, alluded to above, which "worked" satisfactorily elsewhere in the factory but failed completely in the spinning department. The very fact that the bonus had never been earned by the group served to convince them (although, as subsequent developments showed, mistakenly) that an impossible standard had been set. This increased rather than diminished their irritation.

c. "When the work is conceived as a series of self-contained tasks rather than as an indefinite and apparently interminable activity." Various expressions very generally in use amongst the operatives convinced us that they regarded their work as "an indefinite and apparently interminable activity." To which they added forceful epithets.

d. "When the operatives are allowed to work in compact social groups rather than as isolated units." The arrangement and nature of the work precluded any sociability or conversation. Although there were two or three piecers in each alley, they were always remote from each other and isolated, unless emergency, which equally precluded sociability, brought them briefly together.

e. "When suitable rests are introduced within the spell of work." There had been no official rests, few if any unauthorized breaks, and no suggestion of rest-pauses at the time when the inquiry began.

At the beginning of the inquiry there were difficulties of observation owing to the fact that this was merely the latest of many investigations. The men were restless under observation, and the management uneasily aware of this. At this point we were greatly helped by the collaboration of the Graduate Medical School of the University of Pennsylvania in the placing of a small dispensary in the plant with a qualified nurse in charge. This nurse could administer minor remedies or first aid but was permitted also to refer cases to the Polyclinic Hospital in Philadelphia. This was a sufficient reason for her presence, this and the fact that appropriate aid was actually provided for certain individuals in need of medical advice. But the nurse in charge, in addition to her hospital qualifications, was an expert "interviewer." The method she followed was very similar to that described above by Culpin and Smith. She found that the majority of those who visited her were glad to "give a very detailed personal account" of themselves. In all such situations she would listen carefully and would not "interfere with questions." When not occupied in her small office or clinic, she would walk in her uniform through the factory—visiting all departments but giving the greater part of her time to the workers in the spinning department. Any confidences made to her, and they were many, were regarded as inviolable and not communicated to anyone unless professional need arose. In this way she came to know the attitude and personal background of every worker on "the mules" with some detail and intimacy. She thus created a "listening post" of high value to subsequent procedure in the inquiry and, incidentally, became herself something of a social nexus for the group. It was her finding that the reflections or reveries of the workers in the spinning department were uniformly pessimistic. If any one of them was permitted to talk at length, either in the nurse's office or to her in the department, the preoccupations he expressed, whether about himself, his life, his home, or the work, appeared to be almost invariably morbid.

After some discussion of the situation and its probabilities, the management agreed to institute experimentally two or three ten-minute rest-periods in the morning and again in the afternoon for a single team of piecers, constituting about one-third of the total number. In these rest-periods the men were permitted to lie down and were instructed in the best methods of gaining the maximum of muscular relaxation. From the first the men were interested and pleased; they speedily adopted the method of rest which was advised. The experiment seemed to be in some degree successful in the sense that "morale"—whatever that may be—was generally admitted to be improved, certainly by their supervisors and even by the men themselves. This improvement, curiously, extended even to those workers in the department who were not included in the experimental team. The experiment was not really satisfactory, however, at this stage because no measurement of change, or sufficiently objective evidence, was possible. Output records were kept only for the whole group, so any difference of performance of the special team remained unknown.

In October, 1923, however, the management, pleased with the improved condition of the men, decided to extend the rest-period system to include the entire personnel of the spinning department. This had the effect of making the output records significant for the experiment, and from this time on the official daily, weekly, and monthly figures were made available to us. Unfortunately we were never able to secure the departmental records of output for the period prior to October, 1923. All that we know of this period is that the men had never earned a bonus and that the various authorities considered that their best figure for any given month was probably in the neighborhood of 70 per cent.

The first chart shows the daily productivity of the spinning department from October 1, 1923, to June 30, 1924, calculated in terms of efficiency percentage. The actual weight of yarn that is spun does not provide a satisfactory criterion of production, since a thick thread weighs more than a thin one but takes less labor per unit of weight. The Company had therefore devised a scheme by which times were set for the spinning of unit weights of the various types of yarn. The time allowed in

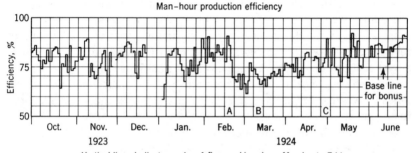

Man–hour production efficiency

Vertical lines indicate weeks of five working days, Monday to Friday

Plate VI. Production—Spinning Mules—Nine Months. (From Elton Mayo, "Revery and Industrial Fatigue," *Journal of Personnel Research*, vol. 3, no. 8, December, 1924.)

each case was experimentally determined, allowance being made for time lost in doffing, machine breakdowns, and so on. The time allowed ranked as 100 per cent and the department was asked to make an average of 75 per cent for the working days in a month in return for the flat-rate wage paid. Beyond this the scheme provided that any month in which the group average exceeded 75 per cent man-hour efficiency on the Company scale, every worker in the group should be paid a percentage addition to his ordinary wage equal to the group percentage in excess of 75. Thus an 80 per cent monthly average would have meant a 5 per cent bonus on his wages to every employee in the department.

The rest-pause innovation was accompanied, from its introduction, by an improvement in the officially recorded productive efficiency. The mental and physical condition of the men was distinctly bettered, their comments to observers were less generally pessimistic than before. Whereas the financial incentive of the bonus had not previously operated to stimulate production, the men now began to be pleased by the fact that they were working less time, earning bonuses as never before, and feeling less tired and irritated. For the first five months of the experiment, the average productive efficiency of the department was 80 per cent, the lowest month was 78¾ per cent, the highest 82.

The system was not, however, altogether satisfactory. It had occurred to someone—not an executive officer—that the rest-period idea might be improved. The men were accordingly made to "earn" their rest-periods. That is, they did not necessarily get a rest at an established time; they were allowed to rest only after completing a certain operation. This meant that they could not always anticipate a definite number of rests at stated periods. On some days, indeed, they might have two rest-periods only. Nevertheless, for the most part they had three or four such intervals in the day and the innovation worked fairly well.

This general condition continued until February 15, when, in response to a heavy demand for deliveries, someone in the factory took it upon himself to order the rest-periods abandoned. (Point marked A on Plate VI.) A week later the carefully built-up improvement in morale had been dissipated and the pessimism had revived in full force. This change was brought to the attention of management and the rest-periods were formally re-instituted. (Plate VI, point B.) Unfortunately the unsatisfactory plan of making the men "earn" their rests was also restored. In March, consequently, the incidence of rest-periods was highly uncertain and irregular. On a given day certain men might have no rests at all; others would have one, two, three, or, rarely, four. In spite of this, the chart shows distinct improvement in the later weeks in March, an improvement which was reflected in a more cheerful mental attitude.

At the end of March the performance of the group showed itself as low —the monthly average had returned to 70 per cent. The president of the Company called a conference and at its conclusion ordered that, during the month of April, the spinning mules should be shut down four times a day for ten minutes at a time, and that all hands from head tenders to "piecers" should lie down and rest as they had been instructed to do. Adequate floor space and sufficient sacking for comfort created difficulties, because forty men had to lie down simultaneously by their machines. This was contrived, however, and the incidence of rest-periods arranged so that the first ten-minute rest came after two hours' work, the second after work for one hour and a half. This left a concluding work-period in each spell of one hour and ten minutes. The experiment was a success; the figures for April showed a ten per cent improvement over March in spite of the fact that the machines had been shut down while forty men rested for forty minutes every day. In May the president ordered a return to the method of alternating rest-periods, one man at a time in each alley —the alley itself to determine the order of succession. In May the efficiency figure was 80¼, in June 85, July 82, and so on. For the sixteen months after April, 1924, the flat average was 83 per cent—the lowest 79½, the highest 86½. There were other changes of interest. For example, the months when production was highest—September and October, 1924, May and June, 1925—were months in which demand was urgent. The months when production was lower—December, 1924, January, 1925—were months in which work was slack and irregular. Before the innovation in method, the contrary was true. It was also noticed that Monday and Friday were no longer the worst days in the week; again, the performance of a given day tended to relate itself to the demand of that day. The irregularity of daily production observable in May (Plate VI,

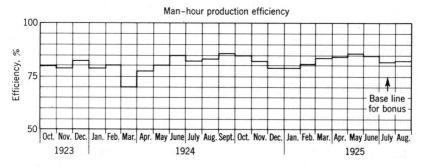

Plate VII. Production—Spinning Mules—Twenty-three Months. (From **Elton Mayo,** "Revery and Industrial Fatigue," *Journal of Personnel Research,* vol. 3, no. 8, December, 1924.)

point C) was due to the fact that, working under the new conditions, the mules were constantly outrunning the carding machines which supplied them with yarn.

The original problem was to devise a method of diminishing a very high labor turnover. In the experimental twelve-month period there was no labor turnover at all. A few workers left the department, one because his family removed to the country, certain others were "laid off" in a slack period. But the problem of an emotional labor turnover ceased to exist. The factory held its workers and had no difficulty in maintaining a full complement even in times of rushed work. The president of the Company in a speech made some years later, claimed that, consequent on the innovation, the labor turnover in the spinning department had fallen from 250 percent to the steady five per cent which was regarded as normal to the whole establishment.

Here, then, is an instance of the manner in which one industrial company worked its way through an acute human problem to a solution very much in accord with the principles later enunciated by Wyatt. At suitable intervals, change was introduced. Payment according to output was to some extent achieved by the consistent earning of bonuses. The work was broken up into self-contained tasks and ceased to be an interminable activity. The social inter-relations within the group improved both within the factory and outside it. Rests were introduced into the spell of work.

Monotony, like fatigue, is a word which is used to denote any sort of induced unbalance in the worker such that he cannot continue work, or can continue only at a lower level of activity. There are many possibilities of such unbalance—different individuals and different situations. Inquiry into such situations looks for some contributing factor or factors in external conditions, something also in the individual himself. The unbalance is, in Cannon's words, both interofective and exterofective; there is a disequilibrium within the individual and between him and his work. In the case cited, the complicating problem was that of the mental preoccupations—pessimism and rage—induced in the workers by the conditions of their work.

the machine age
of mass production:
principles and practice

INTRODUCTION

I N this chapter and in the one that follows the reader will find a strong emphasis on human problems at the worker level and what management can do about them. This is because the most acute problems in the man-machine relationship during the heyday of mass production —1920 to the mid-1950s—were to be found at that level. In most of the selections here reprinted and especially in the following chapter, under "Analyses and Solutions," it becomes obvious that problems arising from the impact of the machine on workers are in the end management problems as well. Without management's understanding and constructive response they remained (and many of them still remain) unsolved.

Although most of us today think we know what mass production is, the first selection, "Mass Production," written by Henry Ford, remains a basic document to which every student of modern technology should return from time to time. Many of the assumptions and methods there discussed are still found in assembly-line production today.

No one has made the points in favor of his great organizational innovation better than Ford himself. The outstanding one, of course, is that mass production has made possible mass consumption; that automobiles, washing machines, refrigerators, and other such aids to living have been made abundantly available to people all over this country and increasingly to those in the rest of the world. Yet some of the assumptions on which mass production is based are today being questioned, as will appear from later selections in this book.

The selection by the "father of scientific management," Frederick W. Taylor, complements that of Henry Ford. At first sight, the excerpts from Taylor's famous paper "The Principles of Scientific Management" may seem to have little place among selections devoted to technology and civilization. Taylor's classic examples of the early application of his principles concern the most primitive kinds of manual labor—a man loading pig iron by hand and shovelers in a steel company. But his approach to these ancient and humble kinds of work illustrates new organizational concepts that are as characteristic of modern industry and as far-reaching in their influence as the assembly line. When Taylor found methods by which a man could reasonably and without undue fatigue handle 47½ tons of pig iron a day instead of 12½ tons, he was making a revolutionary contribution to the modern method of organizing work. He promptly decided that it was inefficient for each man to provide his own shovel and use it for shoveling ore at 30 pounds a shovelful or rice coal at 4 pounds for each shovel. Instead he induced the company to provide eight or ten different shovels suited to the kinds of work being done. All this began a new kind of thinking, the cumulative effect of which has been revolutionary for the organization of both men and machines. Taylor sought not only the "best way" of performing each task and the proper time for every operation, but also the best material, tool, or machine, and the best flow and sequence for the work as a whole.

Taylor's ideas were often misunderstood and frequently misused. He was opposed to a speed-up, and he favored genuine cooperation between management and men and a fair division of the increased profits which his methods made possible. He did not foresee, however, that by greatly increasing the organizational role of management, he was to deprive the worker of participation and initiative in the work process. He made the point that in working out actual methods of scientific management for a specific job, it was frequently those men who had recently worked on the job that provided the ideas and methods, but he did not realize that once these ideas were taken over by management, it often became impossible for other workers to make their own contributions to further progress.

As is to be expected in any great work of innovation, the pendulum has today swung somewhat the other way. Many students of modern factory organization feel that the process of putting all initiative in regard to methods and job design into the hands of engineers and management has gone too far and that the worker himself has more to contribute than is generally assumed under present practices. Likewise, extreme specialization and the breaking down of each job into a few simple repetitive operations has now been reexamined. Not only is this practice criticized because of intrinsic boredom for the individual, but the long-term efficiency of this type of job design is also being challenged. Several of the selections in the following sections comment on these questions either directly or by implication.

Ford carried Taylor's ideas even further by installing the conveyor belt, which mechanically determined not only method—down to the last detail—but the speed of work as well.

Like most innovators, neither Ford nor Taylor—nor their immediate followers—could foresee accurately all the important social and psychological effects of their innovations. Interestingly enough, a good many of these effects were precisely the reverse of Ford's and Taylor's expectations. The fact that these pioneers were less skillful as prophets than as inventors should not blind us to their organizational genius or to their continuing influence on industrial society.

Following the two historical documents of Ford and Taylor, we print a sharp modern criticism of both by Daniel Bell.

One logical development of the "principles" of scientific management is the creation of incentive systems each of which has essentially two parts: a method of measuring exactly how much work the worker performs, per hour or per day, and a monetary reward system designed both to pay him for exactly how much work he does and to motivate him to do more work, and so earn more money. An economic and psychological analysis of how these systems actually work in practice is set forth by William F. Whyte in the fourth selection entitled "Orthodox Incentive Theory, Principles and Problems."

With an unchanging and fully standardized product and process, the defects of the typical incentive systems in industry are not apparent. Few products and processes, however, were as stable as the inventors of incentive systems supposed even at the height of mass-production technologies. Today the dynamic character of nearly all industry has come to be recognized. In the final selection, "Incentives in Time of Change," the difficulties of applying a static pay system, based on an inadequate theory of human motivation, are fully explored.

BIBLIOGRAPHY

Abruzzi, A.: *Work, Workers, and Work Measurement,* Columbia University Press, New York, 1956.

Anderson, E. H.: "The Meaning of Scientific Management," *Harvard Business Review,* vol. 28, no. 6, pp. 678–692, November, 1949.

Bell, Daniel: *The End of Ideology,* The Free Press, New York, 1960.

Cox, David, and K. M. Dyce Sharp: "Research on the Unit of Work," *Occupational Psychology,* vol. 25, no. 2, pp. 90–108, April, 1951.

Durkheim, Emile: *The Division of Labor in Society,* The Free Press, New York, 1947.

Ford, Henry: "Mass Production," *Encyclopaedia Britannica,* 22d ed., vol. 15, pp. 38–40.

Jerome, Harry: *Mechanization in Industry,* National Bureau of Economic Research, New York, 1934.

Katz, R. L.: "Toward a More Effective Enterprise," *Harvard Business Review,* September–October, 1960.

McCormick, Ernest J.: *Human Factors Engineering*, McGraw-Hill Book Company, New York, 1957.
McGregor, D.: *The Human Side of Enterprise*, McGraw-Hill Book Company, New York, 1960.
March, J. G., and H. A. Simon: *Organizations*, John Wiley & Sons, Inc., New York, 1958.
Ogburn, W. F.: "National Policy and Technology," *Technological Trends and National Policy*, Report of the Subcommittee on Technology to the National Resources Committee, 1937.
Taylor, Frederick W.: *The Principles of Scientific Management*, Harper & Brothers, New York, 1911.
Veblen, Thorstein: *The Instinct of Workmanship*, B. W. Huebsch, New York, 1914.

1.   MASS PRODUCTION

From Henry Ford, "Mass Production," Encyclopaedia Britannica, 22d ed., vol. 15, pp. 38–40.

The term mass production is used to describe the modern method by which great quantities of a standardized commodity are manufactured. As commonly employed it is made to refer to the quantity produced, but its primary reference is to method. In several particulars the term is unsatisfactory. Mass production is not merely quantity production, for this may be had with none of the requisites of mass production. Nor is it merely machine production, which also may exist without any resemblance to mass production. Mass production is the focussing upon a manufacturing project of the principles of power, accuracy, economy, system, continuity, speed, and repetition. To interpret these principles, through studies of operation and machine development and their co-ordination, is the conspicuous task of management. The normal result is a productive organization that delivers in continuous quantities a useful commodity of standard material, workmanship and design at minimum cost. The necessary, precedent condition of mass production is a capacity, latent or developed, of *mass consumption*, the ability to absorb large production. The two go together, and in the latter may be traced the reasons for the former. . . .

I. The principles of mass production

As to shop detail, the keyword to mass production is simplicity. Three plain principles underlie it: (a) the planned orderly and continuous progression of the commodity through the shop; (b) the delivery of work instead of leaving it to the workman's initiative to find it; (c) an analysis of operations into their constituent parts. These are distinct but not separate steps; all are involved in the first one. To plan the progress of material from the initial manufacturing operation until its emergence as a finished product involves shop planning on a large scale and the manufacture and delivery of material, tools and parts at various points along the line. To do this successfully with a progressing piece of work means a careful breaking up of the work into the sequence of its "operations." All three fundamentals are involved in the original act of planning a moving line production.

This system is practiced, not only on the final assembly line, but throughout the various arts and trades involved in the completed product. The motor car final assembly line offers an impressive spectacle of hundreds of parts being quickly put together into a going vehicle, but flowing into that are other assembly lines on which each of the hundreds of parts have been fashioned. It may be far down the final assembly line that the springs, for example, appear, and they may seem to be a negligible part of the whole operation. Formerly one artisan would cut, harden, bend and build a spring. In 1939 the making of one leaf of a spring was an operation of apparent complexity, yet was really the ultimate reduction to simplicity of operation.

A typical operation described. For its illustrative value let us trace the course of a spring leaf after it has progressed from iron ore through ingot, bloom and billet stages, and is rolled into strips. (1) Beginning as a strip of steel prepared by the steel mill, it is placed in a punch press for cutting and piercing. The workman puts the strip into press until it hits a stop, then trips the press. The cut-off and pierced piece falls on a belt conveyor which runs along the loading end of a series of heat-treating ovens. (2) A second workman takes the pieces from belt conveyor and places them on conveyor which passes through the furnace (in which temperature is automatically controlled); thence they are deposited at a certain temperature by this conveyor at the unloading end of the furnace. (3) The heated piece is lifted with tongs by a third operator and placed in a bending machine which gives the leaf its proper curve and plunges it in oil, the temperature of which is maintained at a definite degree by apparatus beyond the operator's control. (4) As the bending machine emerges from the oil bath, the same operator removes it to a conveyor that delivers it to an annealing furnace. (5) A fourth operator places the leaf on a conveyor that passes through the annealing furnace. (6) The same workman sends it by conveyor through a water-cooling bath, thence to the spring assembly line.

As a set of springs on the Ford car requires on an average 14 leaves, and 25,000 springs are a normal day's output, this operation must be visualized as employing a great battery of lines similar to the one briefly described.

As all the leaves in a spring are of different length and curve, from the bottom or master leaf to the top leaf, this operation must be visualized as one of many carried on simultaneously by different batteries of machines, each battery working on its own special size. All of these lines, with their various machines and operations, are converging on the point where the leaves are assembled into springs. The leaf whose progress has been described is the simplest one.

The operation proceeds as follows:

(7) A fifth workman removes the leaf from the conveyor on its arrival at assembly line. (8) A sixth workman sprays the arriving leaves with a lubricant. (9) A seventh workman inserts a bolt through leaves assembled as a spring. (10) An eighth workman puts a nut on the bolt and tightens it. (11) A ninth workman puts in the clip bolts and tightens them. (12) A tenth workman inspects the completed spring. (13) He hangs spring on conveyor. (14) Conveyor carries it to loading dock where the eleventh workman removes it.

One workman under the old system could attend the leaf through all these phases, or even make a complete spring, but his production would be limited. Where large quantities of the same article are to be made, the simplest operation may involve the whole time of one man. A one-minute operation will require one man a full day of eight hours to accomplish it on 480 pieces. Now this simple part, a spring leaf, must be identical in strength, finish and curve with millions of others designed to fulfil the same purpose, and this becomes a complicated and delicate procedure requiring automatic machinery, the most accurate measuring devices, pyrometer controls, "go" and "no go" gauges—in fact, the best facilities that can be provided by modern management. The leaf described, which is a minor matter when compared with the whole great process, becomes a major matter when considered by itself; it must have its own supply of material delivered in sufficient quantities at indicated places—for example, steel at 1; heat at 2; power and oil at 3; heat at 5; water at 6; bolts at 7; lubricants at 8; bolts at 9; nuts at 10; clips at 11. In this process the secrets of many arts and trades are employed.

The story of this minor part illustrates what is meant by orderly progression of the article through the shop. It goes to meet other parts of the motor car which have come from other parts of the plant by similar processes. The story illustrates also what is meant by delivering the work to the workman: every workman's task is prepared for him by some other workman, and delivered to his hand. The third principle also is illustrated—the analysis of a single job into its constituent operations. The simplicity of the part here described should not be permitted to exclude from view the multitude of other operations, ranging from the heaviest forgings to the lightest manipulations in bench assembly of delicate electrical instruments. Some gauge inspections involve measurements to the ten-millionth part of an inch.

The economies arising from this method are obvious. The machinery is constantly in use. It would be economically impossible to maintain all this equipment for the service of men occupied in the entire operation of making springs. Presses, furnaces, bending machines, oil baths would be idle while the workman progressed from operation to operation. Under mass production it is the work, not the man, that progresses from operation to operation. Otherwise use-convenience in the commodity would be lessened, while price-convenience would be destroyed. There is also the economy of reduced inventories, in lapse of time between raw material and finished product. Mass production justifies itself by an economy whose benefits may quickly be transmitted to the purchaser.

II. The effects of mass production

But it is not the history and principle of mass production which provoke the widest discussions; the *effects* of it have been placed under scrutiny. What have been the effects of mass production on society?

1. Beginning with management, where unquestionably mass production methods take their rise, there is a notable increase in industrial control, as distinguished from financial control. The engineer's point of view has gained the ascendancy and this trend will undoubtedly continue until finance becomes the handmaid instead of the mistress of productive industry. Industrial control has been marked by a continuous improvement of the standards, for standardization does not mean stagnation, but the instant adoption of the better method to the exclusion of the old, in the interest of production. Financial control was not, in its heyday, marked by a tendency to make costly changes in the interests of the product. The economy of scrapping old equipment immediately upon the invention of the better equipment was not so well understood. Engineering control, entrenched in mass production methods, brought in this new readiness to advance. Management has been kept close to the shop and has reduced the office to a clearing-house for the shop.

Managers and men, as well as the manufacturing process, have been brought to greater singleness of purpose.

2. The effect of mass production on the product has been to give it the highest standard of quality ever attained in output of great quantities. Conditions of mass production require material of the best quality to pass successfully through the operations. The utmost accuracy must control all these operations. Every part must be produced to fit at once into the design for which it is made. In mass production there are no fitters. The presence of fitters indicates that the parts have been produced unfit for immediate placement in the design. In works of art and luxury this accuracy is achieved at the cost of careful handiwork. To introduce hand methods of obtaining accuracy into mass production would render mass production impossible with any reference to price-convenience. The standard quality of the product is guaranteed by the fact that machines are so constructed that a piece of work cannot go through them unless it exactly accords with specifications. If the work goes through the tools, it must be right. It will thus be seen that the burden of creation is on management in designing and selecting the material which is to be produced by the multiple processes utilized in mass production.

3. The effect of mass production on mechanical science has been to create a wide variety of single-purpose machines which not only group similar operations and perform them in quantity, but also reproduce skill of hand to a marvellous degree. It is not so much the discovery of new principles as the new combination and application of old ones that mark this development. Under mass production the industry of machine making has increased out of all comparison with its previous history, and the constant designing of new machines is a part of the productive work of every great manufacturing institution.

4. The effect of mass production on employees has been variously appraised. Whether the modern corporation is the destruction or salvation of arts and crafts, whether it narrows or broadens opportunity, whether it assists or retards the personal development of the worker, must be determined by observable facts. A cardinal principle of mass production is that hard work, in the old physical sense of laborious burden-bearing, is wasteful. The physical load is lifted off men and placed on machines. The recurrent mental load is shifted from men in production to men in designing. As to the contention that machines thus become the masters of men, it may be said the machines have increased men's mastery of their environment, and that a generation which is ceaselessly scrapping its machines exhibits few indications of mechanical subjection.

The need for skilled artisans and creative genius is greater under mass production than without it. The Ford Motor Company employs more than 15,000 skilled mechanics in the construction and maintenance of the machinery of production, besides other thousands engaged directly in the production of cars. It has been debated whether there is less or more skill as a consequence of mass production.

The present writer's opinion is that there is more. Practical production men assert that mass production requires an increasing degree of mass intelligence.

The common work of the world has always been done by unskilled labour, but the common work of the world in modern times is not as common as it was formerly. In almost every field of labour more knowledge and responsibility are required.

2. THE PRINCIPLES OF SCIENTIFIC MANAGEMENT

From Frederick W. Taylor, The Principles of Scientific Management, *Harper & Brothers, New York, 1911, pp. 9–73.*

The principal object of management should be to secure the maximum prosperity for the employer, coupled with the maximum prosperity for each employe.

The words "maximum prosperity" are used, in their broad sense, to mean not only large dividends for the company or owner, but the development of every branch of the business to its highest state of excellence, so that the prosperity may be permanent.

In the same way maximum prosperity for each employe means not only higher wages than are usually received by men of his class, but, of more importance still, it also means the development of each man to his state of maximum efficiency, so that he may be able to do, generally speaking, the highest grade of work for which his natural abilities fit him, and it further means giving him, when possible, this class of work to do.

It would seem to be so self-evident that maximum prosperity for the employer, coupled with maximum prosperity for the employe, ought to be the two leading objects of management, that even to state this fact should be unnecessary. And yet there is no question that, throughout the industrial world, a large part of the organization of employers, as well as employes, is for war rather than for peace, and that perhaps the majority on either side do not believe that it is possible so to arrange their mutual relations that their interests become identical.

The majority of these men believe that the fundamental interests of employes and employers are necessarily antagonistic. Scientific management, on the contrary, has for its very foundation the firm conviction that the true interests of the two are one and the same; that prosperity for the employer cannot exist through a long term of years unless it is accompanied by prosperity for the employe, and vice versa; and that it is possible to give the workman what he most wants—high wages—and the employer what he wants—a low labor cost—for his manufactures. . . .

It should also be perfectly clear that the greatest permanent prosperity for the workman, coupled with the greatest prosperity for the employer, can be brought about only when the work of the establishment is done with the smallest combined expenditure of human effort, plus nature's resources, plus the cost of the use of capital in the shape of machines, buildings, etc. Or, to state the same thing in a different way: that the greatest prosperity can exist only as the result of the greatest possible productivity of the men and machines of establishment—that is, when each man and each machine are turning out the largest possible output; because unless your men and machines are daily turning out more work than others around you, it is clear that competition will prevent your paying higher wages to your workmen than are paid to those of your competitor. And what is true as to the possibility of paying high wages in the case of two companies competing close beside one another is also true as to whole districts of the country and even as to nations which are in competition. In a word, that maximum prosperity can exist only as the result of maximum productivity. . . .

Why is it, then, in the face of the self-evident fact that maximum prosperity can exist only as the result of the determined effort of each workman to turn out each day his largest possible day's work, that the great majority of our men are deliberately doing just the opposite, and that even when the men have the best of intentions their work is in most cases far from efficient?

There are three causes for this condition, which may be briefly summarized as:

First. The fallacy, which has from time immemorial been almost universal among workmen, that a material increase in the output of each man or each machine in the trade would result in the end in throwing a large number of men out of work.

Second. The defective systems of management which are in common use, and which make it necessary for each workman to soldier, or work slowly, in order that he may protect his own best interests.

Third. The inefficient rule-of-thumb methods, which are still almost universal in all trades, and in practising which our workmen waste a large part of their effort.

This paper will attempt to show the enormous gains which would result from the substitution by our workmen of scientific for rule-of-thumb methods. . . .

To explain briefly: owing to the fact that the workmen in all of our trades have been taught the details of their work by observation of those immediately around them, there are many different ways in common use for doing the same thing, perhaps forty, fifty, or a hundred ways of doing each act in each trade, and for the same reason there is a great variety in the implements used for each class of work. Now, among the various methods and implements used in each element of each trade there is always one method and one implement which is quicker and better than any of the rest. And this one best method and best implement can only be discovered or developed through a scientific study and analysis of all of the methods and implements in use, together with accurate, minute, motion and time study. This involves the gradual substitution of science for rule of thumb throughout the mechanic arts. . . .

In order that the work may be done in accordance with scientific laws, it is necessary that there shall be a far more equal division of the responsibility between the management and the workmen than exists under any of the ordinary types of management. Those in the management whose duty it is to develop this science should also guide and help the workman in working under it, and should assume a much larger share of the responsibility for results than under usual conditions is assumed by the management.

The body of this paper will make it clear that, to work according to scientific laws, the management must take over and perform much of the work which is now left to the men; almost every act of the workman should be preceded by one or more preparatory acts of the management which enable him to do his work better and quicker than he otherwise could. And each man should daily be taught by and receive the most friendly help from those who are over him, instead of being, at the one extreme, driven or coerced by his bosses, and at the other left to his own unaided devices.

This close, intimate, personal cooperation between the management and the men is of the essence of modern scientific or task management. . . .

Under the old type of management success depends almost entirely upon getting the "initiative" of the workmen, and it is indeed a rare case in which this initiative is really attained. Under scientific management the "initiative" of the workmen (that is, their hard work, their good-will, and their ingenuity) is obtained with absolute uniformity and to a greater extent than is possible under the old system; and in addition to this improvement on the part of the men, the managers assume new burdens, new duties, and responsibilities never dreamed of in the past. The managers assume, for instance, the burden of gathering together all of the traditional knowledge which in the past has been possessed by the workmen and then of classifying, tabulating, and reducing this knowledge to rules, laws, and formulae which are immensely helpful to the workmen in doing their daily work. In addition to developing a science in this way, the management take on three other types of duties which involve new and heavy burdens for themselves.

These new duties are grouped under four heads:

First. They develop a science for each element of a man's work, which replaces the old rule-of-thumb method.

Second. They scientifically select and then train, teach, and develop the workman, whereas in the past he chose his own work and trained himself as best he could.

Third. They heartily cooperate with the men so as to insure all of the work being done in accordance with the principles of the science which has been developed.

Fourth. There is an almost equal division of the work and the responsibility between the management and the workmen. The management take over all work for which they are better fitted than the workmen, while in the past almost all of the work and the greater part of the responsibility were thrown upon the men. . . .

Perhaps the most prominent single element in modern scientific management is the task idea. The work of every workman is fully planned out by the management at least one day in advance, and each man receives in most cases complete written instructions, describing in detail the task which he is to accomplish, as well as the means to be used in doing the work. And the work planned in advance in this way constitutes a task which is to be solved, as explained above, not by the workman alone, but in almost all cases by the joint effort of the workmen and the management. This task specifies not only what is to be done but how it is to be done and the exact time allowed for doing it. And whenever the workman succeeds in doing his task right, and within the time limit specified he receives an addition of from 30 per cent to 100 per cent to his ordinary wages. These tasks are carefully planned, so that both good and careful work are called for in their performance, but it should be distinctly understood that in no case is the workman called upon to work at a pace which would be injurious to his health. The task is always so regulated that the man who is well suited to his job will thrive while working at this rate during a long term of years and grow happier and more prosperous, instead of being overworked. Scientific management consists very largely in preparing for and carrying out these tasks. . . .

One of the first pieces of work undertaken by us, when the writer started to introduce scientific management into the Bethlehem Steel Company, was to handle pig iron on task work. The opening of the Spanish War found some 80,000 tons of pig iron placed in small piles in an open field adjoining the works. Prices for pig iron had been so low that it could not be sold at a profit, and it therefore had been stored. With the opening of the Spanish War the price of pig iron rose, and this large accumulation of iron was sold. This gave us a good opportunity to show the workmen, as well as the owners and managers of the works, on a fairly large scale the advantages of task work over the old-fashioned day work and piece work, in doing a very elementary class of work.

The Bethlehem Steel Company had five blast furnaces, the product of which had been handled by a pig-iron gang for many years. This gang, at this time, consisted of about 75 men. They were good, average pig-iron handlers, were under an excellent foreman who himself had been a pig-iron handler, and the work was done, on the whole, about as fast and as cheaply as it was anywhere else at that time.

A railroad switch was run out into the field, right along the edge of the piles of pig iron. An inclined plank was placed against the side of a car, and each man picked up from his pile a pig iron weighing about 92 pounds, walked up the inclined plank and dropped it on the end of the car.

We found that this gang were loading on the average about 12½ long tons per man per day. We were surprised to find, after studying the matter, that a first-class pig-iron handler ought to handle between 47 and 48 long tons per day, instead of 12½ tons. This task seemed to us so very large that we were obliged to go over our work several times before we were absolutely sure that we were right. Once we were sure, however, that 47 tons was a proper day's work for a first-class pig-iron handler, the task which faced us as managers under the modern scientific plan was clearly before us. It was our duty to see that the 80,000 tons of pig iron was loaded onto the cars at the rate of 47 tons per man per day, in place of 12½ tons, at which rate the work was then being done. And it was further our duty to see that this work was done without bringing on a strike among the men, without any quarrel with the men, and to see that the men were happier and better contented when loading at the new rate of 47 tons than they were when loading at the old rate of 12½ tons.

Our first step was the scientific selection of the workman. In dealing with workmen under this type of management, it is an inflexible rule to talk to and deal with only one man at a time, since each workman has his own special abilities and limitations, and since we are not dealing with men in masses, but are trying to develop each individual man to his highest state of efficiency and prosperity. Our first step was to find the proper workman to begin with. We therefore carefully watched and studied these 75 men for three or four days, at the end of which time we had picked out four men who appeared to be physically able to handle pig iron at the rate of 47 tons per day. A careful study was then made of each of these men. We looked up their history as far back as practicable and thorough inquiries were made as to the character, habits, and the ambition of each of them. Finally we selected one from among the four as the most likely man to start with. He was a little Pennsylvania Dutchman who had been observed to trot back home for a mile or so after his work in the evening about as fresh as he was when he came trotting down to work in the morning. We found that upon wages of $1.15 a day he had succeeded in buying a small plot of ground, and that he was engaged in putting up the walls of a little house for himself in the morning before starting to work and at night after leaving. He also had the reputation of being exceedingly "close," that is, of placing a very high value on a dollar. As one man whom we talked to about him said, "A penny looks about the size of a cartwheel to him." This man we will call Schmidt.

The task before us, then, narrowed itself down to getting Schmidt to handle 47 tons of pig iron per day and making him glad to do it. This was done as follows: Schmidt was called out from among the gang of pig-iron handlers and talked to somewhat in this way:

> "*Schmidt, are you a high-priced man?*"
>
> "*Vell, I don't know vat you mean.*"
>
> "*Oh yes, you do. What I want to know is whether you are high-priced man or not.*"
>
> "*Vell, I don't know vat you mean.*"
>
> "*Oh, come now, you answer my questions. What I want to find out is whether you are a high-priced man or one of these cheap fellows here. What I want to find out is whether you want to earn $1.85 a day or whether you are satisfied with $1.15, just the same as all those cheap fellows are getting.*"
>
> "*Did I vant $1.85 a day? Vas dot a high-priced man? Vell, yes, I vas a high-priced man.*". . .
>
> "*Well, if you are a high-priced man, you will do exactly as this man tells you to-morrow, from morning till night. When he tells you to pick up a pig and walk, you pick it up and you walk, and when he tells you to sit down and rest, you sit down. You do that right straight through the day. And what's more, no back talk. Now a high-priced man does just what he's told to do, and no back talk. Do you understand that? When this man tells you to walk, you walk; when he tells you to sit down, you sit down, and you don't talk back to him. Now you come on to work here to-morrow morning and I'll know before night whether you are really a high-priced man or not.*". . .

Schmidt started to work, and all day long, and at regular intervals, was told by the man who stood over him with a watch, "Now pick up a pig and walk. Now sit down and rest. Now walk—now rest," etc. He worked when he was told to work, and rested when he was told to rest, and at half past five in the afternoon had his 47½ tons loaded on the car. And he practicaly never failed to work at this pace and do the task that was set him during the three years that the writer was at Bethlehem. And throughout this time he averaged a little more than $1.85 per day, whereas before he had never received over $1.15 per day, which was the ruling rate of wages at that time in Bethlehem. That is, he received 60 per cent higher wages than were paid to other men who were not working on task work. One man after another was picked out and trained to handle pig iron at the rate of 47½ tons per day until all of the pig iron was handled at this rate, and the men were receiving 60 per cent more wages than other workmen around them.

The writer has given above a brief description of three of the four elements which constitute the essence of scientific management: first, the careful selection of the workman, and, second and third, the method of first inducing and then training and helping the workman to work according to the scientific method. . . .

Although the reader may be convinced that there is a certain science back of the handling of pig iron, still it is more than likely that he is still skeptical as to the existence of a science for doing other kinds of laboring. . . . For example, the average man would question whether there is much of any science in the work of shoveling. Yet there is but little doubt, if any intelligent reader of this paper were deliberately to set out to find what may be called the foundation of the science of shoveling, that with perhaps 15 to 20 hours of thought and analysis he would be almost sure to have arrived at the essence of this science. . . .

For a first-class shoveler there is a given shovel load at which he will do his biggest day's work. What is this shovel load? Will a first-class man do more work per day with a shovel load of 5 pounds, 10 pounds, 15 pounds, 20, 25, 30, or 40 pounds? Now this is a question which can be answered only through carefully made experiments. By first selecting two or three first-class shovelers, and paying them extra wages for doing trustworthy work, and then gradually varying the shovel load and having all the conditions accompanying the work carefully observed for several weeks by men who were used to experimenting, it was found that a first-class man would do his biggest day's work with a shovel load of about 21 pounds. For instance, that this man would shovel a larger tonnage per day with a 21-pound load than with a 24-pound load or than with an 18-pound load on his shovel. It is, of course, evident that no shoveler can always take a load of exactly 21 pounds on his shovel, but nevertheless, although his load may vary 3 or 4 pounds one way or the other, either below or above the 21 pounds, he will do his biggest day's work when his average for the day is about 21 pounds.

The writer does not wish it to be understood that this is the whole of the art or science of shoveling. There are many other elements, which together go to make up this science. But he wishes to indicate the important effect which this one piece of scientific knowledge has upon the work of shoveling.

At the works of the Bethlehem Steel Company, for example, as a result of this law, instead of allowing each shoveler to select and own his own shovel, it became necessary to provide some 8 to 10 different kinds of shovels, etc., each one appropriate to handling a given type of material; not only so as to enable the men to handle an average load of 21 pounds, but also to adapt the shovel to several other requirements which become perfectly evident when this work is studied as a science. A large shovel tool room was built, in which were stored not only shovels but carefully designed and standardized labor implements of all kinds, such as picks, crowbars, etc. This made it possible to issue to each workman a shovel which would hold a load of 21 pounds of whatever class of material they were to handle: a small shovel for ore, say, or a large one for ashes. Iron ore is one of the heavy materials which are handled in a works of this kind, and rice coal, owing to the fact that it is so slippery on the shovel, is one of the lightest materials. And it was found on studying the rule-of-thumb plan at Bethlehem Steel Company, where each shoveler owned his own shovel, that he would frequently go from shoveling ore, with a load of about 30 pounds per shovel, to handling rice coal, with a load on the same shovel of less than 4 pounds. In the one case, he was so overloaded that it was impossible for him to do a full day's work, and in the other case he was so ridiculously underloaded that it was manifestly impossible to even approximate a day's work.

Briefly, to illustrate some of the other elements which go to make up the science of shoveling, thousands of stop-watch observations were made to study just how quickly a laborer, provided in each case with the proper type of shovel, can push his shovel into the pile of materials and then draw it out properly loaded. These observations were made first when pushing the shovel into the body of the pile. Next when shoveling on a dirt bottom, that is, at the outside edge of the pile, and next with a wooden bottom, and finally with an iron bottom. Again a similar accurate time study was made of the time required to swing the shovel backward and then throw the load for a given horizontal distance, accompanied by a given height. This time study was made for various combinations of distance and height. With data of this sort before him, coupled with the law of endurance described in the case of the pig-iron handlers, it is evident that the man who is directing shovelers can first teach them the exact methods which should be employed to use their strength to the very best advantage, and can then assign them daily tasks which are so just that the workman can each day be sure of earning the large bonus which is paid whenever he successfully performs this task.

There were about 600 shovelers and laborers of this general class in the yard of the Bethlehem Steel Company at this time. These men were scattered in their work over a yard which was, roughly, about two miles long and a half mile wide. In order that each workman should be given his proper implement and his proper instructions for doing each new job, it was necessary to establish a detailed system for directing men in their work, in place of the old plan of handling them in large groups, or gangs, under a few yard foremen. As each workman came into the works in the morning, he took out of his own special pigeonhole, with his number on the outside, two pieces of paper, one of which stated just what implements he was to get from the tool room and where he was to start to work, and the second of which gave the history of his previous day's work; that is, a statement of the work which he had done, how much he had earned the day before, etc. Many of these men were foreigners and unable to read and write, but they all knew at a glance the essence of this report, because yellow paper showed the man that he had failed to do his full task the day before, and informed him that he had not earned as much as $1.85 per day, and that none but high-priced men would be allowed to stay permanently with this gang. The hope was further expressed that he would earn his full wages on the following day. So that whenever the men received white slips they knew that everything was all right, and whenever they received yellow slips they realized that they must do better or they would be shifted to some other class of work.

Dealing with every workman as a separate individual in this way involved the building of a labor office for the superintendent and clerks who were in charge of this section of the work. In this office every laborer's work was planned out well in advance, and the workmen were all moved from place to place by the clerks with elaborate diagrams or maps of the yard before them, very much as chessmen are moved on a chess-board, a telephone and messenger system having been installed for this purpose. In this way a large amount of the time lost through having too many men in one place and too few in another, and through waiting between jobs, was entirely eliminated. Under the old system the workmen were kept day after day in comparatively large gangs, each under a single foreman, and the gang was apt to remain of pretty nearly the same size whether there was much or little of the particular kind of work on hand which this foreman had under his charge, since each gang had to be kept large enough to handle whatever work in its special line was likely to come along.

When one ceases to deal with men in large gangs or groups, and proceeds to study each workman as an individual, if the workman fails to do his task, some competent teacher should be sent to show him exactly how his work can best be done, to guide, help, and encourage him, and, at the same time, to study his possibilities as a workman. So that, under the plan which individualizes each workman, instead of brutally discharging the man or lowering his wages for failing to make good at once, he is given the time and the help required to make him proficient at his present job, or he is shifted to another class of work for which he is either mentally or physically better suited. . . .

The question which naturally presents itself is whether an elaborate organization of this sort can be made to pay for itself; whether such an organization is not too heavy. This question will best be answered by a statement of the results of the third year of working under this plan.

	Old plan	New plan task work
The number of yard laborers was reduced from between	400 and 600 down to about	140
Average number of tons per man per day	16	59
Average earnings per man per day	$1.15	$1.88
Average cost of handling a ton of 2240 lb.	$0.072	$0.033

And in computing the low cost of $0.033 per ton, the office and tool-room expenses, and the wages of all labor superintendents, foremen, clerks, time-study men, etc. are included.

During the year the total saving of the new plan over the old amounted to $36,417.69, and during the six months following, when all of the work of the yard was on task work, the saving was at the rate of between $75,000 and $80,000 per year. . . .

As another illustration of the value of a scientific study of the motives which influence workmen in their daily work, the loss of ambition and initiative will be cited, which takes place in workmen when they are herded into gangs instead of being treated as separate individuals. A careful analysis had demonstrated the fact that when workmen are herded together in gangs, each man in the gang becomes far less efficient than when his personal ambition is stimulated; that when men work in gangs, their individual efficiency falls almost invariably down to or below the level of the worst man in the gang; and that they are all pulled down instead of being elevated by being herded together. For this reason a general order had been issued in the Bethlehem Steel Works that not more than four men were to be allowed to work in a labor gang without a special permit, signed by the General Superintendent of the works, this special permit to extend for one week only. It was arranged that as far as possible each laborer should be given a separate individual task. As there were about 5000 men at work in the establishment, the General Superintendent had so much to do that there was but little time left for signing these special permits.

After gang work had been by this means broken up, an unusually fine set of ore shovelers had been developed, through careful selection and individual, scientific training. Each of these men was given a separate car to unload each day, and his wages depended upon his own personal work.

3.   THREE TECHNOLOGICS: SIZE, MEASUREMENT, HIERARCHY

From Daniel A. Bell, The End of Ideology, *The Free Press, New York, 1960.*

The contemporary enterprise was set up to obey three peculiar technologics: the logic of size, the logic of "metric" time and the logic of hierarchy. Each of the three, the product of engineering rationality, has imposed on the worker a set of constraints, with which he is forced to wrestle every day. These condition the daily facts of his existence.

For the man whose working day is from eight in the morning to five in the afternoon, the morning begins long before the time he is to arrive at his place of work. After a hasty wash and a quick breakfast, he is off in his car or on the streetcar, bus or subway; often he may have to spend an hour or more in getting to the plant. (There seems to be a law, as Bertrand Russell has noted, that improvements in transportation do not cut down traveling time but merely increase the area over which people have to travel.)

Although this is the most obvious fact about modern work, few writers have concerned themselves with it, or with the underlying assumption: that large masses of human labor should be brought to a common place of work. The engineer believes that concentration is technologically efficient: under one roof there can be brought together the source of power, the raw materials, the parts and the assembly lines. So we find such huge megaliths as Willow Run, now used by General Motors, a sprawling shed spanning an area two-thirds of a mile long and a quarter of a mile wide; or such roofed-over, mile-long pavements as the Boeing plant in Wichita, Kansas.

This belief in the efficacy of size was conditioned by the type of energy first used—the limited amount of power available through the use of steam. Since steam dissipates quickly, the engineer tended to crowd as many productive units as possible along the same shaft, or within the range of steam pressure that could be carried by pipes without losses due to excessive condensation. These considerations led, too, to the bunching of workers in the layout of work, since the machines had to be located along a straight-line shafting.

The introduction of electric power and electric motors opened the way to greater flexibility and within the plant these opportunities were taken. Newer work-flow designs have avoided the antiquated straight-line shafts and aisles of the older factory. Yet the outward size of the factory remained unchallenged. Why? In part because the engineer conceives of efficiency in technological terms alone; and he is able to do so because a major cost—the travel time of the worker—can be discounted. But the question can be posed: should large masses of persons be brought to a common place of work? Which is cheaper to transport: working men twice daily, or materials and mechanical parts, let us say, twice a week? As Percival and Paul Goodman so pertinently note in their book, *Communities:* "The time of life of a piece of metal is not consumed while it waits for its truck; a piece of metal does not mind being compressed like a sardine." What the Goodmans propose is production in "bits and pieces" rather than integrated assembly. If the plants were located near workers' communities, the men would not have to travel; the processed materials would be brought to several places for manufacture, and the parts would then be collected for assembly. Yet the question is rarely considered, for few industries pay directly for their workers' travel time. Calculations in terms of market costs alone do not force the enterprise to take into account such factors as the time used in going to and from work, or the costs of roads and other transport to the factory site, which are paid for by the employee or by the community as a whole out of taxes.

In his travel to and from work the worker is chained by time. Time rules the work economy, its very rhythms and motions. . . .

One of the prophets of modern work was Frederick W. Taylor, and the stop watch was his bible. If any such social upheaval can ever be attributed to one man, the logic of efficiency as a mode of life is due to him. With "scientific management," as enunciated by Taylor, we pass far beyond the old rough computations of the division of labor; we go into the division of time itself.

The stop watch itself was not new. Before Taylor, work had been timed; but only for the entire job. What Taylor did was to split each job into its component operations and take the time of each. This, in essence, is the whole of scientific management: the systematic analysis and breakdown of work into the smallest mechanical component and the rearrangement of these elements into the most efficient combination. Taylor gave his first lectures to American engineers in 1895 (the year, one might note wryly, that Freud and Breuer published their *Studies in Hysteria,* the "breakthrough" of psychoanalysis). But it was in 1899 that Taylor achieved fame when he taught a Dutchman named Schmidt to shovel 47 tons instead of 12½ tons of pig iron a day. Every detail of the man's job was specified: the size of the shovel, the bite into the pile, the weight of the scoop, the distance to walk, the arc of the swing and the rest periods that Schmidt should take. By systematically varying each factor, Taylor got the optimum amount of barrow load. By exact calculation, he got the correct response.

But Taylor also knew what such a mechanical regimen would do to a man or, rather, what sort of man could fit into this strait jacket. "One of the very first requirements for a man who is fit to handle pig iron as a regular occupation," he wrote, "is that he shall be so stupid and so phlegmatic that he more nearly resembles an ox than any other type." [1]

The logic of Taylorism was obvious: each man's work could be measured by itself; the time in which an operation could be performed could be established "without bargaining" as an impersonal "standard time"; pay could then be computed on the basis of the amount of work done and the time taken to do it.[2] In the modern economy, shading of time is so important (as Benjamin Franklin, the prototype of Max Weber's ethical protestant, remarked, "time is money") that a large company like General Motors contracts with its workers on a six-minute basis. (For purposes of payroll calculation, General Motors divides the hour into ten six-minute periods and, except for the guarantee of three-hours "call-in" pay, the worker is paid by the number of tenths of an hour he works.)

The significance of Taylorism lies in its attempt to enact a social physics. Once work was scientifically plotted, Taylor felt, there could be no disputes about how hard one should work or the pay one should receive for labor. "As reasonably might we insist on bargaining about the time and place of the rising and setting sun," he once said. For a managerial class which at the turn of the century had witnessed the erosion of its old justificatory mystique of "natural rights," the science of administration *per se* provided a new foundation for its moral authority.

While Taylor analyzed the relations of work to time, another engineer, Frank Gilbreth (1868–1924), carried the process one step further: he detached human movement from the person and made of it an abstract visualization. Not only could the pattern of machine work be broken down into elements, but human motion, too, could be "functionalized," and the natural movements of arms and legs could be ordered into a "one best way" of usage.

Gilbreth (whose contemporary fame rests, ironically, on the movie story of the frenetically organized domesticity of his large family, *Cheaper by the Dozen*) isolated eighteen basic patterns of kinetic units or motions, e.g. reach, move, grasp, which he modestly called *therbligs* (or Gilbreth spelled backwards). And, from the analysis of therblig combinations, Gilbreth came to his principles of "motion economy." For example: two

---

[1] Taylor was not the first to understand such consequences. One hundred and fifty years earlier, Adam Smith wrote: "The understandings of the greater part of men are necessarily formed by their ordinary employments. The man whose life is spent in performing a few simple operations . . . has no occasion to exert his understanding. . . . He generally becomes as stupid and ignorant as it is possible for a human creature to become," *The Wealth of Nations* (Modern Library, 1937), p. 734.

[2] Which is why the "protestant" industrial economy cannot adopt the system of "family wage," to be found in Italy and other countries where Catholic social doctrine applies, whereby a man with children receives more wages than the one who has none, though both do the same work.

hands should not be idle at the same instant except during rest periods; motions of the arms should be in opposite and symmetrical directions, and so on. The penalty for violating these rules is waste.

There was one further step in the exorable logic of rationalization. While Taylor systematized factory operations and Gilbreth sought to reduce waste motion, Charles Bedeaux sought to combine these into a unit measurement of human power, not unsurprisingly called a "B," which would correspond to the "dyn," or the unit in physics of mechanical power. So defined, "a B is a fraction of a minute of work plus a fraction of a minute of rest always aggregating unity but varying in proportion according to the nature of the strain." Using this detailed calculus, Bedeaux formulated a complicated but mathematically neat system of wage payments which took into account not only the work done but the varying fractions of nonwork or rest required in different operations, and increased or decreased payments correspondingly.[3]

The fragmentation of work, although atomizing the worker, also created a dependency and a hierarchy in work, for inherent in the division of labor is what Marx called "the iron law of proportionality." Thus, in the manufacturing process, the ratios between different numbers of workers required in different work processes are ordered by technological complexities. Marx cited an example in type manufacture: One founder could cast 2,000 type an hour, the breaker could break up 4,000 and the polisher could finish 8,000 in the same time; thus to keep one polisher busy the enterprise needed two breakers and four founders, and units were hired or discharged, therefore, in multiples of seven. In many other operations, notably an assembly line, similar inflexible ratios are established, and the hiring and firing of numbers of workers is dictated by the multiples of those ratios. But such dependency presupposes coordination, and with such coordination the multiplication of hierarchies.

The logic of hierarchy, the third of the logics created by modern industry, is, thus, not merely the sociological fact of increased supervision which every complex enterprise demands, but a peculiarly technological imperative. In a simple division of labor, for example, the worker had a large measure of control over his own working conditions, i.e., the set-up and make-ready, the cleaning and repairing of machines, obtaining his own materials, and so on. Under a complex division of labor, these tasks pass out of his control and he must rely on management to see that they are properly done. This dependence extends along the entire process of production. As a result, modern industry has had to devise an entire new

---

[3] At the height of its use the Bedeaux system was used in the United States by 720 corporations, employing 675,000 workers. During World War II, charges against Bedeaux of collaboration with Vichy, plus the bitter hostility of the unions to this method of mechanical wage calculations, brought the system into disuse here.

managerial superstructure which organizes and directs production. This superstructure draws in all possible brain work away from the shop; everything is centered in the planning and schedule and design departments. And in this new hierarchy there stands a figure known neither to the handicrafts nor to industry in its infancy—the technical employee. With him, the separation of functions becomes complete. The worker at the bottom, attending only to a detail, is divorced from any decision or modification about the product he is working on.

These three logics of size, time and hierarchy converge in that great achievement of industrial technology, the assembly line: the long parallel lines require huge shed space; the detailed breakdown of work imposes a set of mechanically paced and specified motions; the degree of coordination creates new technical, as well as social, hierarchies.[4]

NOTE BY THE AUTHOR

Besides the Bell selection, other comments and discussions on the way work is organized today should be explored by the interested reader. For example, the relation of scientific management to organizational theory is admirably discussed in March and Simon, *Organizations*, Chapter 2. For an inquiry like this one, men's assumptions about what they do and why they do it are strategic. For assumptions underlying scientific management and current engineering and managerial practice, the following are especially recommended: "Toward a More Effective Enterprise," by R. L. Katz, and Douglas McGregor's *The Human Side of Enterprise*. One of the major conclusions which emerges from these and other recent studies of work, organization, and technology is that the Machine has too often been falsely labeled "villain." Many of the harmful human effects—as well as economic wastes and inefficiencies—which stem from traditional ways of organizing men and machines are resultants not of mechanization per se, but of mechanized or limited assumptions about human nature in its work relationships.

---

[4] It is remarkable how recent is the assembly line, both as a mode of operation and as a linguistic term. Oliver Evans developed a continuous production line for milling grain in 1800, and the packinghouse industry in the 1870's had adopted the use of overhead conveyors for the processing of slaughtered animals. But the assembly line as a modern achievement owes its success largely to Henry Ford and the establishment of an auto line at Highland Park, Michigan, in 1914. And only in 1933 did the Oxford English Dictionary legitimatize the term when its supplement in that year added the contemporary meaning of the word. See Siegfried Giedion, *Mechanization Takes Command*.

4. ORTHODOX INCENTIVE THEORY, PRINCIPLES, AND PROBLEMS

From William F. Whyte, Money and Motivation, Harper & Row, Publishers, *Incorporated, New York, 1955, pp. 2–5, 200–202.*

As represented by F. W. Taylor, and his followers in the scientific management movement, managerial thinking begins with one of the basic assumptions of orthodox economic theory: that man is a rational animal concerned with maximizing his economic gains. Of course, no economist believes this assumption to be true to the facts, but the tendency has been to reason from the assumption as if it were close to actuality.

If we assume that man's goal in the factory is to make money, then it naturally follows that we can get him to produce more if we pay him in accordance with the amount he produces. Thus the theory of economic motivation leads directly to the development of a piecework incentive system.

The second major assumption is that each individual responds to economic incentives as an isolated individual. Under such conditions there would be no need to investigate the effect of fellow workers upon the individual under consideration. While most management people realize that this individualism is never quite to be found, there is a tendency to think that people should respond in this individualistic fashion and that management should encourage them to do so.

The third major assumption is that men, like machines, can be treated in a standardized fashion. While individual variations are recognized, it is assumed that there is a "one best way" to do a job so that variations in method of work can and should be eliminated. There are expected to be variations in speed and endurance, but by studying fast and slow workers an average is to be obtained for "the standard workman." The theories of scientific management are based upon standards: standard hours, standard machines and standard workmen, and so on. For example, an incentive engineer's handbook defines the standard hour in this way: "a unit of measurement of the amount of work expected of an operator or a piece of equipment in one actual hour at a pace equivalent to standard performance." It is interesting to observe the way in which machines and workers tend to be linked together as part of the equipment of the factory.

Management also seems to assume that machines and workers are alike in that they are both normally passive agents who must be stimulated by management in order to go into action. In the case of the machines, management turns on the electricity. In the case of workers, money takes the place of electricity.

Since the theory requires a system of economic incentives, it also requires people and procedures and policies to administer this system. If the worker is to be paid in terms of the amount of work accomplished, then it is necessary to have some standards of the amount of work expected. Management must arrive at a price to be paid for each unit of production. The price is generally established through the work of time-study men. Their first task is to see to it that the job is being done according to the most efficient methods. They then are expected to time selected workers on the actual job operation. The price per piece is set on the basis of these measurements.

Management generally adds two guarantees to make the system more attractive to the workers. In the first place, his regular hourly pay is guaranteed whether or not he makes the standard. Let us assume that his regular pay is $1.50 an hour and that the standard on this operation is 10 pieces an hour, which would mean a price for him of 15 cents apiece. Then, if he produced only 8 pieces he would still get his guaranteed $1.50, but if he produced 12 pieces he would earn $1.80.[1]

The second guarantee involves rates or prices set for the particular job. It is generally understood that the rate or price is not to be changed unless there has been a significant change in the machine or method of operation which would justify the establishment of a new rate. This is designed to assure the worker that he can produce an unlimited amount with no fear that in the future he will have to produce more pieces on the same job with the same methods to make the same money.

In spite of such guarantees, we find almost universally that workers set a quota on what constitutes a fair day's work and refuse to go beyond this amount even when it is well within their ability to do so. This situation exists whether the plant is unionized or not. It exists where the workers hate and distrust management. . . . It exists even in cases where the workers evince considerable loyalty for the company and for management in general.[2] . . .

Does the fault lie perhaps with the use of poor techniques in administering incentive systems? If management just used the "right" methods of time study and rate setting, would the problems be solved? The fact that these problems have existed down through the years, in similar form, in a great variety of factories, suggests to us that the fault cannot lie solely with poor techniques. The persistence and generality of the prob-

---

[1] There is a bewildering variety of incentive schemes in existence today. The example here is of what is known as a straight-line or 100 per cent incentive, where the same price is paid for each piece. There are systems where a smaller price is paid after the standard has been reached and there are others which pay a higher price beyond the standard. The straight-line incentive is probably the most common today, and we will deal with that. However, we will seek to avoid the complications of the technical side of incentive systems since this is a book on morale and motivation rather than one on incentive systems per se.

[2] F. J. Roethlisberger and W. J. Dickson, *Management and the Worker* (Cambridge: Harvard University Press, 1939).

lems suggest that there is something basically wrong with the policies and procedures on which piece-rate systems are based.

Rate setting: the problem of change

[The problem of rate setting] is particularly difficult because American industry is so dynamic. New machines and processes are constantly being created. Old machines and methods are constantly being altered. The rate that is acceptable today may be obsolete tomorrow.

How does management meet this challenge of change? The problem has two aspects. There is first the problem of changing a rate when a mistake has been made in the rate-setting process.

Workers expect management to revise upward a rate that has been proved to be too tight. Can managers similarly expect workers to accept the downward adjustment in a rate that has been set too loose? The *Supervisor's Guide to General Electric Job Information* is interesting on this point. Note the following paragraphs:

> *The fact that rate setters sometimes have been wrong and rates have had to be cut should be faced squarely by the supervisors.*
>
> *No rate setter is perfect. However, it must be pointed out that these occasional mistakes are made on the up side as well as on the down side. No employee thinks it is wrong to adjust a rate upward when a mistake on the down side has been made.*
>
> *There should be just as fair recognition of the necessity and right to make a downward adjustment in a rate as an upward adjustment.*

This statement has a fair and reasonable sound. It seems just as fair to change rates set too high as it is to change rates set too low. But in practice how does management discover that a "mistake" has been made in rate setting? Workers have the impression that this discovery will take place only if they turn out exceptionally high earnings on the job. In fact, we know of cases where the industrial engineers were under instructions to take a new look at any job showing earnings over a certain figure. As to whether rate changes were then put into effect the record is not clear, but the regular appearance of these incentive engineers to check unusually high earnings could hardly have failed to create the impression that it was dangerous to go beyond a certain quota.

If we move from possible mistakes in the rate-setting process to consider changes in job methods and content, the picture becomes still more complicated. Most union contracts provide for changes in rates based on changes in job methods and/or content. But we usually find the qualifying adjective "substantial" or "major" describing the change. It seems generally agreed that management should not be allowed to change a rate on the basis of a trivial change in the job. If this were allowed, then management could make some trifling change in any job as an excuse for setting a new rate. In fact, we have heard workers in some plants charge that this was exactly the excuse that management manufactured and used.

In this connection it is interesting to note a comment by John Mills, an engineer: [3]

> *Reward is supposed to be in direct proportion to production. Well, I remember the first time I ever got behind that fiction. I was visiting the Western Electric Company, which had a reputation of never cutting a piece rate. It never did; if some manufacturing process was found to pay more than seemed right for the class of labor employed on it—if, in other words, the rate-setters had misjudged—that particular part was referred to the engineers for redesign, and then a new rate was set on the new part. Workers, in other words, were paid as a class, supposed to make about so much a week with their best efforts and, of course, less for less competent efforts.*

It is the function of the engineer to improve machines and methods so as to reduce the cost of production. Roethlisberger and Dickson have properly pointed out that low production on an incentive job may call it to the attention of the engineers, who will then try to improve the cost situation by changing the job. Thus it is not only high production and high earnings that bring a job to the attention of the engineers. Nevertheless, we can expect the engineers to pay special attention also to jobs where worker earnings are exceptionally high. If the rate is demonstrated to be loose, then it is a natural invitation for the engineer to come in to see if he cannot institute a change which would justify changing the rates so that management could get the same production for less money. It is not only the lure of cutting costs that operates here. Management is dealing also with problems in intergroup relations. If the rate for one work group is so loose that it permits them to make earnings well above that of their fellows at the same skill level, that situation in itself may lead to disturbances within the ranks of workers. One way of adjusting to this disturbance is through making a change in machine or work method and instituting a new rate.

Even if we leave out of consideration rate changes that are clearly motivated by management's desire to find an excuse to cut the rate, we still come face to face with major questions of judgment.

When does a change become a major or a substantial change? It is obvious that two men of equal good will and sincerity can hold different opinions on this point for many cases.

There is the further troublesome problem of a series of minor changes. It often happens in industry that a job will be modified step by step over

[3] *The Engineer in Society* (New York: D. Van Nostrand & Co., 1946), p. 93.

a period of months or even years. No single change in itself would qualify as major or substantial, and yet the sum total of these modifications might change a rate that was average in earnings to one that was very loose. At what point in the series of minor changes should management be allowed to intervene with a new rate?

Even if all parties agree that the change in the job is so substantial that a new rate must be set, the problem is still far from a solution. Let us assume that the old job was yielding incentive earnings of 50 per cent over base pay. Let us assume that the average earnings figure on other incentive jobs was only 30 per cent above base. In setting the new rate for this group of workers, should the rate setter aim at a 30 per cent or a 50 per cent bonus?

The workers on the job and their union officers will naturally argue that the new rate should provide earnings equivalent to those under the old one. The management may well feel that the old rate was out of line with the general plant picture and that earnings on the new rate of 30 per cent above base are quite adequate. So, even if we assume that the rate setter would be able to predict accurately the earnings possibilities of the job—and we have seen how risky this assumption is—there is no easy answer to the question of what earnings he should aim to make possible. This situation opens up a wide area of conflict.

5. INCENTIVES IN TIME OF CHANGE

From Charles R. Walker, Toward the Automatic Factory, *Yale University Press, New Haven, Conn., 1957, pp. 52, 53, 161–175.*

William F. Whyte, reviewing some of the problems of rate-setting under incentive plans, writes: "If there were no changes in machines and processes, the problem of rate setting would be relatively minor. . . . This area of industrial life would proceed rather peacefully. Our problem is particularly difficult because American industry is so *dynamic.* New machines and processes are constantly being created. Old machines and methods are constantly being altered. *The rate that is acceptable today may be obsolete tomorrow.*" [Italics added.] [1]

The incentive problems associated with a time of technological change were brought out strikingly during the break-in period on the first continuous seamless pipe mill in the United States—Number 4 Seamless—at the Lorain, Ohio, Works of the U.S. Steel Corporation. For the first 18 months after the mill was opened, in January, 1949, it was operated without the incentive. This break-in period was hard on everybody. More

[1] Whyte, *Money and Motivation,* Harper & Brothers, New York, 1955, p. 200.

arduous work, whether mental or physical, was being performed by men and supervisors alike than when the mill was finally broken in and running smoothly. If in the life of a mill such periods are brief, everyone takes them in their stride; if not, they take them the way the crews on Number 4 took them. The men had expected to work at base rates while the mill was breaking in, but by May and June of 1949 they were highly impatient for the installation of incentives. The industrial engineers, however, continued to feel that operations were not sufficiently normal to justify rate-setting. The response of the crews was a slowdown designed to pressure management into "putting in the bonus." Incentives finally went into effect in October, 1950. However, frequent and lengthy delays caused by mechanical breakdowns, as well as dissatisfaction with various aspects of the incentive plan itself, aroused considerable bitterness among the men and discouraged them from even attempting to "make bonus." Later, when the mill was running more smoothly, they began to increase their earnings although, as we shall see, they still had real complaints about the incentive plan.

The point that emerges is this: From the point of view of all the workers, all during the period when they went home with the greatest degree of mental and nervous fatigue, and when management expected their utmost cooperation, financial incentive for working, as the record shows, was the lowest—at first "no bonus" over and above base pay, and then for a time small incentive earnings. Later, with far less effort or anxiety, their incentive was at a maximum, rising at times to 35 and 40 per cent above base pay. . . . [2]

Both men and management have in the past always taken such a situation for granted. Will they continue to take it for granted in an age of accelerated technological change?

Now turn to the same period from management's point of view. The overhead on as costly and complex a mill as Number 4 is very great. Every hour, day, or week in which the mill is down or is operating below the break-even point is costly. It was during this experimental period of operation, when management was trying every device to get the mill rolling, that the men were at their most cynical about the mill's future, and that the crews welcomed shutdowns instead of making every effort to prevent them. . . . In addition to lack of faith in this period, there was lack of financial reward.

What of the future? The author hazards the prediction that as American

[2] It has been stated in defense of incentive plans of this character that the later enjoyment of high earnings under the plan is a "reward" for working hard during the break-in period and after. This in the author's judgment does not meet the difficulty. A carrot for a donkey is not an incentive if he is promised it for next year. One reason it took the workers on Number 4 so long to "operate the mill at normal" was that the men wanted the reward here and now if they were going to be "financially motivated."

industry advances further and further into the technological work environments of the future a way will be found to provide work motivations for break-in periods, when the demand for faith, imagination, nerve, and sometimes muscle is often the greatest.

A few of the possible approaches to this problem may be suggested. One of them is to associate workers' interests closely with management's, so that they will be willing to bear the risks and frustrations of a long break-in or experimental period. Profit-sharing plans and yearly salaries are ways of making this approach. The record of so-called Scanlon plans, which are based upon rewarding workers for reducing unit labor costs, and which encourage worker participation in solving production problems, is suggestive reading for managements seeking a solution to this problem.

Closely related to the question of continual change in process, product, and earning power is the question of mechanical delays. . . . Under the incentive plan in force on Number 4, the industrial engineers had handled the matter of mechanical delays as follows: They kept a record of the time taken up by mechanical delays over a period of months, then calculated a daily average and "absorbed them" in the rate of pay. That is, the men were paid enough more in their individual rates so as not to be penalized for the time the mill was down due to no fault of their own. This arrangement appeared eminently fair to the industrial engineers who had designed the plan and who administered it. It did not appear so to the men. Every man in each of the three crews felt angry and indignant. There were no exceptions. The following comments illustrate what was on the workers' minds:

> *The bonus plan is definitely not a better system on Number 4 than in the old mills. We work our fool heads off and then something happens and we can't make it. You take like last night we had a mill change and we were doing it pretty fast and would have made good bonus. We went along for five hours on good production and we were on our way to make, I would say, about 25 per cent. At 8:30 we had two mechanical breakdowns. That took the steam out of everything we were working for. We knew right then and there that we were never going to make 25 per cent bonus, so the rest of the night we just loafed along.*

> *If you go like mad and then a delay comes, everybody knows they can't make a nickel. I do think that the company is making a mistake on that whole business of the delay time. . . . They'd be surprised if they would figure out in a turn how much pipe did not get made for them because the men just didn't have the incentive to put out.*

These comments can be further clarified by simple arithmetic. Assume a man's base pay to be $2 per hour, and his incentive earnings 25 per cent over and above his base pay. It is obvious then that if he worked at incentive pace for eight hours, and if there was no mechanical delay causing the mill to shut down, he would then net $20, instead of the $16 he would have earned had he not been working at an incentive pace. The incentive offered enables him to earn ten hours' pay (at $2 an hour) in eight hours. But consider what happens if there is a substantial mechanical delay during which the mill does not operate. Assuming that the delay occurs at the beginning of the fourth hour and lasts for two hours, his working day, hour by hour, will look like this:

Hours	Base rate and possible incentive earning	Base rate
1st	$ 2.50	$ 2.00
2nd	2.50	2.00
3rd	2.50	2.00
4th	0.00	2.00
5th	0.00	2.00
6th	2.50	2.00
7th	2.50	2.00
8th	2.50	2.00
	$15.00	$16.00

The two contrasting columns of figures tell what was on the minds of every worker on each of the crews on Number 4 Seamless Mill. The first three items in column 1 mean that the worker had worked at incentive pace and *earned* $2.50 an hour, or 25 per cent above his base rate. The zeros at the fourth and fifth hours means that he had earned nothing during those hours because the mill was down. However, he will receive $16 for his day's work, not $15, because in accordance with his union contract he must be paid his base rate so long as he remains in the mill *ready* to work. But that is no more than he would have received had he not spurred himself to work at an incentive rate for the sixth, seventh, and eighth hours. He was saying in effect, "If management wants me to work at incentive pace after a mechanical delay which isn't my fault, they'll have to 'clock out that delay' and pay me something for it, so I won't lose my whole bonus."

What does the industrial engineer say to the two columns of figures and to the workers' argument? Essentially this: "There's nothing unfair about the arrangement. The delays have been carefully averaged out, and the man has been paid for that average in his regular incentive rate. He has nothing to complain about; in fact he should have the incentive to work right through the day at incentive pace." This comment, as well as the workers' comments, deserve study because they throw light on the problems of financial incentive plans during both periods of technical change and other times. The second sentence in the industrial engineer's statement is simply a statement of fact, and it appears, at least on first examination, to justify the first sentence asserting the fairness of the arrangement. The key, however, to the engineer's point of view lies in the last part of the last sentence, "he *should have the incentive* to work right through the day at incentive pace." Here the industrial engineer and his plan have somehow jumped the track of their purpose of *motivating* the crews to produce more pipe. He has shifted to a moral plane. The plan is clearly *not* motivating them but it *ought* to. Why *ought* the worker to be motivated? Because mathematically the plan is correct and the engineer has accounted for those delays. But psychologically it couldn't be more wrong. And this was conceded at once by all Number 4 supervision and most of local management. We need to add a word at this point in defense of the plan and of the industrial engineers who devised and defended it. In mills where delays are short and few and far between, Number 4's method of absorbing, as against clocking out, delays works perfectly. In short, they had precedent behind them.

The lesson or lessons of the delay episode on Number 4 for the period we are discussing would appear to be these:

First, it is quite possible that in a given situation a proposed incentive plan may be mathematically correct but psychologically and humanly wrong. Therefore, where application of an incentive plan results in the development of *unforeseen* and mutually unacceptable features, it is advisable that provisions be made for prompt adjustment or alteration in the plan to correct such situations before they become serious. Under some circumstances an incentive plan may actually become an anti-incentive influence!

Second, the grave dangers in inflexibility are pointed up. The method of calculating delays, a minor feature in the total incentive plan, became a *cause célèbre* for many months on Number 4 Mill, and was all but unanimously regarded as the greatest stumbling block to higher production and good morale in the whole department. And yet there appeared to be no possible principle or procedure under the terms of the plan by which any compromise could be reached. This is the danger of formalism and overstandardization, which frequently affect large industrial organizations.

Third and finally, a plan devised for a relatively stable situation often fits badly into a dynamic one. Even after the delays were so few as hardly to be an issue, the men feared and resented this feature of the plan. Why? "Management plans to make some more technical improvements on the mill," they said. "That will mean more delays, and so those improvements will mean less bonus for us." This suggests a very much larger and more crucial issue than the delay question with which management must grapple in an age of more and more rapid technological change. How can workers be brought to welcome rather than resist periods of rapid and continual technical change which are likely to characterize the age of automation?

One of the commonest and most persistent criticisms of Number 4's incentive plan by crew members and also by certain members of supervision was that the coverage was too narrow. . . . At the beginning only the twenty-seven members of the hot mill crew [out of a possible 150 men] were included in the bonus. A first step in broadening that coverage occurred when the crane man and crane follower were brought in through a separate incentive application. But the crews continued to agitate for an even broader coverage; they wanted maintenance, both mechanical and electrical, to share. Why were these men so anxious to share the benefits of Number 4's growing prosperity with their fellow workers? The reasons were both economic and social.

Their economic motivation the crew members continually made explicit when interviewed. They insisted that the attitude and competence of indirect labor, especially mechanical and electrical maintenance, had a direct bearing on the amount of bonus earned by every member of the three hot mill crews. If maintenance men were to have as great an economic interest in "keeping the mill rolling" as the crews had, repairs would be made faster and better. So much for the economic reasons for advocating a wider coverage. What else? It is common knowledge that the average hourly wage earner is sensitive to and usually acutely aware of the rate of earnings of his fellow workers. The consensus of Number 4 crews was that indirect labor was entitled to share in the mill's earnings, since these men palpably and substantially contributed to them. Even when it was suggested that the crews might earn more by keeping maintenance from sharing in the incentive take, the men still insisted that coverage should be broadened.

As industry becomes more automatic, the author believes, the tendency will grow to recognize the cooperative and interrelated character of every man's contribution to production, rather than meticulously to isolate and pay for segments of individual effort. In fact as the trend toward automatic machinery advances it may be said that the distinction between direct or productive labor and indirect or nonproductive labor tends to lose its old significance. All labor becomes concerned with the uninterrupted maintenance of a high production rate.

What happened on this question on Number 4 Seamless is of great significance to this inquiry. Following the period covered by this history, the steel corporation greatly extended incentive coverage of hourly wage earners in Lorain. This was in accordance with corporate policy. On Number 4 Seamless the policy has resulted in the coverage of the roll setup man and helper (highly skilled nonproductive workers) and of all mechanical and electrical maintenance workers. Certain laborers are not yet covered at this writing, but it is management's plan and policy to see that all personnel in the mill are covered. Details of this development and its full implications are beyond the scope of this case history. From the standpoint of this inquiry the policy appears to give objective recognition to the interdependence of all categories in a modern steel plant.

As a last note in this brief review of incentives in a time of change, some light may perhaps be thrown on the new character of work in a semi-automatic mill by noticing the men's criticism of management's methods of measuring their work. What they said in various ways may be summed up as follows: "All right, if we're only going to get paid for that part of our work which management can measure, then that's the only work we'll do."

The simplest way to understand what was on these workers' minds is to consider their comparison between work on the old mills and work on the new. The former, to put it broadly, demanded muscle; the latter brains. Or "You do less physically on Number 4, but on most jobs you have to think more." And when they considered "thinking," it was obvious that here was something which, unlike muscular movements, was very difficult to measure. The real point that occurred to them, however, was that it was difficult to assign a *time* for thinking, a time when the brain, like the muscles, would cease to be active and enjoy "idle time," as the muscles did under the incentive plan. One remembers the comments that when one quit work on the old mills only the muscles were tired, but now "my brain keeps on working." Again, apropos of measuring work,

> I get my best ideas about my job and the new passes for the nine-stand when I'm in the can, or at lunch, or on the way home. But under the incentive plan that isn't "true work."

The designer of the incentive plan has an answer for this operator:

> We accounted for your ability to think by giving you a high job class, and your high job class is reflected in your incentive earnings under the plan. .

That appears to be a reasonable answer. Why doesn't the worker "see" it? Having talked with the crews and their supervisors for over four years, I would say this: Instinctively the worker feels that some of the demands on his abilities are different ones in this new work situation, so management should *somehow*—he doesn't say or know how—give recognition to that difference. He doesn't know how, I repeat, but he thinks about it critically whenever the incentive plan, with its necessary emphasis upon an elaborate apparatus for *measuring work,* is being discussed.

Perhaps a better illustration of this same general criticism of the plan comes out of the workers' comments on "watching" instead of doing. On the old mills there was far more "true work," to use a technical phrase, that is work which can be strictly measured, like the motions of the piercer plugger, by the stop watch of the time study man. In contrast, with the automatics on Number 4, the men point out, "most of the time we do nothing but watch."

"I know that," replies the industrial engineer, "and that we call 'attention time.' We measure that and credit you for it."

"We don't think," the worker answers, "that in a mill like this you can really tell the difference, the way you say you can, between just sitting on your tail in front of the machine, which you call idle time—and for which your plan gives a man no credit—and being alert, thinking and ready for action, which you call attention time. Take the stripper man, for instance. You call it attention time when the pipe is going through his machine and the conveyors around him. You call it idle time *after* the pipe has left his area. But in those seconds—under some circumstances they're minutes —the *good* stripper man is on the alert for signals from other areas, and planning what to do next."

A certain kind of answer to this criticism is implicit within the terms of the plan. If what the worker says is true, then could not the inequity be corrected by extending or increasing attention time credit and reducing the amount of idle time for which no credit is given? And would not this and similar "corrections" remove all reasonable objections to the plan? Not if my interpretation, based upon a good many hundreds of conversations over several years, is correct. What the crews are really saying, I believe, is this: "Here on Number 4 you have a *new* setup. Mechanically, electrically it is designed along *new* lines, and in accordance with *new* principles. It is the first continuous seamless tube mill in the United States. To run it successfully we have to act differently, think differently, feel differently. Our relations with each other are different, our relation with our bosses is different. There should be some way in which these differences are recognized in the way management acts toward us and in the way we are paid."

I have studied complaints of workers about incentives for a great many years. As a rule the complaints of the workers and of their union representatives have been that the standards were wrong or unfair and that the rates were too "tight." A few workers on Number 4 complained of a few standards, but the most striking thing about criticisms of the incentive plan was that nearly every worker started by saying: "I have no kick about the standards or the rates; the industrial engineers have been fair," and so on. No, the criticisms were of a different character, as in the present instance, when they challenged the practice of measurement itself.

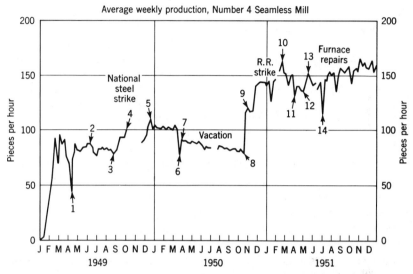

Numbers 1, 2, 3, etc., on curve correspond to explanations of *dips* and *rises* in production given in text of the book from which this selection was taken. These dips and rises were caused by mechanical difficulties. All the others were the results of human situations, such as the one connected with the "delay question" as explained in the text.

Managements that have had the most experience with the new age of automation would tend, I believe, to agree with some of the criticisms of Number 4 crews. In an article entitled "Automation and Industrial Relations" Baldwin and Shultz make a number of comments which are interesting in the light of Number 4's experience. Automation, they suggest, challenges the still prevalent management philosophy which says:

. . . (1) *brake the work process down into the smallest possible components, (2) fit jobs into a rigid structure that emphasizes the* duties and the boundaries of the job rather than its part in the process, *and (3) put everyone possible on an* individual or small-group incentive system *gearing pay to output on the particular job. This philosophy inevitably has tended to identify the individual with an ever more narrow task,* giving him positive incentives to restrict his interests and no incentive at all to think beyond his immediate work environment. . . .

Automation is likely to challenge these habits of thought fostered by discontinuous and highly specialized methods of production. . . . [it] requires a new way of thinking . . . that emphasizes continuous movement of work through a total process rather than stop-and-go progress, thought of as the sum of independent operations.[3] *[Emphasis supplied.]*

Baldwin and Shultz then quote one management group which suggests that seniority standards will undergo an evolution stemming from "the need for a more flexible work force." They comment:

In this view, the development of a work force willing and able to adapt itself to the changing needs of an evolving work process would mean more than application of seniority protections to broader units of work. As a standard for continued employment, "ability to learn" would gradually replace "ability to do" the job. [Emphasis supplied.]

Summary:

In this brief review of incentives in a time of technical change, we have turned up more questions than answers. If questions are good enough in any inquiry, they should point *toward* the answers. That at least is our justification for asking them. To sum up the questions:

How can we provide an incentive for the difficult, break-in period characteristic of these times of rapid technological change?

How can financial incentive plans under conditions of rapid change be prevented from turning into anti-incentive plans?

How can sufficient flexibility be introduced into the principles of any plan and into its administration so that such a relatively minor crisis as the delay question can be promptly resolved and not allowed to fester and disrupt months of operations?

How can thought and effort which are impossible or difficult to measure but of enormous importance both to labor and management be encouraged and rewarded?

How can incentive plans be administered so as to take account not only of financial but of other motivations involving the whole and not simply economic man?

[3] George B. Baldwin and George P. Shultz, "Automation: A New Dimension to Old Problems," Industrial Relations Research Association, *Proceedings of the Seventh Annual Meeting,* Detroit, Dec. 28–30, 1954, pp. 124–5.

man-machine problems: analyses and solutions

INTRODUCTION

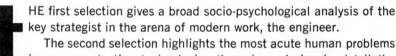

HE first selection gives a broad socio-psychological analysis of the key strategist in the arena of modern work, the engineer.

The second selection highlights the most acute human problems in mass-production technologies through analyzing in detail the somewhat extreme example of an automobile assembly line.

One of the social arguments most frequently made in favor of automation is that meaningless routines will be eliminated from factory work and that the computer will do the same for the office worker. All of this is foreseen together with enormous time-saving, dollar-saving, and brain-saving services for management. The author believes that this is a sound prediction of a trend which is well under way. But two important reservations should be made. The human problems of mass-production technologies will be with us for many years. It takes time and careful planning to substitute successfully computer routines for job routines in the average manufacturing corporation. It should also be emphasized that most industrial processes are and will continue to be amalgams of old and new technologies. Finally, even when the full potential of automatic machines and the computer is realized, many jobs at many levels will still be done better and more cheaply by men and women.

The reader's attention is called to two important points in the selection "Basic Human Problems in Mass-production Technologies." The first is that as a method of analyzing realistically the human impact of technology on men and women, eight work dimensions are utilized: knowledge and skill requirements, pacing or rate of performance, and so forth. These same dimensions will later be applied to the analysis of a highly automated plant in a subsequent chapter (see page 158) and so give the reader a basis of comparison for dimensions of human impact. The second point is that not all assembly work and in fact not all routine work has a negative or undesirable effect on the worker. This point is illustrated by a brief analysis of a type of assembly technology which produces favorable human reactions and effects.

The third selection is a short one, underscoring the often forgotten phenomenon that mass-production technologies, and indeed all others, not only impinge on the worker favorably or unfavorably but profoundly influence managerial thinking and values as well.

The next two selections deal with the all-important problem of economic rewards under mass-production and other technologies. The final selection in the preceding chapter, "Incentives in Time of Change," raised many questions in this strategic area but did not answer them. Here certain answers are provided in two selections, "Enterprise for Everyman" and "The Scanlon Plan through a Psychologist's Eyes." As a takeoff for both selections, actual cases in the application of a specific payment plan are utilized, and the underlying psychological principles for any healthy method of economic reward in modern industry are outlined.

The fifth selection, "Increasing Satisfaction and Cutting Costs through Redesigning Machine-Man Relations," in a sense brings us back to the basic human problems with which the chapter began, but this time at another level, the therapeutic intervention of management. Perhaps the most important point emphasized in this selection is that frequently it is possible to introduce a radical design into an old technology which will both enhance the human value of jobs for men in the factory and be more profitable for management.

Earlier in this introduction we emphasized the mixed evolution that was occurring in the technologies of modern industry. To draw a sharp line between the era of mass production and the era of automation and the computer is too often a distortion of the facts. The final selection, "A Cross-industrial Study of Technology and Work," admirably documents this point. The authors of the study remark that "industries were chosen for broad diversification as to technology and nature of work, as well as company size and regional setting." The one common denominator that appears, however, in this mixed package is that in each case the technological component of the work emerged, whether positively or negatively, as the decisive determinant of the job's human value.

Although some of the selections in this chapter were written with a special view to solving human problems in mass-production factories, most of them are applicable to a broad range of technologies including the new ones.

BIBLIOGRAPHY

Argyris, Chris: *Personality and Organization,* Harper & Row, Publishers, Incorporated, New York, 1957.

Cartwright, Dorwin, and Alvin Zander (eds.): *Group Dynamics: Research and Theory,* Harper & Row, Publishers, Incorporated, 1953. (For general group theory, see Part I, "Approaches to the Study of Groups"; for certain applications in industry and elsewhere, see Part VII, "Leadership".)

Davis, Louis E.: "Job Design and Productivity: A New Approach," *Personnel,* vol. 33, March, 1957.

————: "Pacing Effects on Manned Assembly Lines," *The International Journal of Production Research* (published by the Institution of Production Engineers, 10 Chesterfield Street, London, W.1.), vol. 4, no. 3, 1966.

———— and R. R. Canter: "Job Design," *Journal of Industrial Engineering,* vol. 6, no. 1, January, 1955.

Elliot, Douglas J.: "Increasing Office Productivity through Job Enlargement," *The Human Side of the Office Manager's Job,* American Management Association, Office Management Series, no. 134, New York, 1953.

Foster, G. M.: *Traditional Cultures and the Impact of Technological Change,* Harper & Row, Publishers, Incorporated, New York, 1962.

Friedmann, Georges: *Où va le travail humain?* Gallimard, Paris, 1950.

————: *Industrial Society,* The Free Press, New York, 1955.

————: *Le Travail en miettes,* Gallimard, Paris, 1956.

————, Pierre Naville, et al.: *Traité de sociologie du travail,* A. Colin, Paris, 1961–1962.

Guest, Robert H.: *Organizational Change: The Effect of Successful Leadership,* Richard D. Irwin, Inc., Homewood, Ill., 1962.

————: "Men and Machines: An Assembly-line Worker Looks at His Job," *Personnel,* vol. 31, May, 1955.

————: "Of Time and the Foreman," *Personnel,* vol. 32, May, 1956.

————: "Job Enlargement: A Revolution in Job Design," *Personnel Administration,* vol. 20, March–April, 1957.

Haire, Mason, et al. (eds.): *Modern Organization Theory,* John Wiley & Sons, Inc., New York, 1959.

Herzberg, F., B. Mausner, and B. Snyderman: *The Motivation to Work,* 2d ed., John Wiley & Sons, Inc., New York, 1959.

Homans, George C.: *Social Behavior: Its Elementary Forms,* Harcourt, Brace & World, Inc., New York, 1961.

Jacques, Elliot: *The Changing Culture of a Factory,* Tavistock Publications, Ltd., London, 1951.

Katz, R. L.: "Toward a More Effective Enterprise," *Harvard Business Review,* September–October, 1960.

Kornhauser, A. W.: *Mental Health of the Industrial Worker: A Detroit Study,* John Wiley & Sons, Inc., New York, 1965.

Landsberger, Henry A.: *Hawthorne Revisited,* Cornell University Press, Ithaca, N.Y., 1958.

McGregor, Douglas: *The Human Side of Enterprise,* McGraw-Hill Book Company, New York, 1960.

Mann, F. C., B. P. Indik, and V. H. Vroom: *The Productivity of Work Groups,* Survey Research Center, Ann Arbor, Mich., 1963.

March, J. G., and H. A. Simon: *Organizations,* John Wiley & Sons, Inc., New York, 1958.

Meltzer, Leo, and James Salter: "Organizational Structure and Performance and Job Satisfaction," *American Sociological Review,* vol. 27, pp. 351–362, 1962.

Merton, Robert K.: *Social Theory and Social Structure,* The Free Press, New York, 1957.

――――: "The Machine, the Worker and the Engineer," *Social Theory and Social Structure,* The Free Press, New York, 1957, pp. 567–573.

Morse, Nancy C., and Robert S. Weiss: "The Function and Meaning of Work and the Job," *American Sociological Review,* vol. 20, no. 2, pp. 191–198, 1955.

Pelz, D. C.: "Some Social Factors Related to Performance in a Research Organization," *Administrative Science Quarterly,* pp. 313–320, December, 1956.

――――: "Motivation of the Engineering and Research Specialist," American Management Association, General Management Series, no. 186, pp. 33–36, New York, 1957.

Richardson, F. L. W., Jr., and Charles R. Walker: *Human Relations in an Expanding Company: A Study of the Manufacturing Departments in the Endicott Plant of the International Business Machines Corporation,* Yale Labor and Management Center, New Haven, Conn., 1948.

Roethlisberger, F. J.: *Management and Morale,* Harvard University Press, Cambridge, Mass., 1947.

―――― and William J. Dickson: *Management and the Worker,* Harvard University Press, Cambridge, Mass., 1939.

Seashore, Stanley E.: *Group Cohesiveness in the Industrial Work Group,* Survey Research Center, University of Michigan, Ann Arbor, Mich., 1954.

Shepard, H. A.: "Basic Research and the Social System of Pure Science," *Philosophy of Science,* pp. 48–57, January, 1956.

Shultz, George P.: "Worker Participation on Production Problems," *Personnel,* pp. 201–210, November, 1951.

Turner, Arthur N.: "Management and the Assembly Line," *Harvard Business Review,* vol. 33, pp. 40–48, September–October, 1955.

――――: "Impersonality and Group Membership: A Case Study of an Automobile Assembly Line," unpublished doctoral dissertation, Graduate School, Cornell University, Ithaca, N.Y., September, 1958.

Vroom, Victor H.: *Work and Motivation,* John Wiley & Sons, Inc., New York, 1964.

――――: "Ego-involvement, Job Satisfaction and Job Performance," *Personnel Psychology,* vol. 15, pp. 159–178, 1962.

Walker, Charles R.: "The Problem of the Repetitive Job," *Harvard Business Review,* vol. 28, no. 3, pp. 54–59, May, 1950.

―――― and Robert H. Guest: *The Man on the Assembly Line,* Harvard University Press, Cambridge, Mass., 1952.

――――, Robert H. Guest, and Arthur N. Turner: *The Foreman on the Assembly Line,* Harvard University Press, Cambridge, Mass., 1956.

Whyte, William F.: *Money and Motivation,* Harper & Row, Publishers, Incorporated, New York, 1955.

Worthy, James C.: "Organizational Structure and Employee Morale," *American Sociological Review,* vol. 15, no. 2, pp. 174–177, April, 1950.

Zaleznik, A., C. R. Christensen, and F. J. Roethlisberger: *The Motivation, Productivity, and Satisfaction of Workers,* Harvard Business School, Boston, 1958.

1. THE MACHINE, THE WORKER, AND THE ENGINEER

From Robert K. Merton, Social Theory and Social Structure, *The Free Press, New York, 1957, pp. 567–573.*

IMPLICATIONS FOR THE ENGINEER

New applications of science to production by the engineer . . . do not merely affect the methods of production. They are inescapably social decisions affecting the routines and satisfactions of men at work on the machine and, in their larger reaches, shaping the very organization of the economy and society.

The central role of engineers as the General Staff of our productive systems only underscores the great importance of their social and political orientations: the social strata with which they identify themselves; the texture of group loyalties woven by their economic position and their occupational careers; the groups to whom they look for direction; the types of social effects of their work which they take into account—in short, only by exploring the entire range of their allegiances, perspectives, and concerns can engineers achieve that self-glorification of their social role which makes for fully responsible participation in society.

But to say that this poses sociological problems for "the" engineer is to make a reference so inclusive and vague as to mean little at all. The large and multifarious family of men called engineers have a far-flung kinship, but they also have much that marks subgroups off, each from the others. There are military, civil, mechanical, chemical, electrical, and metallurgical engineers, and so on down through the hundreds of titles found among the members of national engineering societies. But whatever their specialty, so long as they are concerned with the design, construction, or operation of the equipments and processes of production, they are confronted with social and political implications of their position in our society.

A nascent trend toward full recognition of these implications is curbed by several obstacles, chief among which, it would seem, are (1) the marked specialization and division of scientific labor, (2) the applications of professional codes governing the social outlook of engineers, and (3) the incorporation of engineers into industrial bureaucracies.

Specialization

The intensified division of labor has become a splendid device for escaping social responsibilities. As professions subdivide, each group of specialists finds it increasingly possible to "pass the buck" for the social consequences of their work, on the assumption, it would seem, that in this complex transfer of responsibility there will be no hindmost for the devil to take. When appalled by resulting social dislocations, each specialist, secure in the knowledge that he has performed his task to the best of his ability, can readily disclaim responsibility for them. And, of course, no one group of specialists, the engineer any more than the others, alone initiates these consequences. Rather, within our economic and social structure each technological contribution meshes into a cumulative pattern of effects, some of which none has desired and all have brought about.

The professional ethic

Deriving in part from the specialization of functions, engineers, not unlike scientists, come to be indoctrinated with an ethical sense of limited responsibilities. The scientist, busy on his distinctive task of carving out new knowledge from the realm of ignorance, has long disclaimed responsibility for attending to the ways in which this knowledge was applied. (History creates its own symbols. It required an atomic bomb to shake many scientists loose from this tenaciously held doctrine.)

So, in many quarters, it has been held absurd that the engineer should be thought accountable for the social and psychological effects of technology, since it is perfectly clear that these do not come within his special province. After all, it is the engineer's "job"—note how effectively this defines the limits of one's role and, thereby, one's social responsibility— to improve processes of production, and it is "not his concern" to consider their ramified social effects. The occupational code focuses the attention of engineers upon the first links in the chain of consequences of technological innovation and diverts their attention, both as specialists and as citizens, from succeeding links in the chain as, for example, the consequences for wage levels and employment opportunities. "But we have to include consequences impartially"—this is John Dewey putting the issue in more general form. "It is willful folly to fasten upon some single end or consequence which is liked, and permit the view of that to blot from perception all other undesired and undesirable consequences."

Bureaucratic status

The employment of large numbers of engineers and technologists in industrial bureaucracies further shapes their social perspectives. Knit into a bureaucratic apparatus, many engineers take their place as experts in a subaltern role with fixed spheres of competence and authority and with a severely delimited orientation toward the larger social system. In this status, they are rewarded for viewing themselves as technical auxiliaries. As such, it is not their function to consider the human and social consequences of introducing their efficient equipments and processes or to decide when and how they are to be introduced. These are matters for administrative and managerial concern.

The grounds for assigning these concerns to administrators in business and industrial organizations have seldom been stated as lucidly and instructively as in the following passage by Roethlisberger: ". . . physicists, chemists, mechanical, civil, chemical engineers have a useful way of thinking about and a simple method of dealing with their own class of phenomena. Within this area their judgments are likely to be sound. Outside it their judgments are more questionable. Some of them recognize quite clearly this limitation. They do not want to be concerned with the human factor; they want to design the best tool, the best machine to accomplish certain technical purposes. Whether or not the introduction of this tool or machine will involve the layoff of certain employees, quite rightly, is not their concern as engineers. . . . These men are invaluable to the administrator in any industrial organization."

Max Weber and Thorstein Veblen, among others, have pointed to the danger that this occupational perspective, involving the rationalized abdication of social responsibility in favor of the administrator, may be transferred by engineers beyond the immediate economic enterprise. From this transference of outlook and the resulting trained incapacity for dealing with human affairs there develops a passive and dependent role for engineers and technologists in the realm of political organization, economic institutions, and social policy. The citizen-self threatens to become submerged in the occupational self.

As technical specialists thus attend to "their own" limited tasks, the over-all impact of technology upon the social structure becomes nobody's business through default.

THE NEEDS OF SOCIAL RESEARCH

Engineers may well continue to abjure any direct concern with the social effects of an advancing technology as long as the effects cannot be anticipated and taken into account. To the extent that social scientists have failed to address themselves to this problem, there is no informed basis for the most socially oriented of technologists to act with due social responsibility. Only when those equipped with the skills of social research make available an adequate body of scientific knowledge can those working with the skills of engineering extend their sights from the individual business enterprise to the larger social system.

Just as men for centuries neglected the problems of soil erosion, in part because they were unaware that erosion constituted a significant problem, so they are still neglecting the social erosion ascribable to present methods of introducing rapid technological changes. There is a severely limited market for research in this field. It seems safe to suppose that fewer man-hours of research activity are devoted to the intensive investigation of these problems central to our technological age than, say to the design of alluring packages for perfumes and other such basic commodities or to the planning of competitive advertisements for the tobacco manufacturers of the nation.

The inauguration of a vast program of social inquiry proportioned to the scale of the problem need not wait upon new research procedures. Methods of social research have been advancing steadily and will undoubtedly become developed further through disciplined experience. The effective development of this program does wait, however, upon decisions concerning the organization of the research teams, sponsorship of the research, and the directions of inquiry.

Organization of the research team

Disparate and uncoordinated inquiries by diversely skilled groups have not proved adequate. The problems in this area call for the complementary skills and knowledge of engineers, economists, psychologists, and sociologists. Once this focus of joint inquiry is recognized, systematic efforts to institute a program of collaborative investigation could be begun by representatives of the several professional societies. Common universes of discourse would probably be lacking at the outset, but, as the experience of the TVA suggests, patterns of collaboration between engineers and social scientists can be evolved. The walls insulating the several disciplines raised up by the division of scientific labor can be surmounted if they are recognized for the temporary expedients that they are.

Sponsorship of the research

Of the limited body of social research in industry, the greater part has been oriented toward the needs of management. The problems selected as the focus of the inquiry—high labor turnover and restricted output, for example—have been largely thus defined by management, sponsorship has been typically by management, the limits and character of experimental changes in the work situation have been passed upon by management, and periodic reports have been made primarily to management. No matter how good or seemingly self-evident the reason, it should be noted that this *is* the typical perspective of social research in industry and that it limits the effective prosecution of the research.

These remarks do not, of course, impugn the validity and usefulness of research oriented toward the needs of management. From the fact that this research continues to be sponsored by management, we can conclude only that it has been found eminently useful and valid, within the limits of the definition of problems. But an intelligence staff for one stratum of the business and industrial population may in due course find itself focusing on problems which are not the chief problems confronting other sectors of that population. It may happen, for example, that devising methods of reducing workers' anxieties through sympathetic and prolonged interviews or through appropriate behavior by supervisors is not among those researches which workers regard as central to their interests. They may be more concerned with having research men uncover the varied consequences, for themselves and for others, of alternative plans governing the introduction of technological changes.

This reminds us that social research itself takes place within a social setting. The social scientist who fails to recognize that his techniques of participant-observation, interviewing, sociogramming, and the like represent an innovation for workers and supervisors greater, perhaps, than technological changes in the plant would indeed be a dubious believer in his own findings. Resistance to this innovation can be anticipated, if only because it is remote from run-of-the mill experience of most people. Those who have engaged in social research among workers and administrative personnel need not be told of the mingled suspicion, distrust, uneasy amusement, and, often, open hostility with which they were initially met. Unfamiliarity with this type of inquiry, coupled with its apparent inquisitiveness into areas of tension and private affairs, makes for some measure of resistance.

If the research is subsidized by management and if the problems dealt with are relevant primarily to management, the resistance of workers will be all the greater. It is small wonder that in some quarters of organized labor the preliminary efforts at social research in industry are regarded with a measure of suspicion and distrust comparable to that which attended the introduction of scientific management studies in the 1920's. For if workers have occasion to identify the research program as a new-fangled academic device for countering labor organizations or for scientifically substituting symbolic for material rewards, it will create rather than locate problems.

Social research in industry, therefore, must be conducted under the joint auspices of management and labor, irrespective of the source of funds for the research. The cooperation of large numbers of workers will not be achieved unless they know that they will be beneficiaries of an application of scientific method to a field where rule-of-thumb has largely prevailed.

The directions of research

The initial task of these research teams would be to search out the specific problems which demand attention. The very fact that they undertake the research would indicate that they are not possessed by the opaque faith that forward strides in technology, howsoever applied, must lead to the common good. They would be expected to think dangerous thoughts. They would not hold cultural and institutional axioms to be beyond inquiry. The focus of their attention would be the institutional arrangements adequate to incorporate the full potentialities for production of an unevenly but continuously advancing technology with an equitable distribution of gains and losses contained in these advances.

During the last decade there has occurred a reaction among social researchers against the earlier tendency to focus on the economic consequences of advances in technology. The center of research attention was shifted to workers' sentiments and social relations on the job. This new emphasis, however, has the defects of its qualities. It is not only the sentiments of workers which are affected by technological change. It is not only their social ties and their status—it is also their incomes, their job chances, and their economic interests. If the new research on human relations in industry is to have maximum pertinence, it must be meshed with the continuing research on the economic implications of labor-saving technology.

Nor can the research be effectively confined to studies of "the worker." To single out the worker as though he represented a self-contained sector of the industrial population is to do violence to the structure of social relations which actually obtains in industry. Presumably, it is not only the worker who is subject to preoccupations, obsessive reveries, defects and distortions of attitude, and irrational dislikes of co-workers or supervisors. It might even turn out that the behavior and decisions of management are appreciably affected by similar psychological patterns and that these, as well as a clear-cut sense of economic interests, go far toward determining decisions on the introduction of labor-saving technology.

In the absence of research jointly sponsored by labor and management and aimed at commonly agreed-upon problems of the role of technology in our society, the alternative is to pursue the present pattern of piecemeal research, directed toward those special problems which it is in the interest of special groups to have examined. It is possible, of course, that this alternative will seem preferable to some. It is altogether possible that the several interested groups will find no basis for agreement on the sponsorship and direction of social research in this field. But then, this too would serve its backhanded purpose. Should research by technologists and social scientists under the joint auspices of management and labor be rejected on these grounds, it would be a significant diagnostic sign of the state which industrial relations have reached.

2. BASIC HUMAN PROBLEMS IN MASS–PRODUCTION TECHNOLOGIES: PACING, PRESSURE, AND REPETITIVENESS

Adapted from Charles R. Walker, Changing Character of Human Work under the Impact of Technological Change, National Commission on Technology, Automation and Economic Progress, *1965, Appendix, vol. 2, pp. 296–301.*

In investigating the impact of mass-production technologies on work, the conventional formula of wages, hours, and working conditions is still used. But to successfully analyze work environments in the modern world, several other measurements or work dimensions are strategic for determining both productivity and the human impact.

A series of eight are suggested here as an analytic tool for different industries and technologies. These dimensions are specifically designed to highlight the characteristics of work as affected or determined by the job's technological component, that is, the machines or other "hardware" connected with a man's work. They are:

1. Knowledge and skill requirement.
2. Pacing or rate of performance.
3. Degree of repetitiveness or variety.
4. Relation to the total product or process. (This includes how much of a particular product or process the individual works on as well as his overall relation to the total operation of his plant or unit.)
5. Relationships with people as individuals or groups. (This includes the frequency of interactions and whether these are functionally required by the work or are discretionary.)
6. Style of supervision and managerial controls, whether administrative or technological.
7. Degree of worker's autonomy in determining work methods.
8. Relation of work to personal development, both on the job and with respect to transfers and promotions.

"Degree of responsibility" demanded by the job is not named specifically because this may be deduced from the other dimensions.

The impact of technology on these work dimensions will be analyzed first by examining the classical example of mass-production manufacturing on automobile assemblylines.

Ample research findings for the industry not only dramatically demonstrate the close relation between technology and attitudes and behavior of workers, but significantly most of these data are also applicable to assemblyline technologies in other industries. Although in this industry extreme examples of unfavorable work environments due to technology are confined to a relatively small number of final assemblyline workers, it is here that behavioral effects have the most serious social consequences, for the individual, the industry, and the economy as a whole. The record shows that the prolongation of both legal and illegal walkouts in automobile factories is often due to "local working conditions" in assembly plants. Here the impact of technology on job dimensions is greatest. In the nationwide General Motors' strike in the fall of 1964, of the 28 plants that remained on strike after the official settlement, 22 were assembly plants. Eight others, although accepting the terms of the general settlement, declared they would remain idle until their companion assembly plants had satisfactorily settled "local issues." These 30 assembly plants accounted for 77 percent of General Motors' automaking capacity. Significantly, all the plants except two which agreed to the official settlement were plants not involved in final assembly.

The first four dimensions—knowledge and skill requirements, pacing and rate of performance, degree of repetitiveness or variety, and relation to the total product or process—are clearly related and flow from "principles" of mass production.

Typical jobs on the "main line," or moving conveyor, serve to illustrate these dimensions and their interrelationship. Consider the job of the automotive worker who installs toeplates:

I put in the two different toeplates that cover the holes where the brake and clutch pedals are. I am inside the car and have to be down on the seat to do my work. On one kind of car I put in the shift lever while another man puts in the toeplates.[1]

While doing his job this man rides along in the car performing two operations, and must complete the job in 2 minutes, or else he will be carried too far. He then returns to his station, climbs into another car, and begins all over again. Thus his pace is strictly governed by the moving line. Such a job is also highly repetitive. Only slight variety is introduced when the worker installs a shift lever instead of a toeplate on certain cars. The job demands very little skill and has a learning period of just 2 days. Although the worker gets in and out of cars 20 or 30 times an hour, his expenditure of physical energy on the actual operation is slight.

A somewhat similar situation can also apply to jobs not on a moving belt. For example, a blower-defroster assembler who works off the main line describes his job as follows:

I work at a bench on blower-defrosters. The blowers come in two parts. I take one part and attach the blower motor to it. I then connect the fan to

[1] Job descriptions given here come from interviews with actual job holders. But since details of assembly jobs vary from year to year, and change with the introduction of new models, the descriptions are cited only as generally typical of assembly work. They do not reproduce in detail any current job descriptions for any one company.

the motor shaft. Then I take the other half of the air pipe and put two parts together with 14 screws. I test the motor to see if it works, and if it does, I put in the 15th screw which grounds it to the pipe. The materials are brought to me and put in a pile by a stock chaser. After I finish, I put each assembled blower on one of six shelves.

Here pace is only indirectly determined by the main line, since the worker has some choice of pace in keeping his shelves stocked with a supply of blower-defrosters. There is little variety since he performs only three operations. However, a slight variation is introduced through differences in models. His job operations require a minimum of skill: "I learned it in a couple of hours, though it took me about a week to get up speed."

For both these jobs skill requirements are clearly low, the jobs are strictly paced and repetitive and only a small fraction of the product is worked on. These characteristics also appear to be required by the technology.

A good general description of the overall engineering design of an automobile assembly is given in the Department of Labor's occupational handbook:

Final assembly is the process of putting together in sequence the individual parts of the subassemblies, with the completed vehicle rolling off the end of the line. Overhead wires feed electric power to nut tighteners, welding equipment, and other tools used by workers on the assembly line. A conveyor carries the motor vehicles forward while men at work stations attach the necessary parts and subassemblies in proper sequence.

Generally the assembly of a car starts with the frame which forms the foundation of the motor vehicle. All other parts and subassemblies are attached to it. Large and heavy subassemblies, such as the engine and the body, are lowered by hoists into position on the chassis as it comes down the line. The finishing accessories, such as bumpers, hubcaps, and floor mats, are added near the end of the line. Finally, the headlights are adjusted, the wheels are aligned, and gasoline is pumped into the fuel tank, and thus another new motor vehicle is driven off the line under its own power.[2]

Studies of final assemblyline work in a major automobile company by the Technology Project of Yale University found the average time cycle for jobs to be 3 minutes. As to learning time, a few hours to a week sufficed. Learning time for 65 percent of the force was less than a month. In one of the plants, 31.7 percent of the work force performed 1 operation to complete each job cycle; 12.8 percent, 2 operations; 22.8 percent, 3 to 5 operations; 16.1 percent, 5 to 10 operations; and 15.5 percent, 10 or

[2] U.S. Department of Labor, *Occupational Outlook Handbook,* 1959, p. 502.

more operations. For 1.1 percent, it was impossible to determine clearly the number of operations performed.

In examining the technological work environment which characterizes final assembly in the automobile industry, it is important to remember that the effects, in terms of strict pacing, repetitiveness, etc., are extreme. While skill demands and learning time are considerably higher for other sections of the auto industry, nearly half of all automobile manufacturing workers in 1960 filled assembling, inspecting, materials handling, and other semiskilled jobs. Another fourth were employed as foremen, mechanics and repairmen, machinists, tool and die makers, and in other skilled occupations. Clerical workers were about a 10th of those employed, and the remainder worked in professional, technical, sales, and managerial occupations and as laborers and guards.[3]

If we were to ask whether automation has modified these findings, the answer would of necessity be yes and no. The "transfer machine," or "Detroit automation," has transformed the manufacture of engines, and in introducing numerical control for retooling, automobile manufacturers have linked automatic machine tools to perform a variety of operations. But final assembly itself, the classic example of mass-production technology, has not been substantially altered. The reason is simple: To automate an operation which involves fitting together some 10,000 separate parts would not be economically feasible.

The frequency and character of interpersonal relations on the assemblyline, the fifth dimension, are largely determined by mechanical factors, and for most workers are reduced to an occasional exchange of a few words with those nearest on the moving line. Noise, rapidity of the moving conveyors and the demands of the work itself for unremitting attention are the principal deterrents to verbal interaction. Furthermore, few jobs on an automobile assemblyline require a functional or team relationship. For the most part, workers are stationed serially along a moving conveyor, each quickly performing his own individual function which must be completed before the part moves to his neighbor. A certain quota of men along a certain length of the main line (or on subassembly lines or at benches) are assigned to a foreman. In a sense these men constitute separate work groups; however, they have little cohesiveness or sense of unity. Just as the pacing and repetitiveness of the work reduce to a minimum *horizontal* relations between workers, so they also limit vertical relations, i.e., interaction with foremen. And, not surprisingly, investigators report that dislike of rigid pacing and repetitiveness is greatly accented by correlative restrictions on interpersonal relationships of all kinds. The sense of constriction and pressure on the lines is also affected by the

[3] "Employment Outlook in Motor Vehicles Manufacturing," *Occupational Outlook Report Series*, Bureau of Labor Statistics, Bulletin No. 1375–101.

availability of relief men. For example, no worker is permitted to leave the line to go to the toilet until a relief man has been located to take his place. Accordingly, the worker speaks of himself as tied to the line.

Since the speed set for the line "supervises" the *pace* of work, and in fact determines the number of completed cars that come off the end of the line each hour, the sixth dimension, style of supervision, may be thought to be comparatively unimportant. But, nonetheless, the role of the foreman is of primary importance, and perhaps unexpectedly, a foreman actually can choose from a variety of styles of supervision. He may reinforce or amplify the coercion inherent in the pacing and repetitiveness of the job, or he may in a variety of ways lighten that pressure and humanize the job for his workers.[4]

The seventh dimension, degree of autonomy in determining work methods, has been skillfully eliminated as far as humanly possible by careful engineering calculation. Some latitude does creep back when there is a model change. Then work is reassigned; but before the final re-subdivision of tasks has been completed, the individual may be permitted to perform more operations and work on a somewhat larger fraction of the final product.

The eighth dimension, relation of work to personal development both on the job and with respect to transfer and promotions, is easily the most important, and from the individual's standpoint embraces, in a sense, all the others. Whether they are blue-collar, white-collar, or administrative workers, people will commonly endure severe restrictions and hardships in their careers if the work itself is psychologically rewarding or if it is clearly a rung of the ladder leading to a satisfactory job future. Jobs in final assembly comparable to those outlined are neither.

After remarking on the inherent impersonalization of the moving conveyor, Robert Blauner has summarized the lack of psychological rewards in final assembly work this way:

> *The alienation of meaninglessness is further intensified by the workers' lack of a clear identification with a particular job. The division of labor is so extreme that most jobs are basically the same. In addition, because there are many lines operating at once, there are a number of men performing exactly the same tasks. One cannot, therefore, derive a sense of function as the left-front hubcap assembler. Fractionalized job assignments, cyclic rather than task-directed work rhythms, and the anonymous atmosphere of the large plants all dilute the sense of meaning, purpose, and function on the assembly line.*[5]

[4] For further expansion of these points see: Charles R. Walker, Robert H. Guest, and Arthur N. Turner, The Foreman on the Assembly Line, Harvard Press, Cambridge, Mass., 1956.

[5] Robert Blauner, Alienation and Freedom: The Factory Worker and His Industry, The University of Chicago Press, Chicago, 1964, p. 108.

As to the potential for a progressive work career through promotion or transfer, the wage floor in auto assemblylines is indeed high, but it is flat. Since nearly all jobs have been broken down into a relatively simple set of motions, little gradation in skills exists between a job in one section of the line and another. Translated in terms of wages, there is little spread between the lowest and highest job classes. In one plant, for example, Yale Technology Project investigators found that two-thirds of the workers in the two largest departments received exactly the same wage; the promotion ladder among production workers was virtually nonexistent. Robert Guest, commenting on the same point said:

> By applying principles of work rationalization, the industrial engineer, in the best interests of efficiency, has simplified the tasks so that differences in skill from one job to the next were all but eliminated. It was difficult for the average worker to move vertically through a series of distinct steps in promotion. In this connection, it should be added that over the years the union itself, through collective bargaining, had encouraged the trend toward uniform wage standards by raising minimum levels without increasing the relative amounts between job classes.
>
> From a careful examination of the actual work careers of over 200 workers we have found only a few who had experienced any substantial change in job classification during a period of from 12 to 15 years.[6]

As one might expect, individual workers reacted with varying degrees of intensity to the assemblyline technology. One worker disliked most of all the repetitiveness of the job; another, the pacing of the line; another, restriction of movement or of interaction; another, the lack of opportunity for advancement. A small minority appeared indifferent to any of these factors. On the positive side, the relatively high-wage rate for all jobs was the most commonly liked feature of assemblyline work. This was especially true for younger men. Many older workers with families felt they had wasted their lives in a skill-less occupation, but were now hesitant to leave and sacrifice seniority. Most of the work force pointed out that layoffs substantially reduced annual earnings.

Despite individual differences, overall attitudes were markedly consistent. The Yale Technology Project found that a majority of workers were satisfied with wages, but 9 out of 10 disliked intensely the pacing and repetitiveness of their jobs. The plant for which these findings were first reported was relatively new and many of the workers were fresh to factory work. In order to test their validity, investigators spent 2 years more in another study of a much older plant where workers had long seniority records in assembly work. The findings in the older plant were

[6] Robert H. Guest, "Men and Machines, An Assembly-Line Worker Looks at His Job." The Yale Technology Project, Yale University, New Haven, Conn., reprinted from *Personnel*, May 1955.

the same, with only minor differences, the most important being less satisfaction with the economic rewards.

For many methodological reasons, it is less satisfactory to measure worker attitudes than actual behavior. The technology project sought, therefore, to relate work dimensions to actual behavior. Some evidence in early studies of hourly wage earners made by the British Medical Council indicated that a correlation might exist between certain mass-production characteristics of industrial jobs and absentee and turnover records. A mass-production index was accordingly constructed for each worker's job, consisting of the following scalable factors: (1) Degree of repetitiveness; (2) degree of mechanical pacing; (3) skill as measured by length of learning time; (4) frequency of break in job routine; (5) frequency of social interaction; and (6) size of interacting group. This index was applied to each worker's job, and the resulting profiles were then correlated with company records of absenteeism and turnover.

A statistically significant correlation was found to exist between absenteeism and mass-production characteristics. Men with highly repetitive jobs—conveyor paced and the like—were far more likely to take time off from work than those with other types of jobs. Quit records showed that twice as many workers left jobs with extreme mass production as with moderate mass-production characteristics. Both factors were reflected in higher costs of production.

The unfavorable impact of mass-production characteristics isolated and measured in the technology project studies has been confirmed by the substantial Kornhauser study, conducted over several years under a grant from the National Institute of Mental Health and recently made public:

> The outstanding finding is that mental health varies consistently with the level of jobs the men hold. When we compare the factory workers by occupational categories, the higher the occupation (in respect to skill and associated attributes of variety, responsibility and pay) the better the mental health. Those in skilled jobs have highest mental-health scores, followed by the semiskilled and, lowest of all, the men in routine, repetitive types of work.[7]

All assembly technologies do not, of course, produce unfavorable worker reactions similar to those discussed above. For example, the reaction is quite different and far more favorable in a division of the same automobile company studied where small parts are assembled on a moving belt. Clearly one must ask under what conditions reactions are favorable, or what kind of assemblyline technology provides work dimensions

[7] Arthur Kornhauser, *Mental Health and the Industrial Worker*, John Wiley & Sons, Inc., New York, 1965. See especially pp. 260 ff.

that enhance rather than depress the morale and mental and physical health of workers.

A study of repetitive work in an assembly plant in the electronics industry suggests some answers.[8]

The study was set in a large assembly department of a manufacturer of high-quality electronic products. Operators were divided into teams of from three to six girls working either at benches, where the product was moved by hand from one assembler to her neighbor, or at small conveyors, which moved the parts. The typical job cycle for each team member was 1 minute or less. The final product was assembled by attaching 10 or more small and delicate parts, often under a magnifying glass, and the result was then inspected on the bench under a microscope. Samples of every team's output were subjected to a complex series of tests by a quality control department. Most operators worked under a group incentive plan that paid a uniform bonus to each member of the team for all products produced above a certain quality standard.

A large majority of the operators found the work rewarding. They did not complain of repetitiveness or of mechanical pressure from the moving conveyor. At an earlier stage of this study, a variety of interferences with this satisfactory situation had been reported; however, most had been eliminated by the time these findings were reported.

It was found that the assembly process can be organized to provide a form of psychological "traction" rather than the distraction or coercion characteristic of the automobile assembly line.[9] Thus, repetitive assembly work does not necessarily imply unfavorable work characteristics under conditions when (1) the product is attractive; (2) interpersonal relations are not excluded; (3) pride in an unusual kind of skill and quality is possible; and (4) the smooth pull of the process is not interrupted by excessive supervisory attention. All these conditions were fulfilled in the work environment of the electronics assemblyline studied.

3. INFLUENCE OF MASS-PRODUCTION TECHNOLOGY ON MANAGEMENT

From Arthur N. Turner, "Management and the Assembly Line," Harvard Business Review, *vol. 33, pp. 47–48, September–October, 1955.*

The policies and practices which management adopts necessarily grow out of a certain way of thinking about technology and human relations. For example, whether management tries to help foremen counteract some

[8] Arthur N. Turner and Amelia L. Miclette, "Sources of Satisfaction in Repetitive Work," *Occupational Psychology,* vol. 36, No. 4, October 1962, pp. 215–231.

[9] Cf. W. Baldamus, who fully develops these concepts in *Efficiency and Effort: An Analysis of Industrial Administration,* Tavistock Publications, London, 1961.

of the pressure and impersonality associated with the assembly line will depend on its interpretation of the cause of these problems and its judgment as to whether they are undesirable and need to be counteracted. When management itself is thoroughly involved with a particular technology, and committed to its basic concepts, it is difficult to see what the human implications of that technology may be. There is a natural temptation for managers to carry over into their thinking about human motivation the assumptions that seem to underlie the assembly line technology.

Work simplification

Consider, for example, the assumptions which underlie the traditional principles of work simplification. If it is true that work gets done most efficiently when every job is made as simple as possible and motions are highly repetitive, does it not follow that workers in general are content with uninteresting work and actually shun the additional responsibility of more complex jobs? Some members of management, in order to rationalize to themselves the nature of mass production work, go so far as to believe sincerely that this is the case.

The trouble with such assumptions is that, *even if true* (which is extremely doubtful in view of all the evidence), they are not useful guides to action.[1] What about the worker who is not "average"? Even more important, what are the *results* of such assumptions in supervisory behavior and company policy?

The management which believes that workers dislike responsibility does not try to give it to them. And if management assumes that workers like repetitive jobs, it is not likely to support experiments to make the work more interesting or challenging. Consequently, workers tend to feel that management does not *want* them to take responsibility and does not *expect* them to have an interest in their work; for workers, like everyone else, often behave according to how they think other people want and expect them to behave. The very fact that they feel this way creates a problem, whether they would in fact have responded to more interesting jobs or not. The vicious circle of attitudes can only be broken, I am convinced, when management boldly acts on new, positive assumptions about workers' capacity and willingness to take a real interest in their jobs.

Power of coercion

Much the same basic problem exists in relation to mechanical pacing and pressure. The assembly line is primarily an efficient method of moving work in process. But in management's thinking it frequently

[1] For more detailed presentation of such evidence, the reader is referred to the subsequent selections on job enlargement in this chapter. C.R.W.

becomes much more than this. It becomes the agency that gets the work done in the time allowed. Now, if this is assumed, some important further assumptions follow. For example, in order to justify the coercion of the line it is difficult not to assume that by and large people fail to work well unless they *are* coerced. Perhaps no manager would endorse this assumption stated so baldly, but is there not an inevitable danger that it will follow in his thinking, at least subconsciously, if he holds to the first belief?

Admittedly, the moving line has something to do with compelling the completion of each job in a predetermined time. And sometimes certain people *do* have to be coerced in order to do good work, just as under certain (exceptional) circumstances some people prefer repetitive jobs. But basically the cause-and-effect relationship is the other way around. As one manager said:

> *People say, "The men start working as soon as the line starts." It should be the other way around. It should be, "The line starts when the people start to work." It's some sort of reverse thinking that everyone gets into, that motivation is mechanical and not human. You don't carry that kind of thinking over when you talk about your car. There you realize that the car won't go unless the human wants it to go.* But on the assembly line people get their thinking mixed up.

Perhaps this executive was overstating the case. However, he clearly recognized the danger that assembly line technology may tempt management to make certain questionable assumptions about human motivations and capacities. Even if one believes that these assumptions are statistically verifiable, morally right, or socially acceptable, he should still look askance at them. What about the *consequences* of them? If he holds them, how is he likely to act, and how will his actions affect other people? In short, how do they work out in practice?

Let us look at the matter from a pragmatic point of view. These negative assumptions can lead to a serious loss of potential. A management that justifies minute subdivision of the task into its simplest component parts, on the ground that many men prefer repetitive and relatively meaningless jobs, will not benefit from a release of creative interest in the job. Similarly, a management that emphasizes the coercive element in the moving line, on the ground that no one works effectively without externally imposed pressure, will not find the improved productivity that comes from people working hard because they want to and because they participate in setting the goals which are to be reached.

The foreman who gives his men the benefit of the doubt, who is willing to assume that his men want to and are able to do well and that their interest can be stimulated, gets the best results in the long run. But to do so he requires a great deal of support from his superiors and from the total management organization. That is why it is so important for the influence of assembly line technology to be consciously, purposefully counteracted. Otherwise negative assumptions about human ability and motivation may become unthinkingly accepted by managers down the line.

4. SOLUTIONS TO THE MONEY–MOTIVATION PROBLEM

INTRODUCTORY NOTE

From the standpoint of money and motivation in the factory the ninety-odd Scanlon plans now in operation under very varied conditions are believed to be significant for the following reasons:

1. They eliminate the kind of grievances which often accompany the usual incentive plan, as discussed in earlier selections.

2. They do so by adopting a theory of motivation better suited to the complexity of manufacturing companies operating under modern conditions.

3. They answer operationally the hard question which plagues most profit-sharing plans: What should management do when there is no profit to share?

4. They are successful in solving the problem of "overcoming resistance to technological change."

The first selection below describes briefly the plan itself. The second, by the late Douglas McGregor of MIT, analyzes the social and psychological implications of the plan and the reasons why most of its applications in American industry have been successful. Professor McGregor's analysis, however, has broader implications. It outlines in fact a general model for successful man-management-machine relations with or without the application of any specific "plan." The reader is referred to Professor McGregor's well-known book *The Human Side of Enterprise*, and to *The Professional Manager*, for a fuller development of his ideas on the human problems of industry. For the references see the bibliography.

a. "Enterprise for everyman" [1]

From Russell W. Davenport, "Enterprise for Everyman," in Frederick Lesieur, (ed.), The Scanlon Plan, Technology Press, MIT, Cambridge, Mass., and John Wiley & Sons, Inc., New York, 1958, pp. 17–34.

[1] Reprinted by special permission from the January, 1950, issue of Fortune. Copyrighted 1950 by Time, Inc.

There is nothing about the Lapointe Machine Tool Company that would lead the visitor to suspect that it houses the makings of a far-reaching management-labor revolution. It is a small, neat factory in Hudson, Massachusetts, where the executives walk up three flights to get to their varnished offices and most of the 350 employees eat lunch at home because they live nearby. Founded in 1903 by a French-Canadian named La Pointe, it was later purchased by John J. Prindiville, whose son, big, six-foot-six John Jr., is now President and owner of the equity stock. It is a modest enterprise with a reputation for high quality; there is even a trace of modesty in its boast that it is "the world's oldest and largest manufacturer of broaches and broaching machines." Yet the social achievement at Lapointe is something to make one pause and consider, for the discoveries that its management and union have made concerning the enterprise system could have repercussions around the civilized world.

Labor relations at Lapointe were just about like labor relations anywhere else, which is to say that there was mistrust on both sides leading on occasion to ill will. There was constant trouble, for example, over the piecework incentive system. . . . There were numerous production delays, spoilage was too high, and deliveries were bad. In short, the picture was a typical one as industrial relations go—worse than some, not so bad as others.

In 1945 the plant was organized by the United Steelworkers, and about a year thereafter the Steelworkers called a national strike for a postwar wage increase. The Lapointe contract still had six months to run, and many of the men didn't want to go out anyway. However, the decision was to strike. Management thereupon sought an injunction, on the ground that the contract had been violated, and won a favorable decision from Judge Charles C. Cabot of the Massachusetts Superior Court. The union was enjoined from picketing the plant or otherwise interfering with operations. Early in April the strike at Lapointe ended. But there was bitterness in the air, and the situation was not improved by the realization that the machine-tool industry, after its war boom, had fallen on lean times. The unsettling possibility of a layoff hovered constantly over the shop.

It so happened about this time that Jack Ali, then president of the union, picked up a copy of *Life* (December 23, 1946) and his eye fell on an article by John Chamberlain with the intriguing title of "Every Man a Capitalist." Mr. Ali read it. It told about a small maker of steel tanks called the Adamson Company, where union and management had come together to install an amazing productivity plan, with the result that the company's profitability had increased two and a half times and the men had taken home bonuses ranging up to 54 per cent of a high basic wage. The author of the plan was one Joseph Scanlon, of whom Mr. Ali had never heard. However, he took the article to the union executive committee and together they became tremendously excited. After two evenings' discussion, the committee got in touch with Executive Vice President Edward M. Dowd, second-in-command to Mr. Prindiville—a big man, up from the ranks, whose intimate knowledge of the broaching business is matched only by his sure-footed understanding of the men in his shop: Mr. Dowd turned a willing ear to what the committee had to say and on reading the article was deeply stirred.

There then followed some very active weeks. Messrs. Dowd and Ali journeyed out to East Palestine, Ohio, where they went over the Adamson plan in detail. They discovered that Mr. Scanlon was now teaching at M.I.T., scarcely forty miles from Hudson, and they presently made their appearance in his office. Mr. Scanlon, in turn, sent them to Roy Stevens, the regional field representative of the United Steelworkers. When they had obtained this gentleman's blessing they returned to the Scanlon office and began to dig down to bedrock. In the meantime Mr. Dowd had had frequent conferences with Mr. Prindiville, who was at once interested, and after some deliberation gave them the green light. Negotiations with the union were begun. And by December 1, 1947, the Scanlon Plan was installed at Lapointe.

The Scanlon development

Now the Adamson experiment that started this chain of events was no mere accident in labor-management relations. It had its roots in the painful Thirties, when a group of labor leaders in the steel country evolved certain principles that have within them the power to revolutionize labor's relationship to enterprise, and vice versa. One of these leaders was Joseph Scanlon, whose versatile career included cost accounting, a spell as a professional boxer, a return to cost accounting (his basic profession), and then a shift over to the production side as an open-hearth worker. In 1936, during the formation of the S.W.O.C., Mr. Scanlon was on the open hearth of a marginal steel company, where he took a leading part in the organizing drive and was elected president of the new local.

Like many other steel manufacturers, this company was close to the rocks in 1938. Costs were high, the ink was red, liquidation seemed inevitable. Mr. Scanlon and his fellow union officers felt that something had to be done. They persuaded the president of the company to join with them in a visit to Pittsburgh to see Clinton Golden, then vice president of the Steelworkers and Phil Murray's good right arm. . . .

Mr. Golden advised them to go back and try to work out a plan by which union and management could join together to save the enterprise. And the upshot was a pioneer union-management productivity plan, which provided that the workers would get a bonus for tangible savings in labor costs. Despite the fact that the primary aim of this plan was merely *survival*, it worked almost like magic and became the seed of all of Mr. Scanlon's future work. Costs were cut so much that the company actually began to make a profit, and the workers got a bonus to boot. One suggestion by the union production committee, for example, cost less than $8,000 in new equipment but saved about $150,000 in one year.

Scores of other companies doing business with the union found themselves in this same tough position in the late Thirties. Primarily to save the jobs of union members, Messrs. Murray and Golden brought Mr. Scanlon into the national headquarters to work on these cases. Sometimes at the request of the company, often at that of the union, productivity plans based upon union-management cooperation were installed in forty to fifty companies. The largest of these early-period plans was at a basic steel company employing about 4,000 people; the smallest was at a water-heater company with 150 employees. According to Mr. Scanlon, "The successes were just as marked in the larger companies as in the small ones."

Out of this work came a book—*The Dynamics of Industrial Democracy,* by Clinton S. Golden and Harold J. Ruttenberg—and a proposition. The proposition was that collective bargaining, as thus far developed, was a primitive affair and that the future task of labor and management would be to evolve a more mature relationship. In this new relationship collective bargaining would include, not merely wages, hours, working conditions, etc., but intelligent cooperation between the bargaining parties. Such cooperation could not be expected if the workers were shoved to one side, kept ignorant of the business, and treated as pawns in a game going on over their heads. A new principle must be introduced, which has since come to be called the principle of *participation*. . . .

Unfortunately, when he uses the word participation, the average executive usually has something rather superficial in mind. He seeks to develop in the worker a *feeling* of participation, a *sense* of belonging. But is this quite honest? To make the worker feel that he is participating without giving him a real participation is, after all, to fool him; and deception is a flimsy, not to say an inflammable, foundation for industrial relations. Real participation consists in finding a means by which to reward labor for any increase in productivity and *then in building around this formula a working relationship between management and labor that enables them to become a team.* Once a team has been established, it is found that labor's prime interest, just like that of management, becomes *productivity*.

Such, at any rate, was the fruitful vein that Messrs. Dowd and Ali had come upon at the Adamson Company, the most spectacular of the Scanlon developments. The performance of Adamson, indeed, had attracted the attention of Douglas McGregor, then head of the industrial-relations section at M.I.T., and Mr. McGregor had persuaded Mr. Scanlon to come to M.I.T. There, with the help of economists, engineers, statisticians, and other experts on the M.I.T. faculty, Mr. Scanlon's work entered a new phase, in which he [drew] upon his vast experience in the labor-management field to give advice in the installation of real participation plans to those companies that [sought] him out.

The formula

The first task in the application of the Scanlon plan is to find a "normal" labor cost for the plant under consideration and then to devise a means for giving labor the benefit of anything it can save under that "norm." In every case, therefore, some kind of link must be found between the worker and over-all shop productivity. Because every company is different, the nature of this link differs in almost every case, . . . At a manufacturer of silverware it is ounces of silver processed; at a wholesale warehouse it is tons warehoused; at a steel foundry and machine shop in the Deep South it is pounds of castings produced. At the Market Forge Company, a versatile steel-fabricating shop in Everett, Massachusetts, it is a calculated percentage of operating profits per month.

This last method, linking laborsaving to the profit and loss statement, is of course the basis of many profit-sharing plans. But Mr. Scanlon [felt] and Market Forge itself agrees, that it is the least desirable of any of the links, because the connection between the worker's productive efficiency and the final profit is too remote for many to grasp. It was adopted at Market Forge because the types of jobs coming into that shop are so variable that a labor-cost figure was impossible to determine. Notwithstanding this seeming weakness, a high level of participation has been developed at Market Forge, where more than 300 recorded suggestions for improved productivity have been put into effect in the past two years.

At Lapointe, where measurement was relatively easy, Mr. Scanlon decided on the most direct and understandable accounting handle—the ratio of labor cost to total production value, the latter figure being equal to monthly sales plus or minus the change in inventory. Since this labor ratio is a highly competitive figure, Lapointe [did] not make it public. However, the principle can be illustrated, and all the Lapointe moves intelligently followed, by taking the average for the whole machine-tool industry. According to the Department of Commerce the ratio of wages and salaries to the value of shipments for the entire industry for 1947 was 40.7 per cent—which, to speak in round figures, we may call 41 per cent. In actuality, the company felt that the "norm" derived from its war records was too high, and the union consequently agreed to a reduction of three points. If this were applied to the industry-wide average, the norm would be 38 per cent, and the plan would work as follows. If total shipments for a given month were $70,000, and inventory change was plus $30,000, total production value would be $100,000 for that month. The "normal" payroll would then be calculated at 38 per cent, or $38,000. If the actual payroll were only $35,000, the difference of $3000 would go to the workers as their bonus.

Several important points are to be noted regarding this approach. First, labor gets *all* of the laborsaving; management's profit from the plan is derived from increased sales with no corresponding increase in total "burden" (i.e., overhead and labor costs). Second—and absolutely basic to the Scanlon system—the bonus is given to all the workers and not just to those individuals who made productivity suggestions. At Market Forge it goes to every person in the business, including Leo M. Beckwith, the owner—and Mr. Scanlon [preferred] this setup. At Lapointe, however, it goes to all except the fourteen top executives, who have a bonus system of their own, based on sales. Lapointe distributes the Scanlon bonus to every individual every month, as a calculated percentage of his basic rate—that is, his hourly, weekly, or monthly pay.

Mr. Scanlon [believed] that the broadest and most meaningful participation requires a union—in the two or three instances where he has proceeded without one there have been delays and difficulties that a union would have helped to untangle. A firm distinction is made, however, between ordinary union affairs and the productivity affairs; grievances, for example, are handled through the grievance committee and are never discussed in the union-management productivity committees. Preferably, the original suggestion to try the plan should come from the union (as at Lapointe); but if it comes from management, the consent of the union must certainly be obtained, together with the approval of the regional representative. In many instances the plan rests on a simple "memorandum of agreement"; at Lapointe it is actually part of the collective-bargaining contract.

Thus the basic theory is that labor should profit from laborsavings, while the company profits from a better use of its assets (for example, lower unit costs). And in order to maintain this dynamic balance at the original point agreed upon, it is provided that changes can be made in the formula to compensate for changed conditions on either side. Thus, some weeks after the plan actually went into effect, management decided to cut prices by 10 per cent on about half the products. Since this would result in a decrease in production value from a nonlabor source, about three points had to be *added* to labor's norm. This would bring our average norm for the industry back to 41 per cent. If management were to raise prices, the opposite adjustment would have to be made.

If a further general rise in wages were to occur, the union at Lapointe would insist that the workers get it in their wage rates; one of Mr. Scanlon's cardinal principles is that a productivity bonus must not be used as a substitute for a wage increase. But again, in order to maintain the dynamic balance, such a change in the wage level, since it would be an additional labor cost, would require a revision of the norm, here, too, upward. The change can be avoided in only two ways: (1) management may pass the increase along in the form of increased prices, in which event the labor ratio to sales will remain the same; or (2) consideration for the company's competitive position may induce labor to absorb part or all of the increase by agreeing to let the ratio stand as it was. Thus at Lapointe the union and the company undertook to eliminate basic wage inequities, and this resulted in a sizable increase in payroll. Since, however, this cost could not be passed along in prices and still keep the business at a good volume, labor consented to the maintenance of the original norm (41 per cent by our hypothetical figure), instead of insisting on a larger share of the sales dollar. In effect, therefore, the increase in payroll cost came out of increased productivity; and since prices did not go up, the customers of Lapointe were the chief beneficiaries of the difference. This benefit to the customers comes back, in turn, to the company in the form of more secure jobs and profits.

On the other hand, there is built into the agreement a provision that where management makes an investment that will raise labor productivity, without any increased work on the part of the labor force, such investment may entail a recalculation of labor's norm, this time downward. Lapointe has, in fact, invested in about forty major pieces of equipment in the past year. It is impossible to tell how much of this is actually new investment and how much is in reality replacement, though the total would run to six figures. Nevertheless, management feels that this investment is to some extent a fair exchange for labor's extra rise in productivity and has not therefore exercised this provision of the agreement.

All this is collective bargaining of a high order, brought about by the participation principle. The entire factory competes, from the ground up. Because management sees its best hope in the cooperation of the workers, it decides to forgo claims that it would otherwise exact. And because the workers know the company's competitive problem in detail their bargaining for labor's share is oriented to that problem.

One more provision was needed at Lapointe to put the plan in balance. Three times in the first two years the productivity curve has dipped below the norm—that is, labor costs were *greater* than our hypothetical average of 41 per cent. The company had paid out bonuses for the gains; who was to reimburse it for the losses? Owing to the extraordinary understanding that is developed by participation, the men were quick to see the injustice that was being worked on the company, and even though the contract contained no such provision, the union voluntarily agreed to an adjustment. The final arrangement was that the company should hold back half of the first 15 per cent of each month's bonus to take care of possible months when the payroll was greater than labor's norm. This amount is kept in a reserve fund, and whatever is left is distributed at the end of each year.

The reserve has had a salutary effect. It gives management a reasonable protection against temporary but unforeseeable slumps. On the other hand, it gives the workers a better perspective on the business. The desire to protect the reserve gives them the same dread of red ink that management has.

Implementation of the formula

The increased productivity of the shop under the Scanlon system is not achieved by a "speed-up" in the ordinary sense of the word. Possibly the men work harder, and certainly they work more steadily, but the rise in efficiency is brought about chiefly by suggestions as to how time and effort can be saved. These suggestions are handled by shop committees, called "production committees," whose members are always on the job and easily accessible. They are empowered to put any suggestion into effect that does not involve some other department or a substantial outlay of money. Over the production committees there sits the screening committee, composed of representatives of management and labor from the various departments, which rules on suggestions of wider scope. Each suggestion is carefully tagged with the name of the person making it; if it is accepted, some member of the committee is specifically assigned the job of following it up; if rejected, someone is instructed to make a thorough explanation to the worker. At Lapointe the screening committee has received 513 suggestions in twenty-four months. Of these, 380 have been accepted, 28 started, 32 are pending, and 65 have been rejected.

Employers who have installed a casual "suggestion box" system in their plants can have little idea of the kind of thing that goes on in a Scanlon Plan committee. For that matter, the average employer has little conception of the wealth of imagination and ingenuity lying untapped in the heads of the workmen. Under conventional management such ideas are blocked by a number of factors. A worker who has an idea may be given no incentive to suggest it. But even if there is an incentive, he may decide to withhold it, rather than incur the enmity or jealousy of his fellow workers, and especially of his foreman, who may construe the idea as a criticism of his own management. The individual is frustrated; and, moreover, since he can see how a saving could be made, and since management obviously does not see it, his respect for management declines.

Add to this the fact that his communications with management are virtually nil. He has no idea of company problems, and hence no idea of why some moves are made that seem to him (and may in fact be) very stupid.

All this is fertile ground for the kind of animosity that has grown up in some labor circles against what the managers advocate as "free enterprise." Indeed, a number of workers at Lapointe, who feel that they can now talk with freedom, admit that in the old pre-Plan days they never associated themselves or their jobs with the profits of the company and maybe even got a little kick when they heard that the top floor was using red ink.

If one steps from that kind of shop, which often exists even under what is ordinarily called "good" management, and takes one's seat as an observer at a Scanlon Plan screening committee, one passes, with Alice, through the looking glass and into an entirely different world. Like a crack out of a gun the meeting opens with an announcement of the figures for the past month. There follows a roundup by management of the current situation of the company. Then the suggestions are read out, one by one, and debated. A lot of criticism is generated and is of necessity accepted, since it is all directed to the same end—a better profit. Sometimes the workers throw the book at management, sometimes management points out where the shop has fallen down. Engineers argue against machine-tool operators, foremen attack the engineers for unrealistic blueprints, someone demands better maintenance, management points out that more maintenance means bigger labor costs. In the process of this debate, almost every aspect of the business comes up for discussion—sales problems, competitors, orders, bids, spoilage, the business outlook, quality of materials, customers' foibles, management difficulties, etc. The result is a dynamic, working unity, which grows out of the bargaining table and yet wholly transcends it. The sudden realization dawns that here at Lapointe *collective bargaining has come of age.*

The meetings are not recorded verbatim. But minutes are distributed to everyone in the plant, and the important points in the debate are carried by the committeemen back into the shop, where they become the subject of further discussion—at the lunch hour, in the evening, or even at the union meeting. The result is that everyone at Lapointe knows the business and takes pride in his particular contribution.

Company benefits

The extraordinary results of this formula, implemented by the intimate labor-management committees, could make a long and fascinating tale. For our present purposes it will be necessary to concentrate on the most important.

First of all, the Plan has resulted in a good return to the owners. Since Lapointe does not publish its profit figures it is impossible to be precise about this.[2] The profits at Lapointe have not been so spectacular as those at Adamson—indeed it is probable that during the first year of the Plan the company made hardly any profit at all. This goes back to the nature of the machine-tool industry, which has been in something of a slump ever since the war. It is commonly accepted in the industry that Lapointe has been gaining an increasingly large percentage of the business ever since the Plan was inaugurated. During 1948 great strides were made at Lapointe in its ability to compete, which may not have shown up immediately in the profit and loss statement. In 1949 the results have been much more tangible; in contrast to much of the industry the company is now operating at a good profit.

All of this improvement cannot be attributed to the productivity plan. Lapointe has a sharp-eyed management that has been quick to follow up new leads in the hitherto obscure broaching business. It has been rewarded by the fact that modern engineering is finding new uses for broaching—for instance, machine-gun barrels, which were formerly rifled at the rate of one an hour, can now be broached at the rate of sixty an hour. Moreover, an entirely new business is opening up through the fact that certain parts of jet engines cannot be efficiently manufactured except by broaching. These are long-range gains attributable to factors other than labor.

However, management and labor are now cooperating so effectively at Lapointe that it is impossible to tell where the contributions of one ends and that of the other begins. Certain intangible benefits have accrued from this teamwork that affect the company's whole operation. For example, there has been a vast improvement in deliveries. Formerly delivery on ordinary broaches had been from three to five weeks and was often late. Now delivery can be made in from one to three weeks and is usually on time. This has become a great selling point for the company.

A second advantage is the reduction in complaints from spoilage and imperfect workmanship. Lapointe's policy is to take back any unsatisfactory product and fix it without extra cost. Under the Scanlon Plan this means *a loss to the workers as well as to the company*, and as a result great care is taken all along the line. The workers, indeed, get very excited about the big jobs. In one instance, when a new machine for a big automobile manufacturer was being tried out in the Lapointe plant, several of the union committee left their own jobs and gathered around to see whether the automotive manufacturer's engineers were duly impressed. While losses from customer complaints probably never amounted to as

[2] The Kiplinger magazine . . . published figures on Lapointe, but many were inaccurate and were denied by the company.

much as 1 per cent of the business, the intangible result of satisfied customers willing to reorder is a real one, for which management can thank its own foresight in installing a plan that gives the workers an interest in their product.

Moreover, the problem of instructing younger workers has been greatly advanced. Formerly, under the piecework incentive system, a highly skilled workman was reluctant to show a younger man the tricks of his trade. But today the older workers are eager to teach their skills, in order to raise shop productivity. The most dramatic example at Lapointe was that of Robert Juliani, the best and most experienced form grinder, who made $3.57 an hour under the old piecework system. Formerly Mr. Juliani was given no incentive to share his knowledge and skill, but after the plan he reorganized his work, took on two helpers, and taught them many of his ways of doing things. It is estimated that his increased efficiency is in the neighborhood of 300 per cent.

The plan, indeed, has completely solved the problem of "controlled production"—that is, the policy, common to almost all labor, of holding back so that management will never know how fast a man really can work. The very first day it was installed a toolmaker, who had been producing twenty units in eight hours, produced sixty-two units. A surface grinder, whose average weekly earnings had been $76 on piecework, turned out $184 worth of work in four days. And so forth, through innumerable examples.

Labor benefits

On labor's side the benefits have been equally great. The average pay at Lapointe is in line with basic steel for the region, and for two years the workers have taken home an average bonus of 18 per cent over and above this. The bonus has, naturally, varied widely, ranging from zero to 39 per cent in June, 1949. Even better results are expected in 1950.

But the workers, like management, have derived many intangible benefits that cannot be measured in dollars and cents. They seem to enjoy working together and sharing the good and bad times. As one of them said, "Formerly everyone was on his own. Now we all work for each other." Innumerable versions of this observation can be picked up around the plant. One can spend little time here without reflecting that one of the weaknesses of conventional management is its almost exclusive emphasis on the money incentive. For the money incentive cannot satisfy the many demands of human nature—and this goes for management as well as for labor. Other incentives are needed if a man is to lead a healthy and happy life. Among these, two are of the utmost importance. One has to do with one's self—a feeling of accomplishment, a recognition of one's own abilities. This is provided for in the Scanlon Plan through the suggestion system, because a man who makes a good suggestion gets a profound satisfaction out of it; he carries the story home to his wife; he is admired and thanked by his associates. But the Scanlon Plan goes further, in that the reward for such suggestions does not go to the individual alone but to the entire shop. On the one hand, this eliminates jealousy; on the other, it opens up for the ordinary worker a kind of social or community incentive to which he eagerly responds. Cynics to the contrary, men do get a kick out of helping their fellow men; and this is demonstrated at Lapointe, where an atmosphere prevails in the shop that cannot possibly be duplicated under the selfish piecework system.

Yet another intangible advantage that the workers have derived is a strengthening of the union. If any employer becomes interested in this plan as a means of undermining the union, he had better skip it. Mature collective bargaining that has reached the evolutionary stage here described has precisely the opposite result. When the Plan was installed, union membership at Lapointe was about 70 per cent of the working force, exclusive of the office workers, who were not organized. Today all but three or four employees are union members, and the office workers have joined in a body. Interest in the union is keen. The advantage of this from the employer's point of view is that union meetings, instead of being dominated by a few malcontents, are heavily attended; and often enough most of the discussion is devoted to company affairs and how productivity can be increased. The union president, energetic and imaginative Fred Lesieur, who has succeeded Mr. Ali, is enthusiastic about the Plan. The result of all this is that grievances have almost disappeared—only three have been processed in twenty-four months, and none of them has had to go to arbitration.

One of the greatest advantages of this kind of collective bargaining, from the worker's point of view, is the knowledge that it gives him of the business. When a slump is coming, he knows it. He is even given a chance to combat it, in the sense that if he can devise a cheaper way of turning out his product, perhaps the company will be able to take business away from somebody else. In a number of instances the Lapointe workers have actually done this, the most spectacular example being that of an order from a big automotive concern in December, 1948. The workers had been pressing management to accept orders even at the break-even point so as to tide over a bad period. Mr. Prindiville, who sometimes sits in on the screening-committee meetings, had given in to the pressure some months previously to the extent of taking an order from this firm for 100 broaches at $83 per broach. But Lapointe had lost 10 per cent on the deal, and Mr. Prindiville now put his foot down. If this business was to be taken again the price would have to be raised. In view of new competition, it meant that Lapointe almost certainly would not get the business—and at a time when work was scarce.

The gloomy gathering that listened to Mr. Prindiville's pronouncement was then electrified by a question from Jimmie McQuade, skilled grinder and one of the most outspoken members of the screening committee. Who says we can't make those broaches at that price for a profit? Mr. McQuade wanted to know. If you'd give the men in the shop a chance to go over the blueprints before production starts and to help plan the job, there are lots of ways of cutting costs without cutting quality. The idea grew, and the next day the suggestion ran around the shop like wildfire. The order was taken at the old price, this time with a *profit* of 10 per cent —a total gain in efficiency of 20 per cent.

The truth is that the Scanlon Plan has generated a competitive spirit throughout the factory: one hears as much about competition from the workers as from management itself. If there is a question of struggling for existence the whole company struggles collectively, and all the brains available are focused on the fight. The worker is no longer a pawn in a game he does not understand. He is a player. He enjoys it. And his contribution is worth money to all concerned.

The team at work

The effectiveness of such teamwork becomes especially apparent in the crises. Lapointe has been through three critical periods since the Plan was installed, and it has lifted itself out of them principally because the Plan creates an overwhelming incentive to cooperate.

The first crisis occurred in the fourth month. Mr. Scanlon had warned management that output would greatly increase and that they had better begin hustling up some new orders. But management had a normal backlog, and inasmuch as it was having trouble with deliveries it did not dare put on any extra sales pressure. The very first month, however, productivity shot up to 133 per cent (100 equals the predetermined "norm" already defined); the second month registered 128 per cent and the third 121 per cent. The result was that the company's backlog melted away. Management, of course, sprang to action as soon as the danger was realized. Telegrams and telephone calls poured out of Hudson. The salesmen were lashed to activity. Though himself a production man, Vice President Dowd—and even several engineers—took to the road. But broaches and broaching machines are technical tools that sometimes require weeks of designing before production can begin. Consequently the new orders did not give much immediate help, and the next three months were bad; the company ran a loss and the workers got no bonus.

Yet, as it turned out, the strength of the Plan was best demonstrated when things went bad. The workers had had three months of participation; they looked forward to bonuses in the future; and they liked the Plan because it gave them a *chance*—a chance to fight, a chance to pit their skills against other enterprises. Consequently, despite the setback, sentiment among them was overwhelming to continue the Plan, and suggestions kept pouring in for improvements. By June, 1948, a small bonus (4.7 per cent) was earned.

But then there was new trouble. The usual practice of the plant was to shut down for vacations for two weeks in July. Big new orders had come in, but these had to pass through the engineering department for designing, and when the engineers were on vacation no designing would be done. Would anybody dare to ask the engineers to give up their vacations? —especially in view of the fact that, as is usual in machine shops, there was continuous bickering between the engineers and the machine operators, who were inclined to criticize the drawings as unrealistic. A delegation from the union approached Vice President Dowd, who said that he would put it up to the men themselves. When he went to the men, however, he found that agreement had already been reached at the workers' level—the engineers had sacrificed their vacations. They worked hard during July in an otherwise empty plant, and by August drawings were pouring out of the drafting room. Productivity soared again, yielding a bonus of 25 per cent for September and 19 per cent for October. A better example of community incentive could hardly be found.

Still another difficulty then arose. The problem was to devise a machine capable of broaching certain parts of a jet airplane engine. Everybody had said the parts in question could not be broached, but the Lapointe engineers insisted they could be, providing a new machine was developed. The problem centered around a very hard steel, close to the limit for cutting tools, and the company's efforts to solve it resulted in many a setback. Labor watches every job at Lapointe, and the men became impatient when they saw so much work being done on which there would be no shipping dollars. But management went back to the screening committee again and again and said in effect, "Bear with us. This is experimental stuff. If we can get it right, we're in." So the screening committee went along. Then at last the bugs were out, production began, and everybody went to town. The monthly productivity curve shot up, from a dismal low of 71 per cent in December, 1948 (in the middle of the experimental work), to 119, 138, 140, 145, 150, and finally, in the twentieth month of the plan, to 161 per cent.

These three incidents provide three dramatic examples of teamwork. In the first, the workers held on despite an unexpected discouragement. In the second, the engineers came to the rescue of all concerned. In the third, management exercised its proper function with great intelligence, by insisting that temporary losses be sustained in order to grasp a future profit. If this experimental work had failed, a certain field of sales would have been closed to Lapointe. As it is, the firm got in on the ground floor of a new and growing business, and all concerned will profit from that achievement.

Will it work for you?

Many objections will be raised to the Scanlon Plan by those who have never seen it in operation. But perhaps the least fruitful objection of all is the one most commonly encountered: "This plan may work at Lapointe —or wherever—but that is because of special, perhaps accidental, circumstances. *My* plant is different."

Of course, everybody's plant *is* different. Every union is different also. For this very reason, Mr. Scanlon [refused] to crystallize his work into a formula. He [relied] on certain principles fundamental to human nature; and he [adapted] these in almost infinite ways to the particular problems of each particular company. [His plan] has now met with success in varying degrees, in more than fifty enterprises in several different industries, of many different sizes, under many different circumstances; where the original labor relations were good and where they were bad; where profits were good and where they were nonexistent; where labor productivity was easy to measure and where it was virtually impossible; among skilled workers and unskilled workers. There are, of course, shops where this plan would not work. But the burden of the evidence is accumulating that those in which it will not work are the *exceptions*.

Yet there are two prerequisites to the Scanlon Plan, and where they do not exist time would be wasted in trying to install it. One is that the union leadership must be intelligent. This does not mean that the union should be acquiescent: on the contrary, it may be quite aggressive. But real intelligence is needed to bargain at a participation level, which involves an understanding of such things as competition, competitive pricing, profitability, and many other factors that never enter into collective bargaining at the lower level. This prerequisite to Scanlon Plan success is provided at Lapointe by Fred Lesieur, the new union president, who, as a good union man, considers it his *responsibility* to have an intelligent grasp of the productivity side of the business. The other union officers share this responsibility.

Second, and even more important, there must be someone in top management who is vitally interested and *who is able to stand the gaff*. A management that wants to stand off and look down its nose at the workers cannot operate a Scanlon Plan. Nor is it possible to turn this vital area of the business over to a vice president in charge of industrial relations. Someone who actually runs the company or the plant—the president or his executive representative—must be a regular member of the screening committee (he need not be chairman); and this person must be willing to enter into any kind of debate and to accept in a fair and impartial manner any criticism hurled at his own management. He need not worry about his dignity. The men will invest him with the dignity he deserves —no more, but no less.

It is precisely in this respect that Lapointe has been so fortunate. Lapointe has in John Prindiville a man of open mind, who believes that the incentives of enterprise should reach down, through management, to the shop floor. And it has in Ed Dowd a man who became the Plan's prime mover, utterly dedicated to its goals. Mr. Dowd is not afraid of criticism—and is not afraid to give it. The men know he is sincere in his efforts to make the Plan work, and they consequently trust him. Besides, he sets quite a pace. When the argument gets hot, he takes off his coat, and everyone interprets this as permission to do likewise. Comfortably in his shirt sleeves, Ed Dowd pitches into the suggestions, throws upon each of them the light of his enormous knowledge of the business, tosses them back to the committee, and finally designates some individual to "follow it through." When there is a tough one involving important company policy, Ed Dowd takes it himself.

If such men can be found—an intelligent union leader and a forthright management leader—the Scanlon principles can be applied virtually anywhere. And the way is then opened up to a new and creative area of industrial relations—the area of mutual interests. In the process of entering upon this area, and of consolidating it, *everyone* in the shop, high or low, joins the enterprise system.

b. The Scanlon plan through a psychologist's eyes

From Douglas McGregor, "The Scanlon Plan through a Psychologist's Eyes," in Frederick Lesieur (ed.), The Scanlon Plan, The Technology Press of the Massachusetts Institute of Technology, Cambridge, Mass., and John Wiley & Sons, Inc., New York, 1958, pp. 89–100.

Although [Scanlon] was anything but a theoretician and although he was only casually familiar with the research findings of the social sciences, the Plan he conceived fulfills to a remarkable degree the requirements for effective organized human effort that have been highlighted by such research. In addition, the actual experiences of Scanlon Plan companies provide significant verification of the predictions the social scientist makes on theoretical grounds.

The Plan implements Scanlon's underlying belief by establishing three broad conditions within which it becomes possible and natural for all members of the firm to collaborate in contributing to its economic effectiveness. These conditions are:

1. A formally established "area of collaboration" and machinery (production and screening committees) for coordinating such collaborative efforts throughout the whole organization. This is accomplished without undermining collective bargaining or weakening the local union.

2. A meaningful, realistic, common objective (the "ratio") in terms of which such collaborative efforts can be objectively measured.

3. A psychologically adequate system of rewards (noneconomic as well as economic) for a wide range of contributions to the effectiveness of the enterprise. (Traditional incentive wages, profit sharing, and suggestions system awards are quite inadequate in terms of modern psychological theory.)

As a consequence of establishing these three conditions, the employees and the managements of Scanlon Plan companies literally discover a new way of life. The process is not easy; some of the learning is rough indeed. There is little of a sentimental sweetness-and-light atmosphere, but there develops a mutual respect which cuts across even the most violent disagreements. The new relationship permeates in surprising but meaningful ways into every corner of the organization. It is some of these consequences and their relation to social-science theory and findings that I would like to examine.

Scientific management and human capabilities

Many research studies have pointed out that, however persuasive the *logic* of "scientific management" may be, the consequences of its application are often contrary to expectation.[1] Informal but effective collusion to defeat managerial purposes takes many forms, and it is widespread. Less recognized, but perhaps more important than these consequences, is the failure of this approach to make effective use of the potentialities of people. Treating the worker as though he were, in Drucker's words, a "glorified machine tool"[2] is a shameful waste of the very characteristics which distinguish people from machines.

Despite protests to the contrary, the approach of scientific management has been to treat the worker as a "hand" rather than a human being. The consequences of so doing have been attributed to the "natural" cussedness of workers and explained as the price of technological efficiency. Pleasant working surroundings and fringe benefits have been used to alleviate the negative aspects of assembly-line jobs. Fancy communications programs and Madison Avenue sales gimmicks have been used to persuade the worker of the vital importance of his tiny con-

---

[1] Chris Argyris, *Personality and Organization,* New York: Harper, 1957. Chapters IV and V summarize the data succinctly.

[2] Peter Drucker, *The Practice of Management,* New York: Harper, 1954, pp. 280 ff.

tribution to the enterprise. These are understandable but largely ineffective palliatives. However, work simplification and all the other paraphernalia of the industrial engineer—consistent with a view of the worker as a glorified machine tool—remain the commonly accepted way to utilize human effort in industry.

Scanlon knew better. He knew that what Drucker calls "industrial citizenship" [3] is perfectly possible even in the mass-production setting, provided management will recognize that workers have brains and ingenuity as well as muscles. The Scanlon Plan creates the necessary conditions for this discovery. Once these conditions are established, people collaborate because it is to their interest to do so. They don't need to be made to "feel" important; they *are* important and they know it.

The most far-reaching consequence of this creation of genuine industrial citizenship is the virtual elimination of what Argyris calls the sense of "psychological failure" created by the traditional approach of scientific management. Among other things, the notion of the "nonproductive" worker, and the "burden" concept of staff and administrative employees go out the window. Productivity, under the Scanlon Plan, is not confined to direct production workers, nor is the line organization the only part of the enterprise that is seen as carrying its own weight. Productivity is measured by reduction of the labor bill, and *everyone* can contribute to this objective.

Improvement of the ratio, by every means, is everybody's business. The individual's contribution is not limited to doing "a fair day's work." The janitor and the stenographer, as well as the engineer and the manager, can, and often do, exercise human ingenuity in developing improvements entirely outside the limits of their own job descriptions. The area for collaboration covers anything that will contribute to the effectiveness of the enterprise.

The challenging opportunities that are inherent in every industrial organization for people to assume responsibility, achieve status, acquire new skills, learn, develop, exercise creativity become apparent once this area of collaboration is carved out. The idea that workers are paid to do what they are told and management is paid to tell them not only prevents effective collaboration but automatically creates the feeling of psychological failure. It leads either to indifferent passivity or to active hostility. Genuine participation in problem solving removes the causes of these common reactions.

The task of management

It should not be supposed that management loses its responsibility to manage under a Scanlon Plan. Much to the contrary. One of the happier

[3] Peter Drucker, *The New Society,* New York: Harper, 1949, pp. 151 ff.

consequences is that the foreman ceases to occupy the impossible role that has been his in recent years and becomes a manager in the real sense of the term. He is no longer caught in the problem of divided loyalties and conflicting pressures. He is no longer the pawn of a variety of staff groups who "control" him to death under the label of serving him. He ceases to be a paper shuffler, an ineffective disciplinarian, a "master and victim of doubletalk," [4] and becomes a manager willy-nilly. Sometimes the pressures that bring about this transformation are painful in the extreme. However, most supervisors come to relish their new role.

Further up the line there is considerably less tilting with the windmill of prerogatives and more genuine concern with managing the enterprise. One of the interesting phenomena among management people in Scanlon Plan companies is their inability to comprehend the questions that are frequently asked of them concerning their freedom to manage. Authority in the sense of the right to be arbitrary, to force subordinates to do their bidding, ceases to be a meaningful idea because the collaborative relationship almost eliminates the necessity for this kind of order giving.

The management task in Scanlon Plan companies becomes one of genuine leadership. The manager who is primarily a power seeker and a protector of management's right to be arbitrary finds little satisfaction in such a situation. The pattern of managerial behavior which tends to emerge is remarkably close to that of the "democratic" leader in the classic Lewin and Lippitt research.[5] However, this term "democratic" does not mean abdication; it does not imply that "everyone decides everything." Its essence is that it makes effective use of human resources through participation; it provides general rather than close supervision; it is "employee-centered" [6]; it encourages responsible behavior and tough-minded self-control rather than reliance on external authority.

As mentioned above, disagreements flourish in Scanlon Plan companies. Management has the responsibility and exercises the authority in their resolution. The difference is that people usually disagree about the best way to do the job or to reduce costs or to improve the profit margin rather than about whose rights are what or what legalistic interpretation should be put on a work rule. This is a big difference.

The Scanlon Plan typifies Drucker's "management by objectives and self-control." General (as opposed to close) supervision and wide delegation evolve naturally as management discovers that it is no longer neces-

[4] Fritz Roethlisberger, "The Foreman: Master and Victim of Doubletalk," *Harvard Business Review*, Vol. 23, No. 3, Spring, 1945, pp. 283–298.

[5] Kurt Lewin, Ronald Lippitt, and Ralph K. White, "Patterns of Aggressive Behavior in Experimentally Created Social Climates," *Journal of Social Psychology*, Vol. X, 1939, pp. 271–299.

[6] Rensis Likert, "Motivational Dimensions of Administration," *America's Manpower Crisis*, Chicago: Public Administration Service, 1956.

sary to force people to do what needs to be done. It becomes possible to deal with people as mature adults rather than as children and thus to avoid much of the conflict between organizational requirements and the needs of the human personality which Argyris has so well delineated.[7]

Cooperation and competition

The psychological significance of all of this is that the Scanlon Plan "fits together" the purposes of organization with the natural human tendency to collaborate when collaboration is the sensible way to do things. Industrial organizations are complex *interdependent* human entities. Unless the many related functions are smoothly interlocked, unless people are constantly adjusting to each other in terms of common objectives, organizations cannot operate effectively.

Emphasis on individual competition, on narrow job responsibilities, and antagonism toward the natural tendency of humans to form groups characterize much of present-day managerial practice. This emphasis is 180 degrees out of phase with the need for collaboration in a complex system of interdependence.

The Scanlon Plan sets a meaningful common objective and creates the necessary conditions to bring practice and organizational need into phase. Instead of lip service to "teamwork" within a system which stacks the cards against it, the Scanlon Plan makes teamwork the natural way of life. And then it becomes no longer necessary to preach about its value!

Competitive motivations—also natural to humans—are not ignored either. However, instead of competing with fellow workers, or saying, "To hell with the other department (or the other shift); I'm paid to do my job, not to worry about them," the competition is with other companies in the industry. In a capitalist economy what could be more natural?

Resistance to change

A fair amount of research has pointed up the fact that resistance to change is a reaction primarily to certain methods of instituting change rather than an inherent human characteristic.[8] Leo Moore and Herbert Goodwin of the M.I.T. School of Industrial Management have coined the term "improvement management" to describe a way of gaining some of the benefits of scientific management without producing resistance to change.[9] The Scanlon Plan minimizes such resistance because it involves people in the process of creating change rather than imposing it on them.

[7] Chris Argyris, *op. cit.*

[8] Alvin Zander, "Resistance to Change: Its Analysis and Prevention," *Advanced Management,* Vol. 15, No. 1, January, 1950, pp. 9–11.

[9] Leo Moore, "Too Much Management, Too Little Change," *Harvard Business Review,* Vol. 34, No. 1, January–February, 1956, pp. 41–48.

Improvement management is the Scanlon way of life because everyone is interested in improving the ratio.

Significant examples of worker-generated change in the organization of work are common in Scanlon Plan companies. Ironically, these are frequently changes that management tried unsuccessfully to introduce in pre-Scanlon days. Resistance becomes instead active instigation. In fact, the Scanlon Plan company experience with the change process is one of the most clear-cut examples of the way in which the research-based predictions of social science are fulfilled in practice.[10]

It is perhaps needless to point out that restriction of output, featherbedding, collusion to fudge production records, and all the other ingenious group methods of defeating the managerial purposes of traditional incentive plans disappear completely in Scanlon Plan companies. Again, this is exactly what the social scientist would predict on the basis of his research into the causes of these phenomena.[11]

Human motivation

Examination of modern theories of motivation points up further Scanlon's insight into human behavior. The Scanlon Plan production and screening committees, as well as the whole management-employee relationship which develops, provide ideal means for satisfying ego and self-actualization needs which are typically frustrated under the conditions of present-day industrial employment.[12]

There is no undervaluation of economic motives either. However, one happy consequence of the Scanlon Plan is the minimization of conflict over the workers' share of the proceeds of enterprise. The ratio is determined from accounting data, and even in unionized companies there is no instance on record of an impasse over this issue! [13]

The economic rewards of the Scanlon Plan are fully consistent with

[10] See, for example: Lester Coch and John R. P. French, Jr., "Overcoming Resistance to Change," *Human Relations*, Vol. I, 1948, pp. 512–532; Kurt Lewin, "Group Decision and Social Change," *Readings in Social Psychology*, rev. ed., New York: Henry Holt, 1952, pp. 459–473; A. T. M. Wilson, "Some Contrasting Socio-Technical Production Systems," *The Manager*, December, 1955.

[11] William Foote Whyte, *Money and Motivation*, New York: Harper, 1955.

[12] Abraham Maslow, *Motivation and Personality*, New York: Harper, 1954, especially Chapters 4, 5, 8; Douglas McGregor, "The Human Side of Enterprise," *Management Review*, November, 1957, pp. 22–28; E. Wight Bakke, *The Unemployed Worker*, New Haven: Yale University Press, 1940; Robert W. White, *Lives in Progress*, New York: Dryden Press, 1952.

[13] Scanlon was insistent—and wisely so—that the Plan offer management no escape from meeting the standards of wage levels and other conditions of employment established generally by collective bargaining. To use it in this fashion would be the surest way to undermine the union's acceptance of the philosophy of collaboration. The Scanlon Plan would quickly be seen as a device to negate the legitimate gains of the labor movement.

present-day psychological knowledge. First, they are related to factors in the work situation which are controllable by employees. This is in contrast to most profit-sharing plans. Under the latter workers are rewarded in a fashion which is only remotely connected to their direct contribution. (I know of one profit-sharing plan where the profits which were shared for several years resulted primarily from the speculation of the treasurer of the company in the raw-materials market!)

Second, the payoff is within a sensible time span. It is well established that rewards become less effective the more remote in time they are from the behavior which is being rewarded. An annual payoff (typical under profit sharing) is too remote to be of much use as a motivator. The monthly payoff under the Scanlon Plan is meaningfully related in time to the behavior which affects the ratio.

Third, the plant-wide nature of the bonus is realistic in terms of the common objectives of the members of the enterprise. It does not eliminate individual differences in wage rates related to job responsibilities, but it creates the proper perception of "sharing" in a common endeavor.

Fourth, the bonus is paid for *all* contributions to the effectiveness of the enterprise rather than for the narrow contribution of output per man-hour which is common under conventional incentive plans. There are no problems in relating pay to fancy (and largely unrealistic) "standards" for measuring individual performance, particularly for maintenance, clerical, and other service jobs. Moreover, there is no longer any incentive to defeat the time-study engineer or to hide jigs and fixtures which have been invented to "beat the standard" or to establish collusive relations with tool-crib clerks, timekeepers, inspectors, and others in order to "make out." [14]

Finally, the payoff reflects the success of the enterprise in understandable terms. There is no necessity for interpreting the elaborate formulas of the industrial engineers (which workers are quite able to do, by the way), or for fathoming the formalized and often misleading gobbledygook of the balance sheet.

Mention of the balance sheet leads to one other economic point I would emphasize: the education for all participants in the economics of enterprise. American management has spent many millions of dollars in attempts to provide economic education to workers. The results have not been measured, but one may be permitted a certain skepticism. [15]

The Scanlon Plan, however, provides such education in the most direct

[14] William Foote Whyte, op. cit., particularly Chapter 7.
[15] William H. Whyte, Is Anybody Listening? New York: Simon & Schuster, 1952; Douglas Williams in Management Education for Itself and Its Employees, New York: A.M.A., 1954, Part 4.

fashion: through day-by-day involvement in the problems of the enterprise. A casual conversation with Scanlon Plan company employees often reveals an understanding of our economic system which is uncommon even among college graduates. And this fundamental and important educative process costs not one cent! It requires no films or brochures or discussion groups or lecturers. It is obtained in the normal course of daily life by direct, firsthand experience. Scanlon Plan company employees are believers in capitalism and they know *why* they are!

Staff-line conflict

Friction between workers and lower levels of supervision on the one hand and staff departments such as industrial engineering, accounting, personnel, inspection, inventory control, purchasing, and research and development on the other hand is widespread in industry today, and it is a good deal more costly than management usually recognizes. Research studies and reports of participant observers have provided substantial evidence of these phenomena.[16]

A major cause of these frictions is the fact that staff departments are placed in the position of imposing their standards, their plans and procedures, their "expertness" on the line. This is a fact quite generally despite textbook assertions that the staff functions are those of service, advice, and counsel. The staff engineer tells the worker to "follow the blueprint" even when (as happens all too often) the worker's knowledge of his tools and materials tells him that this is foolish or impossible. A substantial amount of paper work by the supervisor is summarized or scrutinized by the accounting department and turned over to others higher in the organization to be used frequently in a disciplinary manner ("Your variances are out of line," or "You have overrun your budget," or "You made an unauthorized expenditure").

The simple psychological fact is that external controls of this kind engender hostility and lead to the exercise of a substantial degree of ingenuity directed solely toward defeating the purposes of those who have instigated the controls. This is the exact opposite of management's desire; it is the antithesis of collaboration. Unfortunately, management at the top is rarely aware of the extensiveness of this internecine warfare, and the staff groups tend to interpret it as evidence of the stupidity or inherent hostility of workers and supervisors. The typical staff reaction is

[16] William Foote Whyte, *op. cit.;* Chris Argyris, "Human Problems with Budgets," *Harvard Business Review,* Vol. 31, No. 1, January–February, 1953, pp. 97–110; Charles A. Myers and John G. Turnbull, "Line and Staff in Industrial Relations," *Harvard Business Review,* Vol. 34, No. 4, July–August, 1956, pp. 113–124; and F. J. Roethlisberger and William J. Dickson, *Management and the Worker,* Cambridge, Mass.: Harvard University Press, 1939, Part IV.

to tighten and elaborate the controls, which of course simply makes matters worse.[17]

The Scanlon Plan, when these groups are included, creates entirely different relations between staff and line. The need for external controls diminishes to the vanishing point as the collaboration toward the common objective of improving the ratio becomes the way of life. The staff groups can help the line in a great many ways if this is what they are set up to do. The line learns to use and to value this help as soon as the staff is relieved of a function which makes them appear to be policemen and spies. Evidence for this fundamental change in relations is to be found readily in Scanlon Plan companies. One nice example was the occasion at the Lapointe Machine Tool Company when the engineers voluntarily postponed their vacations in order to prepare specifications for a new order so that there would be sufficient work to avoid a layoff in the factory.[18]

If the Scanlon Plan accomplished nothing else but to bring about effective collaboration between staff and line it would be a major contribution to organizational effectiveness. But this consequence is simply one of a large number of by-products resulting from a changed way of life. It is, in addition, a convincing demonstration of the well-established psychological fact that self-control is far more effective than externally imposed authority.

Conclusion

There are other ramifications of the operation of the Scanlon Plan which fit consistently with the implications of modern social-science findings. However, those discussed above serve to document my initial assertion concerning this consistency. They demonstrate, also, the difference between the usual personnel "program" and a genuine organizational philosophy, an industrial way of life.

No doubt other patterns of relationship will be found which yield results comparable with or superior to the Scanlon Plan. It is probable that the Plan as Scanlon conceived it would be difficult to establish in some kinds of industrial situations even if both management and union desired it. However, I will venture the prediction that we will succeed in increasing our utilization of the human potential in organizational settings only as we succeed in creating conditions which generate a meaningful way of life.

[17] See Argyris, "Human Problems with Budgets," *op. cit.*, for a penetrating analysis of this set of problems.

[18] Fred Lesieur tells how the machinists in this same company, during pre-Scanlon days, would receive with glee a set of engineering specifications containing a major error and build the equipment exactly "according to specs" with full knowledge that it would ultimately have to be scrapped!

Scanlon's lasting contribution is his recognition—now effectively demonstrated in action—that one cannot successfully tackle this central task of management with gimmicks or procedures or programs. The real task of management is to create conditions which result in genuine collaboration throughout the organization. To create such conditions is to establish a way of life. This is the central conclusion to which the findings of social science are pointing today. And this is the lesson that Joseph Scanlon taught us all.

5. INCREASING SATISFACTION AND CUTTING COSTS THROUGH REDESIGNING MACHINE–MAN RELATIONS

Adapted by Charles R. Walker from Eaton H. Conant and Maurice D. Kilbridge, "An Interdisciplinary Analysis of Job Enlargement: Technology, Costs and Behavioral Implications," Industrial and Labor Relations Review, vol. 18, no. 3, p. 384, April, 1965. For a fuller discussion of cost reductions in this case, see Maurice D. Kilbridge, "Reduced Costs through Job Enlargement: A Case," Journal of Business, vol. 33, no. 4, October, 1960.

A large manufacturer of home-laundry equipment, recognized certain unfavorable effects which he thought stemmed from the assembly-line technology in his manufacturing plants. As a result he undertook a deliberate program of removing jobs from progressive assembly lines and placing operators into newly designed single-operator stations. The term commonly applied to such a regrouping of work content is "job enlargement." In this case management undertook job enlargement and elimination of the assembly line mainly in the hope of favorable productivity and quality gains; not only were these goals realized (the bench-enlarged job resulted in tangible savings of $2,000 yearly, chiefly because the job design sharply reduced nonproductive and balance-delay time), but many of the other work dimensions being considered were favorably affected as well.

The following brief review, from field research reported by Conant and Kilbridge of the Graduate School of Business, University of Chicago, is based on the experience of two of the company's plants employing approximately 2,000 persons, with a United Automobile Workers local as bargaining representative for blue-collar workers.

The case demonstrates, then, that there is an optimum extent for the division of labor on assembly lines. When the excessive division was reversed, hidden costs of nonproductive work and balance-delay (time taken by management to assign and reassign the minute job elements to each worker on an assembly line; a process which must be repeated every time there is a design or model change in the product) were squeezed out of operations and assembly time was shortened. The cost savings identified are based on tangible savings, principally labor costs. Improved quality, greater production flexibility, worker satisfaction, and other considerations are important to the economic arguments favoring job enlargement but are not needed to establish its desirability in this case.[1]

Thus, they suggest that the enlargement of many jobs in the American economy could be undertaken in the interest of cost reduction alone.[2]

The following summary of the effects on worker attitudes of this transfer from line technology to bench-assembly work is based on replies to a questionnaire given to 61 workers with at least 3 months' experience on both line and bench. They expressed approval of enlarged-job attributes in this order:

Freedom from being tied to the job (55).
Quality assignability (53).
Individual incentive opportunity (53).
Ability to contribute quality (52).
Opportunity to make complete assembly (50).
Ability to set own pace (48).
Greater amount and variety of work (47).
Learning time (38).

They most disliked characteristics of line assembly work in this order:

Inability to control quality on the line (51).
Absence of quality assignability (47).
The group incentive on the line (43).
The attachment to line jobs (42).
Line pacing (37).

To this summary, Conant and Kilbridge add the following comment:

There is strong evidence that workers' inability to contribute workmanship (quality) and obtain credit for it was a most important source of dissatisfaction on the line. The general pattern of line response is impressively negative.[3]

[1] Eaton H. Conant and Maurice D. Kilbridge, "An Interdisciplinary Analysis of Job Enlargement: Technology, Costs and Behavioral Implications," *Industrial and Labor Relations Review*, vol. 18, No. 3, April 1965, p. 384.
[2] For a fuller discussion of the cost-reducing aspects of this case, see Maurice D. Kilbridge, "Reduced Costs Through Job Enlargement: A Case," *Journal of Business*, vol. 33, No. 4, October 1960.
[3] Conant and Kilbridge, *op. cit.*, p. 392.

Again there is behavioral confirmation that worker attitudes are reflected in their performance, i.e., the problems of quality that increasingly afflict the automobile industry. In a front-page story on July 21, 1965, the *Wall Street Journal* reported:

> *Some authoritative critics are leveling broad charges that the number of poorly built cars is on the increase.* Consumer Reports *magazine recently charged: "The condition of 1965 cars the Consumers Union bought for test is about the worst, so far as sloppiness in production goes, in the whole 10-year stretch of deterioration that began in 1955 . . . minor, multiple, and annoying defects found in all 25 cars [purchased for test] added up to an overall impression of 'incredibly sloppy workmanship' " . . .*
>
> *One of the greatest quality problems is the danger of human error in the 4,000 to 7,000 assembly operations involved in building each car.*

In an observation study of social interactions on the job, Conant and Kilbridge indicated that opportunities for social interaction were reduced by about one-half on enlarged bench jobs (distances to the operator's nearest and next neighbor were about twice what they had been on the line). Forty-five of the 61 workers queried preferred the social-relations aspect of line over enlarged bench jobs. Significantly, however, this negative factor was insufficient to influence the strong majority preference for enlarged jobs.

The Conant-Kilbridge findings examined against the eight work dimensions [discussed in selection 2, page 95] yield interesting results. Considering the first four—knowledge and skill requirement, pacing or rate of performance, degree of repetitiveness or variety, and portion of product worked on—the majority preferred greater skill, control over rate of performance, variety as against repetitiveness, and work on a larger portion of the product.

Findings on relationships at work, the fifth dimension, were more ambiguous. While a majority of the workers preferred the larger number of social interactions permitted by the assemblyline layout, this was overridden by the positive force of the other characteristics of the enlarged jobs. Designers of jobs should, however, weigh this dimension carefully. Personal interactions at work can be a most powerful source of satisfaction, and under certain circumstances subtracting them from the work situation will cancel out many of the positive elements of work satisfaction.[4]

Style of supervision, the sixth dimension, was not specifically studied

4 Cf. "Job Enlargement in an Electronics Company," Thomas M. Lodahl and Charles R. Walker, unpublished study in Technology and Society Collection, Yale University. This study describes the negative effects of the absence of opportunities for interaction.

by Conant and Kilbridge. As to the seventh, degree of workers' autonomy in determining work methods, autonomy was clearly increased, representing an important source of work satisfaction. The eighth dimension, relation of work to personal development both on the job and with respect to transfers and promotions, was not specifically studied, although replies suggest an awareness of this dimension's importance.

The relevance of the Conant-Kilbridge research lies not only in specific findings as related to the experience of one appliance manufacturer, but in their very wide applicability.

There are several reasons for suggesting that these changes in job design may be relatively pervasive. The problem of balance-delay and associated labor costs is a prime problem in manufacturing assembly today. It has become more acute as consumers have demanded and technology has permitted production of more sophisticated and complicated goods. Henry Ford was pleased to maximize the advantages of his assembly-line technology by informing consumers that they could have any color Model A they desired as long as it was black. Today changing demand patterns, upgraded product performance requirements, new technologies and competitive market forces have required many manufacturers to increase variety, complexity, and quality of products. Firms are attempting, in effect, to produce custom-made products by mass-production techniques. Partial failure in this is forcing more firms to reconsider assembly methods, and in some cases to revert to bench assembly, which fosters job enlargement.

. . . Workers may be affected in large numbers, and it may also happen that traditional sources of dissatisfaction with assembly work will be diminished.

Conant and Kilbridge conclude on this important note:

We recognize, of course, that shifting assembly work from line to bench is only one form which job enlargement can take. The principle has many applications in both factory and office that are quite unrelated to progressive assembly.[5]

---

[5] Conant and Kilbridge, *op. cit.*, pp. 395 and 395r.
See in addition:
Robert H. Guest, "Job Enlargement—A Revolution in Job Design," *Personnel Administration*, vol. 20, No. 2, March–April 1957, pp. 13–14.
Chris Argyris, *Personality and Organization*, Harper & Brothers, New York, 1957, pp. 177–181.
J. Douglas Elliot, "Increasing Office Productivity Through Job Enlargement," *Office Management Series*, No. 12, American Management Association, New York, p. 13.

6.   A CROSS–INDUSTRIAL STUDY OF TECHNOLOGY AND WORK

Adapted from Charles R. Walker, Changing Character of Human Work under the Impact of Technological Change, *National Commission on Technology, Automation and Economic Progress*, 1965, *Appendix, vol. 2, pp. 309, 310.*

The most substantial example of cross-industrial research relevant to work dimensions as defined in the second selection is a 3-year project recently completed by Turner and Lawrence.[1]

The research is valuable and appropriate in three ways: (1) It is the first systematic investigation undertaken to test the weight and impact of the technological component in modern work across a wide spectrum of technologies; (2) it provides a practical methodology for *predicting* worker response to the characteristic attributes of work in the modern world; and (3) it recommends a number of ways for both diagnosing and meeting specific problems related to modern work environments. The Turner and Lawrence investigation introduces important innovations in method, content, and coverage. Sources include the British Medical Council (during and after World War I), the early work of Elton Mayo, the Tavistock Institute in England, the Centre des Arts et Metiers in France, and the Technology Project at Yale University. Of special significance is the frank objective to isolate and analyze each technological component in many industries, and to measure their impact on not only the attitudes but the behavior of individuals at work.

The study examined the work dimensions of roughly 500 workers in a sample of 47 jobs drawn from 11 companies. Industries were chosen for broad diversification as to technology and nature of work, as well as company size and regional setting. The sample also gave representation to other common classifications of American industry, such as job shop, mass production, process, and the "soft-" and "hard-goods" industries.

The term "task attributes" was used to describe and measure work characteristics. A requisite task attribute index (R.T.A.) was constructed and includes work characteristics corresponding generally to the dimensions used in this book and, in some respects, to the mass production index used by the Technology Project for studying the automobile industry.

To conceptualize job characteristics or task attributes as inclusively as possible, the investigators began with three major categories: Activity, interaction, and mental states. Activity included much of what has been described here as pacing, repetitiveness, or variety and autonomy in choosing work methods. Interaction included relations with people on and

[1] Arthur N. Turner and Paul R. Lawrence, "Industrial Jobs and the Worker," Harvard University, Graduate School of Business Administration, Boston, 1965.

off the job, whether functionally required or discretionary. Mental states included knowledge and skill required and responsibility.

The full list of requisite task attributes is given below. The plus or minus factor of personal development is a deduction resulting from the application of the whole R.T.A. index. Promotions and transfers are omitted as a work characteristic because the intrinsic job itself is conceptualized as the object of study, rather than the job in a work sequence or on a promotion ladder.

Hypotheses tested stemmed in a broad sense from the assumption that the technological component is strategic in molding the content of modern work. To frame this assumption in terms that are measurable and testable over a cross-industrial and cross-technological spectrum, each task attribute was quantified. For example, "knowledge required" was measured by learning time; "interactions required" were observed and counted. The entire list of attributes was run through for each job and then considered as independent variables. Workers' responses to the attributes were taken as dependent variables and were then quantified, in the main, by using two yardsticks: High or low attendance at work and expressions of satisfaction or dissatisfaction by workers themselves.

List of requisite task attributes

Activity:

Object Variety:

Number of parts, tools, and controls to be manipulated.

Motor Variety—average of:

Variety in prescribed work pace.

Variety in physical location of work.

Variety of prescribed physical operations of work.

Autonomy—average of:

Amount of worker latitude in selection of work methods.

Amount of worker latitude in selection of work sequence.

Amount of worker latitude in selection of work pace.

Amount of worker latitude in accepting or rejecting the quality of incoming materials.

Amount of worker choice in securing outside services.

Interactions:

Required Interaction—average of:

Number of people required to interact with, at least every 2 hours.

Time spent in required interactions.

Optional Interaction on-the-Job—average of:

Number of people available for interaction in working area.

Time available for interaction while working.

Optional Interaction off-the-Job:
Amount of time worker is free to choose to leave the work area without reprimand.

Mental States:
Knowledge and Skill:
Time required to learn to perform job proficiently.
Responsibility—average of:
Ambiguity of remedial action (to correct routine job problems).
Time span of discretion (maximum time before marginal substandard work is detected).
Probability of serious (harmful or costly) error.

Hypotheses tested were:

1. That satisfaction would be high on jobs with a high R.T.A. index, e.g., jobs high on autonomy, responsibility, and interaction opportunities, and that satisfaction would be low on jobs with a low R.T.A. index, e.g., where autonomy, responsibility, and interaction opportunities were low.

2. That workers on jobs with high R.T.A. scores (more autonomy, responsibility, etc.) would stay on the job more consistently and so have a higher attendance score; and conversely, those on jobs with low R.T.A. scores would have low attendance records.

Generally speaking, these two major hypotheses were validated. Other factors influencing work life—for example, supervision, the union, wages, and personality traits—were also fully considered, and detailed tables were presented on their general effects as supplementary variables. The most important and definitive finding, however, was that no matter how supplementary variables influenced individual worker response, for the total population studied the technologically determined job attributes dominated worker response. This was true whether that response was positive or negative.

Among many practical recommendations for solving work-related problems, the following are particularly appropriate for this report: Where the existing technology imposes simple job characteristics with little variety, responsibility, or skill, Turner and Lawrence suggest that management increase variety through job rotation. Even within highly automated technologies, autonomy and responsibility may be increased "through encouraging worker decisionmaking on many aspects of quality control, scheduling, etc., as well as on issues directly related to task attributes, such as hours of work and rest pauses. . . ." They also recommend that management experiment with a "selective form of job enlargement. Often a careful investigation of a particular situation may show that the particular attributes which are contributing most to workers' dissatisfaction can be considerably 'enlarged' without any significant change in the basic technology."

Turner and Lawrence also say about technological change: ". . . Undesirable consequences . . . can be avoided to the extent that workers actively participate in recognizing the need for change and in planning its impact. [They are then likely] to have both the predisposition and the ability to devise ways of adapting to needed change while preserving existing levels of commitment to the importance of the work itself and of total organizational goals."

This body of cross-technological research would seem to have taken a useful step in bridging the gap between broad statistical surveys of modern work and case material. It should be broadened and applied to several strategic segments of modern work, notably those areas where conversion to automatic or semiautomatic operations is creating drastic dimensional changes for both blue- and white-collar workers and for supervisors and managers.

An examination of case studies of different technologies and the Turner and Lawrence cross-technological research, suggests this operational finding: That each individual occupation (as conceived and described here) consists of two halves, the hardware half or machine complex and the organizational structure in which it is imbedded. The machines and tools the worker uses or the control board he operates are examples of the hardware or machine half of his work environment. The administrative or organizational system as it impinges on him, together with all skills and techniques imparted to him and which he controls or which control him, make up the other half.

It follows—and this has been found in practice—that a man's work in modern industry *can be redesigned* in two ways: By changing the hardware portion of his job, or by changing the organizational structure that surrounds it. It is also possible and useful in some cases to change both.

enter automation and the new technologies

INTRODUCTION

THE first and second selections report on two of the earliest full-scale installations of automation among blue-collar and white-collar workers and remain models of objective reporting and analysis. They underscore the typical human impact of the new technologies on individual men and women and on the organizations of which they are a part. They are entitled "Automation in the Factory" and "Automation in the Office."

The two selections which follow are based on advanced applications of the new technologies. The first is entitled "Automation in Continuous Process Industries," and the second, "Computer-controlled Machines."

Although the selections emphasize the human experience of white- and blue-collar workers with the new and revolutionary technologies, it is apparent that the collar and color distinction is breaking down. Two new phenomena are emerging. One is that the worker's job is either disappearing or being pushed upward toward a more and more technical operation or downward to monitoring. And it is evident that occupational assignments generally have become more fluid, as one might expect in an era of transition and acceleration. The second phenomenon, hinted at but not fully developed in these studies, is that some of the more far-reaching impacts and influences of automation are now upon management, and on society as a whole.

For this reason, we shall turn after this chapter to a consideration of management, organized labor, and government in their new and *reciprocal* relationships with the new technologies. In Chapter 10, The Knowledge Revolution and Industry, the arena of impact begins to widen to include most of modern society.

BIBLIOGRAPHY

Barnes, Louis B.: *Organizational Systems and Engineering Groups,* Harvard Business School, Boston, 1960.

Bright, James R.: *Automation and Management,* Harvard Business School, Boston, 1958.

————: "Does Automation Raise Skill Requirements?" *Harvard Business Review,* vol. 36, no. 4, July–August, 1958.

Hoos, Ida Russakoff: "When the Computer Takes over the Office," *Harvard Business Review,* vol. 38, no. 4, July–August, 1960.

Man and Automation: Report of the Proceedings of a Conference Sponsored by the Society for Applied Anthropology at Yale University, December 27–28, 1955. Technology Project, Yale University, New Haven, Conn., 1956.

Mann, Floyd C., and Richard L. Hoffman: *Automation and the Worker,* Holt, Rinehart and Winston, Inc., New York, 1960.

———— and ————: "Case History in Two Power Plants," in *Man and Automation: Report of the Proceedings of a Conference Sponsored by the Society for Applied Anthropology at Yale University, December 27–28, 1955,* Technology Project, Yale University, New Haven, Conn., 1956. (Also in "Human Relations Research in Large Organizations, II," *Journal of Social Issues,* vol. 12, no. 2, 1956, under the title "Individual and Organizational Correlates of Automation.")

———— and Lawrence K. Williams: "Organizational Impact of White Collar Automation," IRRA *Annual Proceedings,* 1958.

———— and Franklin Neff: "Managing Major Change in Organizations," *Report of a Seminar,* Foundation for Research on Human Behavior, Ann Arbor, Mich., March, 1961.

"Social Consequences of Automation," *International Social Science Bulletin,* vol. 10, no. 1, UNESCO, Paris, 1958.

Touraine, Alain: *L'Évolution du travail ouvrier aux usines Renault,* Centre national de la recherche scientifique, Paris, 1955.

Turner, A. N.: "A Researcher Views Human Adjustment to Automation," *Advanced Management,* vol. 21, no. 5, pp. 21–25, May, 1956.

Walker, Charles R.: "Life in the Automatic Factory," *Harvard Business Review,* vol. 36, pp. 111–119, January–February, 1958.

Wiener, N.: *Cybernetics,* The Technology Press of the Massachusetts Institute of Technology, Cambridge, Mass., and John Wiley & Sons, Inc., New York, 1948.

————: *The Human Use of Human Beings,* Houghton Mifflin Company, Boston, 1950.

World Health Organization: *Study Group on the Mental Problems of Automation,* Twenty-fourth Session, Provisional agenda item 10.3, May 25, 1959.

1.   AUTOMATION IN THE FACTORY

From Floyd C. Mann, and Richard L. Hoffman, "Case History in Two Power Plants," in Man and Automation: Report of the Proceedings of a Conference Sponsored by the Society for Applied Anthropology at Yale University, December 27–28, 1955, published by Technology Project, *Yale University, New Haven, Conn., 1956.*

Anticipating a greater demand for electric power in its service area, an electrical light and power company expanded its production capacity recently by adding a new power plant to its system of older plants. In the design of this new plant, the company incorporated many of the latest engineering advancements. As a result of these equipment changes, the new power plant has many characteristics of the automated factory of the future. These characteristics led us to study the new plant as a prototype of automation.

Our study has focused on the perceptions and attitudes of the workers in this new plant. Not having recent measures of the characteristics of these men, we could not evaluate the actual changes in their attitudes resulting from their new working conditions. The decision was made to compare the attitudes of the men in the new plant with those of a similar group of men in an older plant in the system, where relatively few changes have taken place.

Approximately two years after the beginning of operations in the new plant, questionnaires were administered to the men in both plants. Questions were constructed to assess the men's perceptions and feelings about their working conditions, their jobs, their selection and training, shift work, supervision, and the company in general. The study had the support of the managements in both plants and of the union officials representing the men in the older plant. The men in the new plant were not organized.

IMPACT OF ENGINEERING CHANGES ON THE ORGANIZATION AND ITS PERSONNEL: SOME PRELIMINARY FINDINGS

The first findings from our study of some of the dimensions of the human problems which may accompany automation suggest that this form of technological change will have both positive and negative effects on workers' lives, their job satisfactions and motivations. In the new plant the more highly automated, unit system of production has brought about

[1] This case history by Mr. Mann and Mr. Hoffman relied heavily upon charts in its original presentation. For reproduction here the authors have preferred to substitute a paper which covers the same ground and which has also been published by them, under the title, "Individual and Organizational Correlates of Automation," in The Journal of Social Issues, "Human Relations Research in Large Organizations, II," Vol. 12, No. 2, 1956. [For a fuller treatment see Floyd C. Mann and R. Hoffman, Automation and the Worker, Holt, Rinehart and Winston, Inc., New York, 1960.] James Dent and Thomas Lough made significant contributions as members of the research team on this project during its initial phases. Odile Benoit has been a major collaborator during the analysis phase.

significant changes in the occupational and organizational structure of this plant, as compared to the older plant.

Reduction in work force. The first impression a visitor to the new plant receives is one of a large amount of gigantic, expensive equipment going full blast, but with very few men apparently responsible for its operation. This impression is not an illusion. The personnel requirements of the new plant, relative to its productive capacity, are about half what they would be in the older plants. This reduction in the number of workers needed has taken place principally in the operating jobs. In this plant, there is greater reliance on machine than on human control systems.

Part of this reduction in the number of operating personnel has been effected in the boiler feed pump and valve operations by the simplification of the system and the improvement in the feedback controls described previously. The regulation of the speed of the pumps and of the opening of the valves is now performed automatically under the control of a pneumatic feedback system. Because of these changes, the specific jobs of Auxiliary Operator and Water Tender no longer exist. Any work on the pumps which might be required is performed by helpers, but these occasions are rare.

The job of Flue Blower-Ash Handler which exists in the older plants has been, in part, replaced also. In the description of the flue-blowing process, it was noted that an operator in the new plant directs this process remotely by an automatic, programmed device. The Flue Blower-Ash Handlers do this dirty job manually. The ash handling—removal of ashes from the furnaces—is still manually controlled by the helpers in the new plants.

A further reduction in the number of operating personnel has taken place in the control rooms. Whereas nine men are used on the electrical switchboards in the older plant, only two are specifically responsible for this operation in the new one. Similarly, many fewer personnel are used in the unit control stations than operate the turbine and boiler sections of the old plant. Many functions, such as maintaining the steam temperature, are now done automatically without operator control. This reduction has also been accomplished by the reorganization of the work which accompanied the centralization of control of the boiler-turbine-generator operations in the unit control stations.

The effects of these reduced personnel needs are reflected in a greater feeling of job insecurity for the workers in the older plant. These men recognize that technological developments will soon force them to acquire new skills or to supplement their present skills with others required in the operation of new high pressure equipment. The greater efficiency of the new plant is underscored as it is operated continuously at full capacity. Cutbacks in the load requirements and the work force on the week-ends in the older plant have made it clear to all the workers there that the efficiency of the new plant may affect their future markedly. Four out of five of the men in the older plant report they are likely to be laid off if business conditions in the service area of this utility were to become worse. Only one out of five of the men in the new plant have equivalent fears about their future job security regardless of economic conditions.

An extensive reorganization of the content of jobs accompanied the integration of the boiler-turbine-generator operations and the centralization of their control. The job of "operator" has been redefined and enlarged to include a knowledge of and responsibility for the three major parts of the production system rather than merely a specialized concern with boiler, or turbine, or electrical operations.

In the older plant there is a high degree of job specialization related both to the type of work and to the degree of skill required. There are three major operating job groupings—boiler, turbine and condenser, and electrical. The job classification of the most highly skilled electrical job, Switchboard Operator 1st, is three grades higher than the grades of the most highly skilled turbine and boiler jobs, Turbine Operator 1st and Fireman, respectively. Jobs are also classified within each grouping by the degree of skill required. For example, in the boiler room in the older plant in this study there is the following hierarchy of jobs in order of *ascending skill requirements:* Flue Blower-Ash Handler, Fan Operator, Water Tender, Assistant Fireman, and Fireman. Similar skill hierarchies are present in the turbine and condenser rooms as well as in the electrical control room.

In the new plant the integration and centralization of operations and their controls dictated the combination of the jobs of the boiler and turbine operators into a single enlarged job. This enlargement required by the engineering changes set the stage for management to consider the advantages of further job enlargement. This consideration resulted in a decision to add the electrical operating jobs to the new boiler-turbine combination to ensure the development of personnel trained in all three functions. The only operating job classifications are A, B, and C Power Plant Operators. This organization of jobs is a hierarchy based on degree of skills alone. The older distinctions according to the particular equipment operated have been wiped out.

The A Operator is the most highly skilled classification. Each of these men is expected to have most of the skills and, especially, the knowledge and information previously held separately by the skilled boiler, turbine, and electrical operators. As his job title suggests the Power Operator A must be capable of running all of the major parts of the production system. The B Operator is a less skilled worker, in the process of acquiring proficiency on all the operations. Each B is paired with an A in his work, as he takes work orders and is trained by the more skilled man. The C Operator is really a helper. He performs the low-skilled, less desirable tasks which still remain after mechanization, under the informal direction of a B Operator.

The men who were A and B Operators at the time this study was conducted had transferred from operating jobs in the older plants, where they had performed specialized jobs in one of the three production rooms —boiler, turbine and condenser, or electrical. Each of these men had to learn new parts of the production process to a degree almost equal to the skill they already had in their own specialty. Former electrical switchboard operators now had to learn the steam side of the plant; former boiler fireman, the turbine and electrical; former turbine operator, the boiler and electrical.

As part of the on-the-job training for this job enlargement, job rotation was instituted. The men were rotated weekly between the unit control stations, the electrical control station, and other duties in the plant. Rotation has been continued even after the formal training was completed, so that, at the time of the study, the attitudes of the men towards their jobs were affected both by the fact that the job requirements had been vastly expanded over their previous jobs, but also by the fact that they changed the particular job they were doing for another one every week.

The effects of this job enlargement and rotation are marked. A significantly greater proportion of the men in the new plant report that their jobs are much more interesting and that they are more satisfied with the jobs they are doing than do those in the older plant. This feeling seems to arise generally because their jobs are more challenging. Moreover, more men feel that their jobs fully utilize their abilities. Another part of this greater satisfaction lies in the reduction of the monotony of the jobs permitted by job rotation. Each week the operators are faced with a different responsibility in a geographically and physically different job setting.

On-the-job rotation was only one part of a formal training program the company established to ease the transfer of men from their old specialized jobs to the new enlarged ones. The program ran the gamut from classroom sessions in the theory of operations, given by the technical engineers of the plant, to on-the-job training in all aspects of operation. Visits to other plants to observe particular parts of the production process in operation were also included. Despite this elaborate program, the men were generally agreed that they learned most about their new jobs from doing the jobs themselves while actually running the plant.

Tension and interdependence. More men in the new plant than in the old plant report they feel jumpy or nervous about their work. This tension reflects both the enlargement and the feeling of inadequate training. More than a third of the operators report that their training for these new enlarged jobs was too fast, and that it took more than a year for them to feel at ease on their jobs.

Another factor related to the men's feelings of tension on the job is the degree to which they depend on each other for information about the system. Because they found they learned most about the jobs while actually doing the operations—rather than from the formal class-room parts of the training program—the former steam men relied on the former electrical men, and vice versa. The greater the tension level, the more the men report relying on the other men for suggestions and advice about the particular work problems they face on the job. There seems to be some optimal level of interdependence for the men in these plants. Too much or too little leads to some dissatisfaction with the job itself.

Reduction in physical isolation. Change in physical plant design has also affected the patterns of association among the men. The centralization of the control systems onto one floor in the new plant has brought the greater part of the operating personnel together at three stations. The design of the new plant has virtually eliminated the physical isolation of some of the jobs in the older system, where, for example, the Fan Operator spends his entire working day on the top floor of the plant, seven floors apart from most of the other men. This change in location of jobs gives the men more contact with each other, more chance to talk with others on the job. Although no direct measures are available on this, there is strong indication that the men feel a greater unity, more like a single group than they did previously.

Change in supervisory structure. The change to the unit system of operation, the accompanying enlargement of the jobs of the A Operators, and the placing of the major control stations on one floor, have resulted in a reorganization of the supervisory structure. In the old plant, each shift has at least one boiler room foreman, a turbine and condenser room foreman, and an electrical operating foreman. Each foreman also has an assistant. These men report to the Operating Engineer, who is in charge of coordinating the activities of 50 men through these foremen, and is responsible for running the entire system on a particular shift. The Operating Engineer is in charge of the total plant during the evening and night shifts. He reports to the Plant Operations Engineer, who is a member of the top staff of the plant.

In the new plant, a single foreman (the Operating Foreman) is responsible for operations in the plant, and is in charge of the total plant during the evening and night shifts. He reports directly to the Plant Operations Engineer. There is no longer any need for an Operating Engineer to coordinate the boiler, turbine, and electrical functions. This level of supervision has been eliminated. Thus, the introduction of automation into this power plant has resulted in a streamlining of the organizational structure through the elimination of a level of supervision.

The Operating Foreman in the new plant does not directly supervise all of the men on his shift. He relies on the A Operators who have considerable knowledge of the operating process to direct the work of the B and C Operators. This organization of the direction of the work allows the A Operators to learn the human relations skills required to supervise people while they acquire technical knowledge about the equipment.

Patterns of supervisory behavior. Although a reduction in the number of workers and supervisors needed was easily anticipated by the forecasters of automation, there has been considerable speculation concerning the kinds of supervisory abilities which will be important. Some writers have suggested that technical proficiency will be the major stock in trade for the new supervisors. Concern for human relations will be minimal in the face of the new complicated equipment to be run, and the many fewer people to be supervised. Another group has said just the opposite. They claim that the workers will be the people who need the technical skills, and the job of the supervisor will be even more to supervise—to plan ahead and to maintain high morale and motivation among the workers.

Although our data offer no clearcut answer to this problem in prediction, several relevant findings should be mentioned. Those supervisors who are seen as most satisfactory by their subordinates are also perceived as being the most capable on *both* the technical and on the human relations side of their jobs. Those supervisors considered unsatisfactory are rated low in proficiency on technical and human relations skills. Among those supervisors who were rated as intermediately satisfactory, those who were perceived as competent in human relations, but not in technical ability, more often were considered satisfactory by their subordinates than the supervisors who were seen as good on the technical side but poor in human relations. Using the satisfaction of subordinates with their supervisors as the criterion, then, the good supervisor seems to combine both technical and human relations skills, with human relations ability being the most important. This seems to be equally true in the two plants.

Centralized maintenance. While the maintenance of the equipment in power plants has long been on a preventive rather than a "crash" basis, the introduction of the unit system forced management to reconsider and, ultimately, to redesign the organization of plant maintenance. Before the unit system was installed, maintenance had been an in-plant function. Each man in the maintenance crew was a skilled craftsman— mechanic, electrician, pipe fitter, welder, boiler and stoker repair man, etc.—in a particular trade. In his maintenance activity he performed specific repairs. Under the unit system, when any part of a "unit" is incapacitated, its entire production is lost to the system. In order to minimize the "down time" for the new units, the major maintenance work has been removed from the individual plants, and made the responsibility of an enlarged department of construction and maintenance. The men in this department are usually engaged in the systematic overhaul of equipment and preventive maintenance. They move from plant to plant throughout the year. When an emergency arises, however, the entire group can swarm into the plant to make the necessary repairs as quickly as possible. The men in these construction and maintenance crews have retained their job specialties and particular trades.

Small repair jobs within each plant are still done by in-plant maintenance groups. Within these groups, however, old lines of specialization have been eliminated by combining five maintenance skills for the job of General Mechanic "A." The objective here has been to build multiple-skilled units in which each man is capable of doing several job specialties.

Some of these changes were strongly resisted by the union, but were eventually supported in arbitration. The difficulties met by the company in implementing this reorganization of jobs suggest the possibility that job changes of this order, if done too quickly, may be seen as job degradation rather than job enlargement, and decrease rather than increase work satisfactions.

Continuous operation. Earlier we indicated that the increased capital investment may force automated factories to operate around-the-clock. The smaller work forces which are needed to man these factories will be asked to man them 24 hours a day. Since the production of electric power is a continuous process, our study allowed us to examine some of the problems of shift work. Moreover, the two plants which we contrasted have two different patterns of rotating shifts. One plant uses four shifts on a weekly pattern, while the other uses three with monthly rotation. These differences permitted comparisons of their effects on the lives of the workers involved.

The results of our study indicate that very few shift workers (six percent) actually like shift work. The most favorable attitude expressed by any sizeable group in this regard could only be interpreted as a tolerance for ("I don't mind") shift work. Most of the men dislike working shifts. Shift work creates problems in the worker's physical well-being, his relations with his family, and his relations to his larger social world of friends and entertainment. Our findings suggest that the physical and social costs of working shifts are great.

We find a difference, however, in the workers' tolerance for one shift pattern over the other. The weekly rotational pattern used in the new plant was more tolerable to the shift workers there than the monthly rotational pattern was to the workers in the old plant. Although statistically significant, this difference was small. Even under the weekly rotational system, the majority expressed a distaste for shift work.

The change to centralized maintenance also resulted in the institution of shift work for workers who had previously worked only days. To avoid shift work, many maintenance men chose to remain on the in-plant staffs rather than join the centralized group.

It seems clear that unless some ingenious alternative solutions are developed for easing the difficulties imposed by shift work, this aspect of automation will have generally negative effects on workers' lives.

SUMMARY AND CONCLUSION

The objective of this study has been to explore some of the individual and organizational correlates of automation. It has been our purpose to determine some of the social and psychological dimensions of this type of technological change. Toward this end our first study has been in a new, highly automated power plant. We chose power plants because their continuous production has long had many of the engineering characteristics of the new technology; we chose to study a *new* power plant because its changes in design and control appeared to be even more typical of new automated plants.

The introduction of automation into this power plant has produced major effects on its organizational structure and on the attitudes of the workers toward their jobs. Maintenance has been centralized for the entire system. Fewer levels of supervision are required for the smaller work force in the new plant. Job enlargement and rotation have resulted in greater job interest and satisfaction, but also in a higher tension level on the job. The effects of continuous operation on the workers' lives were generally found to be negative.

The findings in our study provide some indication of the dimensions of change which have accompanied automation in this one particular situation. Some of these changes were dictated by the new engineering design and controls; others were instituted by management as they attempted to create the most effective organizational machinery to meet the demands of the new technology. It should be emphasized that the effects we have described may be specific to the particular situation. For example, the extent to which the operating jobs were enlarged in this plant was a management decision and was not forced by the engineering changes. Automation introduced in a different situation and in a different way will presumably have different effects. This study suggests some of the dimensions of the psychological and social problems to be investigated more intensively; other exploratory studies will be needed to uncover other areas.

2.   AUTOMATION IN THE OFFICE

From Floyd C. Mann and L. K. Williams, "Observations on the Dynamics of a Change to Electronic Data Processing Equipment," Administrative Science Quarterly, *vol. 5, pp. 217–256, September, 1960.*

The introduction of automation in the factory and electronic data processing (EDP) in the office has presented social scientists with unique laboratories for investigating the dynamics of organization and processes of change. This paper will summarize some of our findings concerning one such study—a study of the effects of a change-over to EDP equipment. This paper is titled "observations concerning a change-over" to emphasize that our findings have no firm quantitative foundation; they are based on materials from over three hundred unstructured interviews taken as various phases of the change have unfolded.

The company in which this change-over occurred produces and sells electric light and power. It is one of the largest in the United States, serving well over a million customers. Two major divisions are primarily concerned with the accounts of these million customers: Accounting, which is responsible for all customer billing, bookkeeping, and records, and Sales, which handles all direct contacts with customers relating to service and the payments of their accounts. The installation of EDP to maintain customers' accounts had immediate and direst effect on the Accounting Division, its organization and personnel. Our study, therefore, concentrated on the change as experienced in [this] Division.

The change was initiated with very little fanfare in October 1953, when top management announced that a study would be made of the customer accounting and collection function. One year later, after a number of analyses had been completed and evaluated, it was decided to implement recommendations for reorganization of work within and between the Accounting and Sales Divisions. Among these recommendations was a plan for the consolidation and centralization of all record-keeping and calculating work into one data processing group. This was to be [facilitated by] the installation of electronic accounting equipment. On the data processing side, one master record containing all customer information was to be placed on magnetic tape for use with an IBM 705. In terms of organizational structure, conversion to electronic equipment called for considerable realignment, involving extensive transfers of functions and employees from one major division to another, and *a major reorganization* within the Accounting Division. Indeed, studies of the feasibility of introducing EDP equipment placed key members of management in the relatively rare position of being able not only to rethink the organization of work within specific divisional areas, but to redesign the organization, taking advantage of the climate of change to cut across old divisional lines. Many of the economies which accompanied the introduction of EDP probably could have been made without the equipment *if* the same original and broad gauge thinking had been applied to existing operations and equipment.

The period of transition stretched out over five years and during this long period continuity of operations had to be maintained. Activity in all departments mounted as the date for the installation and initial testing of the 705 equipment and programs approached. The machine was delivered in October 1956—almost three years after the feasibility study was announced.

Pressure mounted during late 1956 until fatigue and stress reached a climax for a number of key personnel. A heart attack dramatized for all both the tempo and the level of tension. The change of records from the old to the new equipment finally got underway in mid-March 1957 and continued during the remainder of the year as personnel, equipment, and procedures were tested, found unsuccessful, or found wanting and replaced. By early 1958 the system was technically sound, and more fully understood and accepted. Attention was then turned to the massive task of reassignment and the establishment of permanent jobs and relationships.

This brief résumé gives some feeling of the change which occurred in the nature and tempo of work in the departments within the Accounting Division. It went from a period in which system maintenance was the principal task through a period when attention was focussed on system creation and revision while still performing all the functions of the old system to a period in which a new equilibrium was being established under the new system.

In the remainder of this paper, we shall discuss, first, some of the major changes in philosophy, policy, and practice that accompanied the conversion. Next, we will be concerned with some of the more specific problems of transition. Finally, we will describe the problems of reassignment and restructuring, and provide a final overview of the organization with its new jobs, new structure, and new relationships.

A change-over on this scale provided a crucial test of the corporation's philosophy of participative management. Over the years much effort had been invested in developing the abilities of the intermediate and first-line supervisors to understand and practice the principles of participative management. The rewards from this investment became apparent again and again as Accounting department heads and their supervisors worked together on the technical problems of the conversion which required a common management approach toward change. Intra-organizational conflict was kept to a minimum because of the similarity of such values as notifying people in advance of each step of the change, involving subordinates in the development of the plans for their part in the change, and employing other democratic human relations principles.

The introduction of electronic equipment caused the development and elaboration of company policy in a number of different areas. Probably the most important was the area of policy regarding the employment security of the personnel affected by the change. It was estimated that the consolidation and simplification of records, the mechanization of additional clerical records, and the use of electronic data processing equipment would result in a marked reduction in both the clerical and the supervisory work forces. The specter of this eventual reduction in labor force could have created a serious morale problem, augmented resistances to reorganization of the system, and even severely retarded the introduction of the new equipment.

Since such potential technological unemployment could affect not only the non-supervisory and supervisory employees directly involved, but members of higher levels of management as well, policies regarding the rights of displaced employees began to be spelled out during this period. The general policy which first evolved was as follows:

> Whenever practicable, regular employees whose jobs have been discontinued will be transferred to equivalent assignments for which they are qualified, and at the same rates of pay. It is recognized, however, that permanent assignments to the same rated jobs may not be immediately possible for all employees. When permanent transfers cannot be made, departments are expected to endeavor to provide the most suitable temporary work possible, anywhere in the company. It is the continuing responsibility of the department head to see that such employees are eventually placed in permanent positions—after training if necessary.

It is worth emphasizing that in the development of this type of policy the company went a step further than previously in formalizing its obligation to its permanent and long service employees. It offered employment security, but not the assurance of a particular job to an employee. Such a policy accomplishes several objectives simultaneously. It demonstrates the organization's concern for the welfare of its personnel, helps ensure the assistance of those on whom the company must rely to accomplish the change-over, and reduces the likelihood of unionization of white collar workers as they experience a major threat to their livelihood.

Of the demands placed on management during this transitional period one of the most important was the need to maintain simultaneously three systems of accounting: the old, the conversion, and the new. Manning, operating, and coordinating all three systems was a rigorous test of the abilities and skills of all levels of management in Accounting.

When change is gradual, managers and supervisors, like employees, become thoroughly familiar with that part of the total work process for which they are immediately responsible. With such a drastic change it was necessary for them to develop a much broader view of the system. But the effective supervisor during such a period must not only change his perspective of his role. He must, along with his superiors, be able to draw upon different combinations of skills at different times. Conceptually, we have found it useful to think of three areas of supervisory skills or competences: technical, administrative, and human relations skills.[1] When an organization is in a relatively stable state, the supervisor has to draw heavily upon abilities that ensure organizational maintenance and effective human relations. By contrast, a transition period places a heavy stress on the supervisor's technical competence and cognitive skills. The problems of the transition period were basically technical, and only technical knowledge could solve them. Human relations skills were not unimportant, but the job of laying out operationally feasible plans for complex changes in the accounting systems demanded technical competence. Supervisors without adequate resources in terms of these three skill components found the going extremely difficult at different periods during the transition.[2]

Training was one of the largest problems continually facing supervisors. Throughout the change period, supervisors complained simultaneously about the lack of time to do adequate training and about the great amount of time being consumed in training. Not only were there many replacements on old jobs who had to be trained but also old employees assigned to new tasks who had to be retrained. Frequently training had to be done on overtime. Training for new jobs was particularly difficult. For example, the first people on new jobs in programming, often had to be trained on a process with materials with which neither the supervisor who was doing the training nor the trainee had had any experience.

[1] F. C. Mann and L. R. Hoffman, *Automation and the Worker: A Study of Social Change in Power Plants,* Holt, Rinehart and Winston, Inc., New York, 1960.

[2] F. C. Mann and L. K. Williams, "Organizational Impact of White Collar Automation," *Proceedings of the Eleventh Annual Meeting, Industrial Relations Research Association,* 1958.

First-line supervisors were faced with quite different morale problems during this period of instability. Some had to try to keep their groups working on activities which all knew would be replaced shortly. Others were trying to develop the required new job skills in older employees who would have preferred to have gone on until retirement doing those things they had grown to know so well over the years. Still other supervisors were finding it difficult to keep ahead of their subordinates who were rushing ahead to learn new procedures, nomenclature, and the intricacies of the electronic data processing world without any inhibiting knowledge about the old system. A few supervisors were encountering the problems attendant upon introducing white collar personnel to shift work. Nearly all were able to see the effects of continued overtime and its high cost in terms of fatigue and decreasing productivity.

Another major problem faced by management was the meeting of schedules and principal target dates which had been set early in the planning phase on the basis of little knowledge. In need of some reference points the tentative dates and schedules soon became fixed goals. Perhaps the most serious psychological stress occurred just before the actual conversion date was missed. It had served well as a goal but as the target date neared it became increasingly obvious to key department heads that the date would not be realized, yet all were reluctant to make the pronouncement which would indicate failure. As a group they finally were able to acknowledge that the rapidly approaching deadline would not be met. This admission of the failure, without any pinpointing of blame, came as a relief to many. Subsequently, conversion dates and other targets became less public, and smaller, more meaningful segments of change were set as sub-goals.

Despite these kinds of problems, management was able to continue a high and sustained level of activity without any crippling dissatisfaction or morale problems throughout the transition period. The high degree of involvement, the feeling of personal development, and the sense of team accomplishment undoubtedly did much to maintain satisfaction in what can best be described as a stressful and at times even a chaotic period.

Non-supervisory personnel experienced different types of stress at different times during the change period. Prior to the actual conversion, employees were concerned as to whether they would be able to meet the demands which the change would bring. This was a period of ambiguity and doubt. As soon as the company announced its intention to introduce EDP equipment, some employees began to question their ability to learn the new duties and to be apprehensive about their ultimate place in the organization. Others expressed a desire to "get going and get it over with."

During the transition when top management was beginning to spell out in ever greater detail the dimensions of the change through meetings of the key department heads and supervisors in each unit, employees became increasingly concerned. As top line personnel became more aware of the complexity of the task they had embarked upon and began to wonder about their own adequacy to handle this type of change, their subordinates sensed these fears and in turn became more anxious as to when they would be brought in on the plans, how they could actually assist in the transition, and how they personally would be affected finally.

Once the conversion actually got underway, however, the demands placed upon the employee were those he shared with his superiors and in contrast to the pre-conversion periods were primarily physical demands. Both worked overtime, both lived in an ambiguous, changing work environment, and both were asked to perform at a more rapid rate and in a more devoted manner than previously. While the manager spent his time in managerial meetings, the non-supervisory employee conferred with co-workers and with his supervisor devising solutions to problems unique to a transition period.

Management's decision not to assign any jobs on a permanent basis until the total change process had run its course was at once assuring and disturbing to many employees. The decision was necessary because the completed system was difficult to visualize. Employees recognized the good intentions implicit in this policy, but the continuing uncertainty was hard to live with month in and month out. When the policy was introduced, it was assumed that the change-over would be completed in a relatively short time—two years or three at the most. But as the transition period stretched out, this continuing ambiguity became a greater problem for both employees and supervisors, all of whom were looking forward to a period of system stability and equilibrium.

Employees were not only confronted with a relatively unstructured picture of their long range future in the company, but the immediate working environment for many was equally ambiguous. Those directly responsible for the introduction of the new system were without guideposts to handle this type of technological change in the office. The few companies with some experience in introducing EDP equipment had not attempted such a total system change. Some employees who did not even remotely understand the system that the managers were hoping to create found themselves in training for a job that no one had really seen in operation. Instruction during much of the change was necessarily at quite an abstract level; it is little wonder the employees expressed fears about learning the new required skills—particularly when their jobs were subject to frequent modifications on short notice.

During much of the change period, then, the employee operated on faith: faith that the demands that were placed upon him would be rewarded in the future, and faith in management's ability to effect the change.

After all company accounts were converted to EDP procedures the transitional period came to an end, and the organization was faced with the task of making the final assignments of personnel to permanent jobs in the new system. The policy which was formulated to handle this mass shifting of over 270 employees was dictated by a combination of existing circumstances, previous commitments, and the general management philosophy of the Accounting Division.

Nearly everyone, management and employees alike, had anticipated higher average job grades as a result of the change. However, these higher job grades did not materialize. The least interesting and the most menial types of jobs had been eliminated, but so had a number of high level non-supervisory jobs. Certain previous job grades in the Accounting Division had been somewhat higher than similar jobs in other parts of the organization, and for the first time in a number of years it was possible to bring these jobs into line with the rest of the company. Moreover, as might be expected, nearly everyone had at the outset overestimated the complexity of the new jobs because there had been no experience with them.

Since company policy was to avoid—insofar as possible—reduction in pay rates and job grades of permanent employees as a result of the change-over to EDP, the elimination of upper level jobs in particular greatly complicated the task of reassignment. Furthermore, earlier commitments to the permanent employees precluded one alternative of the usual selection process, i.e., total rejection of the candidate. The problem, therefore, was one of optimum placement of all employees in a manner that would minimize losses in terms of pay and promotion and at the same time enable the company to maintain a staff that was capable of operating the new, and often more demanding, system. These goals were often incompatible and compromises had to be made. Instead of the usual procedure of making assignments to maximize a prediction of success on the job, many personnel decisions had to be made within the framework of minimizing failure. For example, X was obviously the best man for Job 1; he was also the best man for Jobs 2, 3, and 4 that were open simultaneously. On the other hand, there was person Y who had to be placed and who could adequately perform on Job 1 but not on Jobs 2, 3, and 4. The placement of Y on Job 1 then became imperative even though he was not "the best man for the job."

From an overall company point of view, this approach of trying to find a best fit for all employees was quite acceptable. To the first line supervisor or department head, who later would be judged by the performance of only his own subordinates, the placing of known-risk candidates and the passing up of better candidates for jobs in his own group were more difficult to accept. It was all too clear that some of these assignments meant the department head and his staff would be saddled with such an employee for a long time.

As the reassignment program gained momentum, a review of those individuals who were difficult to place revealed that a few factors—such as age and physical disabilities—were the principal deterrents to a candidate's placement. It became apparent that the very nature of some of the white collar desk jobs which existed before conversion had attracted many individuals with physical disabilities such as speech or hearing difficulties, arthritis, or heart conditions. Many of the new jobs required communication with others including the use of telephones, standing at machines, and a considerable degree of training. Moreover, a large number of the jobs eliminated were at the higher levels—levels where one found the older members of the work group, many of whom had worked their way up on highly specialized jobs. Some of the most difficult jobs the company had to fill under the new system had to be staffed from a population that had the least potential.

The reassignment period was one in which several other changes were being made that demanded the careful attention of management. They were also directing all of the activities necessary to introduce a new customer bill form and to change the physical location of all departments affected by the innovation. A number of the interviewees noted that either one of these changes would have been highly disruptive, even "traumatic" to some people, at any other period. However, perhaps because of the magnitude and duration of the change they had just encountered and the personal significance that the reassignment process held for each individual, nearly everyone—management and employees—was able to take these other changes in stride.

Besides the stresses involved in having to accept high risk job candidates, there was the accompanying problem for management of training new members of the work group who were replacing already trained members. Unlike the usual job candidate who anticipates starting at the bottom and learning the fundamentals, the transferred employee often brought several years of seniority with him along with a set of status claims he was accustomed to having met. Even though it was expected that the transferred candidate would rapidly gain proficiency on the job, the necessary training on the elementary and often less challenging tasks of the new job resulted in situations that violated the candidate's self-image. Frustrations derived from such situations often severely taxed the supervisor's human relations skills. These kinds of problems appeared to be somewhat less difficult when two or more employees were transferred together. Several individuals could better face these new and frustrating roles as trainees in a new work group under a new supervisor if they could share and evaluate their experiences with others having a common background.

As the reassignment process started to affect personally the majority of the workers, more employees became visibly concerned about reassignments. Throughout the period of transition there was little disturbance or resistance until each change was imminent, and this again was true of the reassignment phase. Immediately after the job grades and reassignment plans were announced, supervisors reported that only a minority of the employees showed any signs of psychological distress. The earliest reassignments were made at the highest levels, and although many individuals were not accommodated as they had hoped, there was little change in the behavior of workers as reported by their supervisors. The reaction as reassignment of the middle job grades approached was quite different, however. One of the largest single groups of employees worked at grade 0–9 jobs. The week that the 0–10 jobs were being settled, supervisors began to report symptoms of nervousness and anxiety, lowered performance rates, and other indications of a generally agitated work force. A rash of rumors swept Accounting that week.

While no systematic records were kept, supervisors generally felt that an individual's performance went up again following a decision on his job assignment, whether or not the results were favorable for him. Several supervisors reported of their employees that the waiting for the decision seemed to be much worse than the result of the decision itself.

Throughout the latter part of the reassignment period there was a growing realization by personnel at all levels that the organization which was emerging was going to be quite different from the organization they had known so well before the change-over. There would be no going back to the old system and its comfortable, familiar routines. The new patterns of work flow and relationships which were being established contained the environmental realities to which supervisory and non-supervisory personnel had to accommodate. The following is a brief description of the new organization.

A change-over to EDP appears to accelerate the level of formalization within an organization. The organization of work is further rationalized; rules and regulations are substituted for individual decision-making. Programming itself is a large step in this direction. Decisions formerly left to individual employees to handle within the spirit of a general statement of policy are programmed into the machine. It is this type of decision with known criteria that can be built most readily into machine programs. With the programming of this area of decision-making, important functions and even certain positions within the organization are eliminated. Previously these functions have supported a job occupant's claim to a title and a grade of some status within the system. Such positions are typically perceived as status positions, serving as terminal points for the average employee who rises to these positions through sheer endurance within the system. Occasionally these positions also serve as a proving ground for managerial aspirants.

In this study the elimination of these status positions and the further restriction of the areas of employee decision-making fell as a severe blow on status position occupants. Long service employees were stripped of many of their responsibilities at a time when the right and ability to make such decisions was the principal reward of the job.

The new more highly integrated work process allowed less autonomy in setting a work pace for both individual employees and work groups. Work could not be held over from one day to the next. Each group had to process a specific number of accounts every day or perform specific operations. Deadlines themselves became more important, regardless of how the job had been going, or how the personnel and equipment were performing. Absences and tardiness became increasingly important because of their detrimental effect on the group's ability to complete their portion of the job.

Greater interdependence also resulted in greater vulnerability and a greater need for coordination. A breakdown in one phase of the work flow soon stopped the whole operation. Since a change in one section will quickly affect another's ability to do its job, new procedures and centers for coordination were required.

A different type of relocation of control also occurred as responsibilities for given areas or duties were transferred to other groups, departments, or divisions within the company. Throughout the change period there was evidence that such transfers of responsibility often resulted in the control moving either horizontally or to some higher level in the organization to effect a more efficient coordination. Since various sub-units contributed to different stages of the input, it was necessary that a central control unit be aware of any deviations that occurred. Consequently final responsibility and control was vested in a very few positions.

This shift toward more centralized control and decision-making was required to handle the new level of coordination necessary to maintain what was obviously a more efficient system. On the other hand, such centralization ran directly counter to the company's philosophy of participation—one of its principal objectives being the delegation of responsibility directly to first-line supervisors.

The new system resulted in many changes in job structure and in new and differing patterns of relationships. Some of the jobs that were eliminated were taken over directly by the 705. The new equipment also brought into being two major classes of jobs: programmers and electronic equipment operators. The greater number of key punch operators and other machine groups increased the number of employees who were associated more with the mechanical processing of the data than with the data itself. Because of the obvious distinguishing characteristics of the machine jobs as against the accounting jobs and because promotion is probably more feasible within rather than between the groups, there is an increasing possibility of a rather severe schism between these two groups within the Accounting Division.

Job enlargement does not necessarily accompany a change-over to electronic accounting. In this instance, however, it did. The work of the non-mechanized accounting groups responsible for the steps preparatory to the machine handling of the customer's account was completely reorganized. The specialized tasks previously done in five separate sections were consolidated into "a station arrangement," and each member of a station was trained to handle all five operations as a part of a new enlarged job. This reduction in job specialization resulted in increased efficiency in the allocation of man-power, and it is believed that most employees and their supervisors were more satisfied with these jobs.

In addition to creating new jobs and new combinations of old skills, the system required the development of different relationships. With the loss of autonomy and the introduction of more system pacing, groups became more highly dependent upon each other and individual responsibilities became more obvious and easily evaluated. Such changes allowed the development of tighter standards of performance, and the increasing costs of errors augmented concern for standards. In the sense that failures in performance were easily detected, the machine placed more responsibility upon the individual employee.

There has been little chance as yet to assess how this extensive period of change will affect the organization eventually, but we are able to indicate what some of the major effects have been on the organization and its members to date.

Accounting and Sales Divisions have moved from a relatively autonomous set of departments to a much more highly integrated system. The installation of electronic equipment has brought about changes in policies and procedures which are much more demanding of the individual employee. The level of decision making and control has moved up to fewer and higher positions within the organization. Changes in the job and promotion structure have been quite drastic.

For many individuals this was a period of growth; for others a period of failure and disillusionment. The change severely tested marginal employees and supervisors while at the same time giving more experienced and able personnel the chance of their life to develop and to demonstrate their work potentials.

The change period gave management at all levels a much deeper understanding of the human resources within their organization. It also increased each supervisor's awareness of how his responsibilities interlock and interrelate with other supervisors, superiors, and subordinates. The long period of sharing problems with other managers, and the need for extraordinary cooperation at all levels resulted in a greater appreciation and tolerance for other parts of the organization. Employees and supervisors learned to work together in problem solving groups in a way which neither would have thought possible before the change started. It is already apparent that the principal reasons for which this major organization change was undertaken are being attained; the new system is permitting a reduction in cost and is sufficiently flexible to encompass further expansion. The final effect on the individual members of the organization who were caught up and embroiled in this change is still to be learned.

3. AUTOMATION IN CONTINUOUS PROCESS INDUSTRIES

Adapted from Charles R. Walker, Changing Character of Human Work under the Impact of Technological Change, *National Commission on Technology, Automation and Economic Progress, 1965, Appendix, vol. 2, pp. 296, 304, 305, 306, 307, 308.*

In the following discussions of automation in the factory we shall use the same list of work dimensions applied as an analytic tool to mass and other production technologies. (See p. 95.)

By doing so the reader can make direct comparisons of the human impact of mass-production technologies with the newer automatic or semi-automatic ones. The dimensions, repeated here for easy reference, are:

1. Knowledge and skill requirement.
2. Pacing or rate of performance.
3. Degree of repetitiveness or variety.
4. Relation to the total product or process. (This includes how much of a particular product or process the individual works on as well as his overall relation to the total operation of his plant or unit.)
5. Relationships with people as individuals or groups. (This includes the frequency of interactions and whether these are functionally required by the work or are discretionary.)
6. Style of supervision and managerial controls, whether administrative or technological.

7. Degree of worker's autonomy in determining work methods.

8. Relation of work to personal development, both on the job and with respect to transfers and promotions.

The impact of automation on hours, wages, and union-management relations is discussed in the chapter The New Technologies and Labor. Of all industries, the chemical and oil refining are the most highly automated, having introduced forms of automatic controls very early, long before the term automation was invented. It is not surprising, therefore, that the number of workers in these industries is, comparatively speaking, small and investment per worker is high. In oil refining, the most highly automatic of all, capital investment per production worker is $110,000, compared with an average of $15,000 for all manufacturing in the United States. Output per man-hour increased 5.2 percent a year between 1947 and 1962, as compared with less than 3 percent for all manufacturing. For the chemical industry, the investment figure is $28,000 per production worker. Technologically, these industries belong in the more general category of process industries, of which basic steel is another example.

In applying the eight work dimensions to process technology, major sources of empirical data and findings are the studies of Robert Blauner, Davis and Werling, and the Technology Project of Yale University.[1]

It is interesting to quote Blauner on the first dimension: "The developing mechanization in continuous process technology results in an internal distribution of the blue-collar labor force that is different from the assembly line, mass-production industries. The most dramatic change is the reduction in the number of semiskilled operatives . . . since automatic processes do the work which these men would do in other technological situations. . . . There is also a striking inversion in the number of skilled craftsmen . . ." [2] (i.e., increase in skilled craftsmen compared with assembly-line technologies).

In one chemical plant which Blauner studied in detail, 40 percent of the work force were maintenance workers. In contrast to mass-production technologies, the blue-collar work force was highly stratified with respect to skill, status, job grade, department, and type of work; such stratification was clearly a response to the industry's technology.

As to the second and third dimensions, pacing or rate of performance and degree of repetitiveness or variety, instead of the mass production

[1] Robert Blauner, *Alienation and Freedom: The Factory Worker and His Industry,* The University of Chicago Press, Chicago, 1964, pp. 124–165.

Louis Davis and Richard Werling, "Job Design Factors," *Occupational Psychology,* vol. XXXIV, No. 2, 1960, pp. 109–32.

Charles R. Walker, *Toward the Automatic Factory,* Yale University Press, 1957.

Charles R. Walker, "The Basic Oxygen Furnace," unpublished manuscript, 1965.

[2] Blauner, *op. cit.,* pp. 131 and 134.

job cycles of a few seconds to a few minutes, Blauner writes: "The chemical operator's most standardized operation is his periodic round of readings which he takes every 2 hours. On such a round an operator may check the readings on more than 50 different instruments located at widely different points in his patrol area. There is a considerable variety, then, even in the most routine of the chemical operator's job tasks." [3]

This freedom of physical movement and a considerable choice in the timing of tasks largely eliminates imposed pacing and repetitiveness from the job. Whereas pressure and monotony were the commonest subjective expressions of dislike among the auto assembly workers, these factors appeared in almost none of the chemical workers' expressions of dissatisfaction. Eighty percent said they were free to set their own work pace.

The fourth dimension, relation to the total product or process, is one of the most important in all continuous process industries. The chemical worker, for example, is related to the total industrial operation—or to an important segment of it—in a fashion duplicated in few other work environments. Blauner writes: "The responsibility demanded of the chemical worker is a collective as well as an individual responsibility. Since the process is integrated and continuous rather than divided . . . the responsibility of any one employee for his share of a plant's process is inevitably linked to the responsibility of other workers. . . . [As a result] the very definition of responsibility as a job requirement involves a meaningful connection between the worker's own function and the goals of the entire enterprise." [4]

The fifth dimension, relationship with people as individuals or groups, is especially relevant for two reasons: (1) The operating work force of much of the chemical industry is organized into small groups or teams. ". . . Chemical-process operators are clearly identified with a particular shift and a particular department; the departmental work teams are not only clearly defined, they also have an explicit hierarchy of authority and status." [5] (2) The rate of interaction between workers on the job is relatively high although there are a few semisolitary jobs in chemical plants. The Davis and Werling study reports that blue-collar workers ranked "friends at work" as the most-liked element in the total job situation more consistently than 10 other factors, including interesting work, security, and pay.

With relation to dimension six, style of supervision and of managerial controls, whether administrative or technological, a few characteristics emerge from the nature of the process industries. Many worker-attitude surveys in many industries over the years have found strong preferences

---

[3] *Ibid.*
[4] *Ibid.,* pp. 143 and 146.
[5] *Ibid.*

for "general" rather than "close" supervision, the typical comment being: "I don't want the boss breathing down my neck." Close supervision usually characterizes industries with a highly subdivided technology. In process industries the hand of supervision is lighter. Blauner writes: "The chemical workers interviewed all felt that the load of supervision was light and that they were given considerable scope to do their jobs in their own way. . . . The freedom is possible because the work team which runs an individual plant *takes over many of the functions of supervision in other technological contexts.* A worker will come to work and do his job well, not out of fear of a particular boss, but because he feels the other operators in his crew are depending on him to do his part of the total work." [6] [Emphasis supplied.]

Dimension number seven, degree of worker's autonomy in determining work methods, has been encompassed in discussions of other dimensions. Autonomy in choosing work methods results, in part, from the absence of pressure which allows time for considerable experimentation in meeting new situations. Again, according to the Davis and Werling survey, 50 percent of the respondents stated that they usually plan how they do their job; 34 percent frequently do this; and only 6 percent said they seldom or never are able to plan their work.[7]

Finally, with regard to the eighth dimension, relation of work to personal development both on the job and with respect to transfers and promotions, the process industries contrast sharply with those technological environments which offer little difference in skill levels and a flat wage structure. Workers in the process industries typically function in teams that include a distribution of skills and defined responsibilities at all levels—job grades are likely to run from beginning helper to head shift operator. Thus, each job becomes a step on a natural ladder along which the worker may reasonably hope to progress, with an appropriate increase in training, responsibility, pay, and status.

Dimension four, relation to the total process, is clearly one of the most distinctive and satisfying features of process industries, but tangentially related to it is an element in the industry's work environment that is cordially disliked. This is the shift system, deriving from 24-hour operation. Other investigators have given considerable study to this element.[8] Blauner summarizes worker reaction as follows: "Changing shifts every 2 weeks prevented many workers from settling into satisfactory sleeping routines. *Night and weekend work stands out as the number one source of dissatisfaction of the chemical operators."* [9] [Emphasis supplied.]

[6] *Ibid.*, p. 147.
[7] Davis and Werling, *op. cit.*, quoted by Blauner, p. 139.
[8] Cf. for example, Floyd C. Mann and L. R. Hoffman, in their study of a power-plant, *Automation and the Worker*, Holt, Rinehart and Winston, New York, 1960.
[9] Blauner, *op. cit.*, pp. 141, 142.

Then he gives the following condensed summary of the overall work environment of a chemical plant as seen by the workers themselves:

> . . . as compared to the textile mill and the automobile assembly line, continuous process technology leads to considerable freedom from pressure, control over the pace of work, responsibility of maintaining a high-quality product, choice of how to do the job, and freedom of physical movement.

In spite of such favorable features, however, Blauner asked the chemical worker if he feels and resents being controlled and dominated by the powerful technological complexes among which he works. A head operator in the company's ammonia plant answered in a generally typical fashion:

> If I want something to happen, I'll open a valve, and more product will be distributed to such and such a place. It's the operator who's definitely in charge and he runs the machine. The machine doesn't run him.

"The responses to this question," writes Blauner, "as well as other evidence, indicate that chemical workers do not feel dominated by their imposing technological surroundings but, instead, get feelings of satisfaction from the control of complex machinery." [10]

The average worker on automobile assembly lines welcomes breakdowns in technology as a means of relieving the pacing and repetitiveness of the line as well as his lack of freedom of movement. The auto-worker also welcomes and often prolongs another type of "break" in his routine, through unauthorized or "wildcat" strikes. The chemical worker, on the other hand, appears strongly motivated, as Blauner writes, "to solve the problems caused by a breakdown in the technology and restore production to normal as soon as possible." This is in spite of the fact that "when there is a break in production he must work most frantically and under pressure . . . ."

Blauner concludes that these attitudes toward technology suggest chemical workers are more functionally integrated with the goals of management. It might be added that these workers are functionally integrated *because* the technology *permits* a wider span of interest and responsibility. It follows, then, that a fuller discussion of dimension four, relation to the total operation of the plant or unit which employs the worker, is indicated.

"The most critical feature of automation (in the chemical industry)," writes Blauner, "is that it transfers the focus of emphasis from an individual job to the process of production . . . . In this shift of emphasis

[10] *Ibid.*

from job to process, the worker's role changes from providing skills to accepting responsibility. His scope of operations increases. Continuous-process technology thus reverses the historic trend toward the greater division of labor and specialization." (This is essentially another type of job enlargement.)

In a typical chemical industry crew not all workers have the same degree of understanding or relationship to the total process as the leader. Nonetheless, even the least skilled worker with restricted duties and responsibilities is on the same promotional ladder and is a member of the same functional work group. The net result is that those in the lower ranks tend to identify with the whole crew and the total process. Confirmation of this is reported in a recent study comparing an electronic tube plant, a computer manufacturing factory, and a steel mill.

The perception of workers in low-functional level jobs in steel manufacturing is almost identical to that of workers in high-functional level jobs in that industry and quite contrary to that of the workers in the other two industries. This is quite understandable since in the steel industry: (a) Both high- and low-functional level workers are members of a hierarchical team, operating in relation to a single huge machine; (b) the low-functional level crewmembers identify with the higher jobs which they expect to attain by seniority; (c) the low-functional level workers have a higher function (operating) than their counterparts in the other two industries who are feeding and tending; (d) when the low-functional level steel workers are talking about a less advanced technological situation, they are referring to one that is already highly automated; when the workers in the other two industries are talking about a less advanced technological situation, they are referring to handwork or to jobs in which they were in control of a nonautomatic machine rather than to an automated situation which utilized them functionally largely as feeders and tenders.[11]

Although the technology and job structure of the chemical industry and portions of the steel industry either demand or promote wider identification with the product and total process, even in less favorable technologies such identification can be greatly increased by progressive management policies. Examples can be found in accounts of union-management experience under the so-called Scanlon plans.[12]

The Davis and Werling survey of a highly automated chemical plant

[11] "The Nature of Automated Jobs and Their Educational and Training Requirements," S. A. Fine, Human Science Research, Inc., McLean, Va., prepared for Office of Manpower and Training, Department of Labor Contract. OAM–3–63, June 1964.
[12] Douglas McGregor, "The Scanlon Plan Through a Psychologist's Eyes," in Frederick Lesieur (ed.), *The Scanlon Plan,* Technology Press, MIT, Cambridge, Mass., and John Wiley & Sons, Inc., New York, 1958, pp. 89–100.

found 60 percent of the operators saying they knew all the stages required to complete the product. Surprisingly, this figure was higher than for maintenance repairmen and stockroom and shipping employees.

A feature peculiar to the technological work environment in the chemical and oil refining industries should also be mentioned: The worker's sensory relation to his product is totally eliminated, since the product goes its entire cycle in pipes or reactors out of sight of those manning the controls. Blauner speculated whether this might be a negative factor, and found it was not. In fact, the question had rarely occurred to the respondents. Of course, invisibility of the product does not hold for all process industries; in basic steelmaking, for example, the physical presence of molten steel is most of the time dramatically evident to all who work in the mill.

In summarizing, Blauner isolates and emphasizes four distinctive aspects of the work environment of a chemical plant which "enhance the worker's sense of providing a unique and important function whose purpose he understands." These are process production, team operations, the job requirement of responsibility, and the possibility of physical movement.

"Of these the technological factor of division of labor by process rather than by job seems to be the most important . . . ." [13]

CONTINUOUS PROCESS INDUSTRIES—STEEL

The steel industry is roughly divided into two technological parts: First, those processes commonly called the basic steel industry through which ingredients are "melted" into raw steel products or ingots; and second, those processes by which ingots are transformed or finished into a vast variety of products, called, depending on the general nature of the product, tubing (pipe), flat-rolled products (sheets), etc. Both parts have undergone profound technological revolutions during the past decade.

Basic steel

Significantly the revolution in basic steelmaking has occurred not through an application of automatic devices, although these are present, but through a new application of chemical principles to traditional ingredients. The units for turning molten iron ore and scrap into steel by this new method are basic oxygen furnaces, whose furnace load or "heat" receives at over supersonic speed a draft of oxygen. This enormously accelerates the rate of chemical reaction and multiplies the efficiency of the furnace by from 4 to 800 percent. The older, open-hearth furnace converts its ingredients into steel in 4 to 8 hours; a basic oxygen furnace produces the same quantity of steel in 45 minutes to an hour. In order

[13] Blauner, *op. cit.*, p. 146.

to maneuver the heavy machinery that makes the oxygen furnace operable and to perform metallurgical calculations at necessary speeds, a
variety of automatic devices, including a computer, are necessary. This
whole complex of innovations is now rapidly transforming the work environment for basic steelmakers.[14]

Following is a discussion of basic steelmaking in oxygen furnaces with
relation to work dimensions:

1. *Knowledge and skill requirement.* The higher skills in basic steelmaking have been, to some degree, absorbed by management and by
automatic or semiautomatic technology. Notably, many of the skills in
judgment and decision making of openhearth workers, especially those
of the first helper, have been taken over either by the melter foreman or
by automatic devices and data processing equipment. Some, although
not all, of the other jobs of the several crews necessary to operate the
furnace have lost a number of points in job class. The amount of heavy
hot work has been reduced but by no means eliminated. Total manning
force for a basic oxygen furnace is roughly the same as for an open
hearth; therefore, technological displacement of workers will be due not
to overall reduction in crew members, but to the need for fewer crews as
units of production.

2. *Pacing and rate of performance.* As already noted, these are much
faster. However, their character and impact are wholly different from that
required by machines and assemblyline technologies. Essentially greater
alertness and attention are demanded at certain intervals, rather than
more rapid or dexterous physical movements.

3. *Degree of repetitiveness or variety.* Although the same operational
steps are taken for every *heat* of steel, conditions vary sufficiently, heat
by heat, to guarantee little monotony.

4 and **5** will be discussed below.

6. *Style of supervision and managerial controls.* For the blue-collar
worker, the new steelmaking process, like the old, shares or divides necessary supervision between the melter foreman and the process itself.
While this is not as striking as in the chemical industry, it is an important
feature of the work process.

7. *Degree of worker's autonomy in determining work methods.* For all
of the crew, the degree is substantially less than on the open hearth. But
because metallurgical processes cannot, at least as yet, be wholly standardized in the manner of a machining operation, some latitude remains
as to how and when each step is performed.

8. *Relation of work to personal development, both on the job and with*

---

[14] In 1965 about 10 percent of the basic steel-producing capacity in the United
States was in B.O.F.'s. Within 10 years, it is commonly predicted that the industry
will consider the older openhearth method obsolete.

respect to transfer and promotion. Because of the relative newness of this type of work environment and the absence of studies in depth of its work dimensions, it is too soon to apply this dimension intelligently. However, the opportunity for the worker's personal development does depend on training programs and on management's ingenuity in integrating blue with white-collar careers.

To return to dimensions **4** and **5**—*relation to the total product or process,* and *relationship with people as individuals or groups*—with respect to both, the effect on the individual is positive. Some of the psychological and social elements of satisfaction reviewed for the chemical plant also appear to be present in this new method of basic steelmaking. To illustrate, it is immediately and continuously evident to every member of the furnace crew, white or blue collar, that he is a participant in a *process* that is larger than the work contribution of any single individual and yet which continuously demands that contribution. Further, the "product" of each heat is physically or mentally vividly present and each member of the crew can *see* the completion of the product several times a shift. Finally, to achieve their common purpose, furnace crews must have freedom of physical movement and frequent verbal interactions.

Although working conditions are better than they are on the older open-hearth process, considerable hazard, heat, and heavy physical exertion, especially during emergencies, remain as negative features.

Steel finishing

An early and substantial application of automation to the finishing portion of the industry was studied over a period of years by the Technology Project of Yale University and has yielded useful findings.[15] The study focused on a large automatic pipe mill, built and operated by the United States Steel Corp., in its tubing division. While results were similar to those reported for basic steelmaking, certain dimensional differences were noted, the most important of which concerned pacing, rate of performance, and freedom of movement. The pipe mill was composed essentially of a mechanical complex of automatic devices, with each crewmember attached to a particular work station; therefore, there was little or no freedom of movement and pacing by the total machine complex was continuous. Nevertheless, the effect (after the break-in period) of this pacing is radically different from that in machining or assemblyline technologies.

Although men were stationed at different points, all were, and, in fact,

[15] Charles R. Walker, *Toward the Automatic Factory,* Yale University Press, New Haven, 1957.
"Life in the Automatic Factory," *Harvard Business Review,* January–February 1958.

felt themselves to be members of a close-knit team, manning a single massive unit of machinery. Split-second timing of their own motions, for the most part through the operation of levers, was integrated with every other man's physical and mental activity, and the product as it moved through a variety of finishing processes was continually visible.[16] Again, product visibility at all times contrasts with product invisibility in a chemical plant. On the other hand, the chemical worker does control through levers and buttons a much larger sequence of operations than the workers in automatic pipe mills.

It is a characteristic of the steel industry, as it is of certain others concerned with metalworking, such as aluminum and copper, that the basic work unit is the group rather than the individual. Even where automation reduced the total manpower complement as in the pipe mill cited here, this primary structural feature was not changed, and cohesive crews continued to operate the mill.

As in basic steelmaking, the style of supervisory control was also distinctive. It was *shared* by the men as crews with their supervisors. The importance of these features was generally important to worker satisfaction.[17]

These relatively favorable appraisals are tempered by the realization that declining manpower requirements will continue to affect the attitudes and working lives of employees. Workers in large sections of the chemical industry experience little anxiety over technological displacement. However, in steel the opposite is true: Uncertainty as to future employment lessens present satisfaction with favorable dimensions in the work structure. As one worker in the automatic pipe mill put it:

> As far as I go, this new mill has been good for me because I can sit down or stand up, and I have all the "automatics." (His job consisted of the manipulation of levers.) It's certainly much better than it was when I had that heavy labor of rolling down billets. . . . But . . . look what happens to manpower. On the old mills we had about 21 or 22 operating people (per mill unit), and on this mill we only have 9. That cuts things in half . . . and most of the men . . . took a cut in job class. . . . So . . . you wonder whether all these improvements are good. . . .[18]

This comment was made when employment in the steel industry was still increasing; today the prognosis for manpower is a steady decline in requirements.

[16] These characteristics of work are also noticeable in other modern finishing installations—blooming mills, sheet mills, tin mills, etc.

[17] Walker, *Toward the Automatic Factory, op. cit.,* see especially, "After Three Years," p. 104, and "The Automatic Mill as a Work Community," p. 210.

[18] *Ibid.,* p. 183.

In 1953, the peak year for steel employment, the industry turned out 111.6 million ingot tons of steel with a production and maintenance force averaging 544,000 a month. In the first 6 months of 1965, with production running 2.6 percent higher monthly than in 1953 (partly the result of a strike threat), the production and maintenance force averaged 468,000. Some 100,000 blue-collar jobs have been lost in steel since the mid-1950's. The industry acknowledges that the number of workers needed to produce a ton of steel has declined by 2 percent a year since 1940, and if this continues and production by 1975 is, say, around 145 million tons, employment will be under 400,000. For its part, the union claims management's figures are too low. The union insists the decline has been nearer 3 percent and that the work force will be cut by nearly 40 percent by 1975 unless the demand for steel increases drastically. In addition, the ratio of white- to blue-collar jobs is constantly increasing, having risen from one in nine in 1934 to one in four in 1964.[19]

4. COMPUTER–CONTROLLED MACHINES

Adapted from Charles R. Walker, Changing Character of Human Work under the Impact of Technological Change, *National Commission on Technology, Automation and Economic Progress, 1965, Appendix, vol. 2, pp. 311, 312, 313.*

One of the most rapidly growing systems of automation in manufacturing is "numerical control" or A.P.T. (automatically programmed tool system). Two features about this technique are striking. First, as a cross-industrial technology, it is applicable to many if not all of the 29 metalworking industries. Also being discussed and tested is its extension to other types of operations, such as drafting, riveting, welding, inspecting, and molding, among others. Thus, this automatic technique has implications for many industries with different technologies. Second, applications are sufficiently new and experimental that occupational structures into which numerical control is being fitted are not yet frozen. A Department of Labor study comments: "Because numerical control is a new field where procedures in most of the operations still are being developed, occupations, job titles and duties do not yet follow a well-defined pattern." [1]

This statement is well documented and has been given organizational and behavioral significance by several investigators through interviews

---

[19] Figures from *Business Week,* Aug. 14, 1965, pp. 75–78.

[1] *Outlook for Numerical Control of Machine Tools, A Study of a Key Technological Development in Metalworking Industries,* Bureau of Labor Statistics, Bulletin No. 1437, March 1965, pp. 33–45.

and questionnaires.[2] Major conclusions which may be drawn from all investigations to date are:

(1) Depth and force of the impact of numerical control on the whole organizational structure is profound; and (2) uncertainty still prevails as to its influence on the work dimensions of many individuals. Followup investigations in particular industries are, therefore, called for. L. K. and C. B. Williams, who studied the impact of numerical control through interviews and extensive questionnaires with 33 users and 6 producers, emphasize several major organizational impacts. Each implies certain behavioral and psychological problems attendant on dimensional changes in the work of individuals and groups.

Major users of "automation in the office" have long observed that one of the great benefits of the computer has been the rethinking and the reshaping of organizations which it compels. Hidden costs have often been revealed and improved methods adopted even before savings were realized from the computer itself. Now evidence accumulates that the same preinstallation benefits are being realized from numerical control in the factory.

Williams and Williams in their broad survey document certain predictable impacts. Among these are a number of occupational candidates for displacement, for example, the skilled craft of a tool and die maker. (To date, few of these craftsmen have actually lost their jobs, but no new ones are being trained in many companies.) Another is the technically trained first-line supervisor. For perhaps obvious reasons, many decisions formerly made by the supervisor—allocations of work, to name one—are now made at a higher level and far from the factory floor. Two other predictable results of numerical control are, of course, the creation of a new occupation, that of programing, and the addition of electronic engineering skills to the maintenance department.

However, from the standpoint of this report the most fundamental and far-reaching change is the new location and character of the decision-making process. That decisions would be lifted to a higher point in the organizational hierarchy was predictable, but many of the behavioral effects of this change were not. The nature of numerical control technology dictates several features that characterize the decisionmaking proc-

---

[2] For this discussion of the impact of numerical control on dimensions of human work, the writer is particularly indebted to Lawrence K. Williams and C. Brian Williams, "The Impact of Numerically Controlled Equipment on Factory Organization," *California Management Review*, Winter 1964, and for a broader discussion of new technologies and work, to Peter B. Doeringer, "The Theory of Internal Labor Markets," unpublished Ph.D. thesis, Harvard University, 1965, and Michael J. Piore, "Impact of Technological Change on the Skill Content of Jobs," unfinished Ph.D. thesis, Harvard University, scheduled for completion, spring 1966.

ess and determine its location. Minor decisions on work allocation and quality of product, formerly made over a period of time and on the factory floor, must now be made once and for all. The high cost of equipment implies heavy penalty for idle machines, and there must be no down time. By the same token the cost of planning errors is far greater than it is on conventional equipment. Williams and Williams report, "The error often is not the fault of the operator of the equipment, because his opportunity to deviate from the planned sequence of machine operations is normally restricted. Usually the performance failure can be traced back to design; to a translation of the design into programing information; to a conversion of the programing information into numeric information; or to the preparation of the punched tape."

These wholly new dimensions in the decisionmaking process account for many of the unanticipated consequences for organizational behavior. Certainly departmental units are less independent in a numerically controlled factory than a conventional one. Interaction must, therefore, be close and frequent. As Williams and Williams remark, "Essentially units become interdependent and have fewer areas of freedom. Maintaining productivity becomes a continuing cohesive force." Another result of numerical control is its introduction of a new problem in communication —or put more positively, it demands new channels of communication. Traditional channels, which go up to the top in one division and over and down into another, are too slow and cumbersome; also the particular level within, say, a manufacturing or engineering division at which the failure occurred may be by-passed under the old arrangement. Some companies now use multidepartmental committees made up of representatives from the various levels of their operating units. Another communications problem when computers are used is posed by the introduction of a novel language, the syntax and vocabulary of the computer, which must be learned by many of the personnel. (An advantage of the multidepartmental committee is that it permits and promotes the use of this common medium of communication.)

Another important result of numerical control installations is unexpected: The importance of the skilled machine operator is increased rather than decreased, a result of the new decisionmaking functions and the "once-and-for-all" taping of production runs. Since it is *his* skills and *his* knowledge of actual machine performance that have now been transferred to the tape, his past experience best equips him to anticipate actual outcomes on the factory floor; and by the same token, to correct planning errors made at the source.

Williams and Williams conclude: "The operator is in a position to be of great assistance, or hinderance, to the other members of the numeric control system. He is also in a position to evaluate the performance of the input of these other groups contributing to the numeric control effort. A good operator can feed back performance data and can often correct for errors introduced by others. A low-level operator, who may have little knowledge of what is happening, is not able to feed back information. Above all, he is not in a good position to correct errors. He can only shut the machine down (or worse, cause damage to it) and call for help, thus revealing the performance failure to the whole organization."

It must be emphasized that the whole phenomenon of the numerically controlled department or factory is still in its early stages, and many occupational classifications, including that of machine operator, are still undefined. Nevertheless, the incumbents of certain jobs are in strategic positions and may well retain them for some time.

Williams and Williams suggest that organized labor's policy, as a rule, is to accept the fact of a reduction in the daily exercise of certain former skills but also "to argue that the cost of the equipment and the cost of an error is so great that the classification of the individual should be maintained or even raised. The shift is from claims based on job skill to job responsibility."

The latitude enjoyed and exercised by industrial engineers, managers, and personnel departments is still appreciable, not only with numerical control but with many other installations of automatic machinery as well. Practices observed by Doeringer and Piore show that knowledge and skill required (dimension one) and personal development on the job and pro- motions (dimension eight) are frequently within the control of manage- ment through decisions made by industrial engineers or managers. For example, an automatic installation may result in a new occupation, designed as the simple monitoring of a machine, but the job specification may be written to include a quota of maintenance; or it may, in addition, encompass inspection. Considerable latitude is also introduced in the ladder of promotion as a result of changing technologies—some manage- ments have succeeded in maintaining or creating promotion ladders for blue-collar workers, while others have been disposed to remove highly skilled jobs from the blue-collar category and assign them to exempt employees.

The tendency of certain technological innovations to create ceilings or dead ends for blue-collar workers creates a problem for many hourly employees from the standpoint of a healthy work career. This was empha- sized by the Yale technology project's comparative studies of the impact over a 10-year period of conventional and of automatic technologies on the working lives of men in the steel tubing industry. The question of promotion was summarized thus:

> There are two interrelated factors that are likely to influence strongly the harmony of any automatic mill . . . education and promotion. The

workers believed that there was an all but impassable educational barrier to their own advancement in automatic mills. . . . More and more, they said, the mill man with his practical skill and experience will be unable to rise as in the past unless he has had a technical education. The future belongs to the college boys, the slipstick men (technicians using a slide rule) and the engineers.

The study concluded that:

The nationwide trend toward automation as such will create a large and many-sided educational problem in the next decade. The demand for education both inside and outside the industry will grow. Of this fact there is already much talk and wide recognition. What is less well understood is the two-sided problem stressed by the men . . . . They were saying: "Mills like Number 4 and all other automatic mills of the future, will need more technical men, that's understood; but isn't there a way of bringing in the engineers without losing the hard-won qualities of 'mill-wise' men, with their skill in human relations and in man-boss relations which the 'college boys' haven't got?" [3]

A part of the response to this problem can be found in more night courses by more colleges in more cities for blue- and white-collar workers, and some increase in the quality and scope of on-the-job training in industry. But so far the effort and results are small compared with the need. Fortunately more courses in the social and behavioral sciences are being given in the country's leading engineering schools with the result that new designers of jobs hopefully will be better equipped to weigh both the technical and human factors in the new occupational structures they will be called upon to design.

[3] Charles R. Walker, *Toward the Automatic Factory*, Yale University Press, New Haven, Conn., 1957, pp. 214–215.

the new technologies and management

INTRODUCTION

THE first selection by the English economist Joan Woodward is based upon several years' research in a great variety of industries. The findings given here by Miss Woodward in condensed form and in broad strokes demonstrate that technology increasingly appears to be the decisive and determining factor in the organizational structure of modern industry. The general implication of the research is that those companies where the "fit" between technology and organization is closest will tend to be the most successful.

The second selection, a case study of aerospace systems, takes the reader directly into a research center where he listens to the actual problems of scientists and managers in modern industry as set down in dialogue. The third selection is a pilot study of the problem of coordinating research specialists with both production specialists and market specialists. It is called "Tailoring Management Organization to the New Technologies." The fourth is called "Coordination: A Key Problem in Manufacturing a Complex Product." It is a study of that problem in IBM, one of the most technologically advanced corporations in the modern world, which manufactures a whole series of highly complex and sophisticated products. The fifth and final selection is a freewheeling forecast of what the industrial organizations of the future will look like.

BIBLIOGRAPHY

Argyris, Chris: *Interpersonal Competence and Organizational Effectiveness,* Dorsey Press, Homewood, Ill., 1962.

————: *Integrating the Individual and the Organization,* John Wiley & Sons, Inc., New York, 1964.

Bennis, Warren G.: *Changing Organizations,* McGraw-Hill Book Company, New York, 1966.

————: "Leadership Theory and Administrative Behavior: The Problem of Authority," *Administrative Science Quarterly,* April, 1959.

————: "Theory and Method in Applying Behavioral Science to Planned Organizational Change," MIT paper, presented at the International Operational Research Conference, Cambridge University, September 14, 1964.

Blake, Robert R., and Jane S. Mouton: *The Managerial Grid: Key Orientations for Achieving Production through People,* Gulf Publishing Company, Houston, Tex., 1964.

Blau, Peter M., and William R. Scott: *Formal Organizations,* Chandler Publishing Co., San Francisco, 1962.

Bright, James R.: *Research, Development and Technological Innovation,* Richard D. Irwin, Inc., Homewood, Ill., 1964.

Burns, Tom: *Management in the Electronics Industry: A Study of Eight English Companies,* Social Science Research Centre, University of Edinburgh, 1958.

———— and G. M. Stalker: *The Management of Innovation,* Tavistock Publications, Ltd., London, 1961 (Quadrangle, Chicago, Ill., 1961).

Cooper, W. W., H. J. Leavitt and M. J. Shelly II (eds.): *New Perspectives in Organization Research,* John Wiley & Sons, Inc., New York, 1964.

Davis, Louis E.: "Applying Technology to Social Problems," *New Society,* January 13, 1963.

———— and Ernst S. Valfer: "Intervening Responses to Changes in Supervisor Job Designs," *Occupational Psychology,* vol. 39, no. 3, July, 1965.

Dubin, Robert, George C. Homans, Floyd C. Mann, and Delbert C. Miller: *Leadership and Productivity,* Chandler, San Francisco, 1964.

Etzioni, Amatai: *A Comparative Analysis of Complex Organizations,* The Free Press, New York, 1961.

Gouldner, Alvin W.: *Patterns of Industrial Bureaucracy,* The Free Press, New York, 1954.

———— and Louis R. Pondy (eds.): *Readings in Managerial Psychology,* The University of Chicago Press, Chicago, Ill., 1964.

Greenberger, Martin: "The Computers of Tomorrow," *The Atlantic Monthly,* May, 1964.

———— (ed.): *Management and the Computer of the Future,* published jointly by The M.I.T. Press, Cambridge, Mass., and John Wiley & Sons, Inc., New York, 1962.

———— and Howard W. Johnson: "Automation, Management, and the Future," *The Technology Review,* vol. LXV, no. 7, May, 1963.

Gross, B.: *The Managing of Organizations,* The Free Press, New York, 1964.

Guest, Robert H.: "Today's Trends for Tomorrow's Management," *The Business Quarterly,* The University of Western Ontario School of Business Administration, vol. 31, no. 4, Winter, 1966.

Hall, R. H.: "The Concept of Bureaucracy: An Empirical Assessment," *The American Journal of Sociology*, vol. 69, p. 33, 1963.

Kahn, R. L., and Elise Boulding (eds.): *Power and Conflict in Organizations*, Basic Books, Inc., Publishers, New York, 1964.

————, D. M. Wolfe, R. P. Quinn, J. D. Snoek, and R. A. Rosenthal: *Organizational Stress: Studies in Role Conflict and Ambiguity*, John Wiley & Sons, Inc., New York, 1964.

Leavitt, Harold J., and Louis R. Pondy (eds.): *Readings in Managerial Psychology*, The University of Chicago Press, Chicago, Ill., 1964.

———— and Thomas L. Whisler: "Management in the 1980's," *Harvard Business Review*, November–December, 1958.

Likert, Rensis: *New Patterns of Management*, McGraw-Hill Book Company, New York, 1961.

————: *The Human Organization: Its Management and Value*, McGraw-Hill Book Company, New York, 1967.

McClelland, David C.: *The Achieving Society*, D. Van Nostrand Company, Inc., Princeton, N.J., 1961.

McGregor, Douglas (Warren G. Bennis and Caroline McGregor, eds.): *The Professional Manager*, McGraw-Hill Book Company, New York, 1967.

March, James G. (ed.): *Handbook of Organization*, Rand McNally & Company, Chicago, Ill., 1965.

———— and Herbert A. Simon: *Organizations*, John Wiley & Sons, Inc., New York, 1958.

Mason, Edward S. (ed.): *The Corporation in Modern Society*, Harvard University Press, Cambridge, Mass., 1960. (See especially J. Schmookler, "Technological Progress and the American Corporation.")

Myers, Charles A. (ed.): *The Impact of Computers on Management*, The M.I.T. Press, Cambridge, Mass., 1967.

Parsons, Talcott: *Structure and Process in Modern Society*, The Free Press, New York, 1960.

Rice, A. K.: *The Enterprise and Its Environment*, Tavistock Publications, London, 1963.

Seashore, S. E., and D. G. Bowers: *Changing the Structure and Functioning of an Organization*, Monograph 33, Survey Research Center, Ann Arbor, Mich., 1963.

Simon, Herbert A.: *The New Science of Management Decision*, Harper & Row, Publishers, Incorporated, New York, 1960.

————: *The Shape of Automation for Man and Management*, Harper & Row, Publishers, Incorporated, New York, 1965.

Sofer, Cyril: *The Organization from Within: A Comparative Study of Social Institutions Based on a Socio-therapeutic Approach*, Tavistock, London, 1963 (also Quadrangle, Chicago, Ill.).

Technological Trends in Major American Industries, Bulletin No. 1474, U.S. Department of Labor, February, 1966.

Thompson, James D. (ed.): *Approaches to Organizational Design*, The University of Pittsburgh Press, Pittsburgh, Pa., 1966.

————, P. B. Hammond, R. W. Hawkes, B. H. Junker, and A. Tuden (eds.): *Comparative Studies in Administration*, The University of Pittsburgh Press, Pittsburgh, Pa., 1959.

Woodward, Joan: *Management and Technology*, Her Majesty's Stationery Office, London, 1958.

————: *Industrial Organisation: Theory and Practice,* Oxford University Press, London, 1965.

1. AUTOMATION AND TECHNICAL CHANGE: THE IMPLICATIONS FOR THE MANAGEMENT PROCESS

From Joan Woodward, "Automation and Technical Change: The Implications for the Management Process," Organization for Economic Cooperation and Development, European Conference on Manpower Aspects of Automation and Technical Change, Zurich, February 1–4, 1966; and Industrial Organisation: Theory and Practice, *Oxford University Press, London, 1965, pp. 74, 75, 77–80.*

THE SOCIO-TECHNICAL SYSTEM

It is only during the last decade that behavioural scientists have interested themselves in the central feature of modern industrial society, the production technology on which it is based. In this period, however, the existence of a link between the technology of a firm's manufacturing activities and its organisational structure and management processes, has come to be taken for granted. Indeed this is a current generalisation of industrial sociology. There is a widespread acceptance of the concept of the industrial firm as a socio-technical system, first propounded by the Tavistock Institute about ten years ago. It follows therefore that it must also be taken for granted that changes in either the methods of production or the systems of production planning and control will have an impact on the organisational and behavioural patterns of the firm concerned. This assertion is supported by an increasing amount of empirical evidence. Many case studies of technical change have been undertaken in both the United States and Europe and it has been demonstrated in almost every case that even where technical and organisational change are not planned simultaneously, the latter is an inevitable outcome of the former.

But although the concept of the socio-technical system is useful as an aid to the understanding of industrial behaviour at both management and operator levels, it remains largely an abstraction. The result is that with the exception of the detailed work done on man-machine systems at shop floor level . . . the contributions made by social scientists to the understanding of the effects of technical change, particularly the effects on the management process, are descriptive and general. Case studies have been of a historical kind; accounts are given of what has happened and in many instances the research workers have found it difficult to distinguish between effects arising from involvement in change and the effects of change itself.

Analytically, the central problem in the development of a compre-hensive theory of organisation is to determine the conditions under which behaviour inside organisations becomes standardised and predictable. Techniques have to be found to describe systematically and evaluate quantitatively, complex and intricate manufacturing situations. Only when such techniques are available can the two questions so often on the minds of those responsible for organisational planning be answered on anything other than a hunch basis: firstly how can an assessment be made of the appropriateness of a firm's existing organisational pattern to achieve its objectives, and secondly what is likely to be the effect on the manage-ment process of any specific technical change that is being planned. It is not enough to be able to say that technical change will lead to organisa-tional change, we want to know to what degree and in what direction this organisational change will come about. To do this requires an ability to measure technical variables in the manufacturing situation and to understand what they mean in organisational and behavioural terms. The biggest problem faced in any serious study of the implications of tech-nical change for the management process is the lack of what might be called a natural history of industry which groups together manufacturing processes that have characteristics in common and identifies relation-ships between one kind of technology and another.

THE SOUTH ESSEX STUDIES

A first step towards building up this natural history was taken during a study of the organisational structure of 100 manufacturing firms located in the South of England.[1] Having found that organisational characteristics did not appear to be related either to size of firm or to business efficiency, an attempt was made to relate organisation to technology. The firms were classified according to simple features of the technology characterising their production; first into three main groups and subsequently into eleven sub-groups. The three main groups were firms that produced units or small batches generally to customers' individual orders, large batch and mass production firms and firms producing on a continuous process basis.[2]

[1] See Joan Woodward, *Industrial Organisation: Theory and Practice*, Oxford Univer-sity Press, London, 1965.
[2] The breakdown of eighty firms into three main groups and nine sub-groups is illustrated in the chart on page 178. The three main groups are roughly equivalent to the types of manufacture described elsewhere in this book as job shop, large-scale and mass production, and process industries. Twelve other firms were grouped under two types by Miss Woodward: production of standard parts later assembled into diverse products; and process production, such as pharmaceutical chemicals subse-quently packaged for sale, for example the quantity production of acetylsalicylic acid, becoming packages of aspirin tablets. These eleven categories, comprising in all 92 firms, are the basis of Miss Woodward's analysis. C.R.W.

This classification produced what was in effect a crude scale of technology in terms of three related variables. These were i) stages in the historical development of production processes, ii) the interrelation between the items of equipment used for these processes, and iii) the extent to which the operations performed in the processes were repetitive or comparable from one production cycle or sequence to the next. The production of unit orders to customers' individual requirements is the oldest, and least repetitive form of manufacture, using items of equipment between which materials are transferred in non-standard or non-

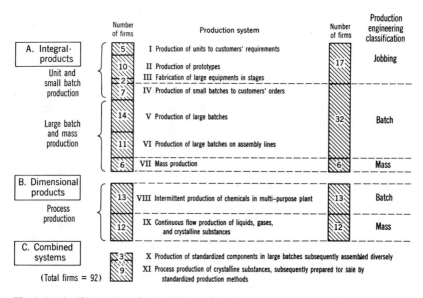

Fig. 1. Production systems in South Essex industry

repetitive sequences. Continuous flow production is the most recent, most advanced, and most repetitive form of manufacture, in which materials flow between items of equipment in standard, repetitive sequences. Moving along this scale it becomes increasingly possible to exercise control over manufacturing operations, the physical limitations of production becoming better known and understood. Targets can be set and reached more effectively in continuous flow production than they can in the most up to date and efficient batch production firms, and the factors likely to limit performance can be allowed for. However well-developed production control procedures may be in batch production firms, there will be a degree of uncertainty in the prediction of results. Production proceeds by drives and a continuous attempt is made to push back physical limitations by setting even higher targets. The difficulties of exercising effective control, particularly of prototype manufacture are greatest in unit production. It is almost impossible to predict the results of development work either in terms of time or money.

It was found that there were significant organisational management differences between the three main groups of firms. For example among the 24 small-batch and unit-production firms, the median number of levels of management authority was only three with a range of two to four. Among the 31 large batch production firms the median was four and the range from three to eight and among the 25 companies in the process production group the median was six and the range from two to seventeen. The fact that there is such an obvious technical impact on the structure of management suggests, at least by inference, that it also influences the functions and character of management.

A closer look at the system of supervision in terms of the span of control and the ratio of managers and supervisors to hourly paid personnel likewise showed the importance of the technological factor. The median span of control of the first line supervisors was twenty-three in unit production, forty-eight in large batch production and fifteen in process production. The ratio of managers and supervisory to other personnel is lowest in unit production and highest in process production. The differences are marked; in process production the ratio of managers and supervisors to other personnel is between 1 to 7 and 1 to 8 whereas in unit production the ratio ranges from 1 to 24 to as low as 1 to 49. In large batch production the ratio ranges from 1 to 14 to 1 to 18. It should also be emphasised that the ratios appeared to be little influenced by the size of the firm. As indicated above, size was a much less important variable in the firms studied, than technology.

There are interesting implications in relation to the location of responsibility for production in these structural differences. In process production an error could cause a considerable loss to the process if it continued unchecked or unnoticed, and one result of this is the concentration of that part of the control function with respect to the technological process that is not implicit in the operation of the plant itself, into the hands of managers and supervisors. The direct control of the technology is transferred from operators to management.

Dubin [3] suggests that a similar transfer of control is characteristic of data processing operations where control of machines becomes critical, especially in programming the machines, and many of the control and overseeing functions in maintaining the quality and quantity of the goods they produce are transferred from worker level to management.

[3] "Supervision and Productivity" by Robert Dubin in *Leadership and Productivity*, Chandler Publishing Co., San Francisco, 1964.

It will have been noticed from the figures given above that in respect of certain characteristics, the ratio of managers and supervisors to hourly paid personnel, for example, firms at the extremes of the technical scale resembled each other. This was true of other less easily measured characteristics. There was a tendency for organic management systems to predominate in jobbing and continuous flow production while mechanistic systems predominated in the middle ranges.[4] Clear-cut definition of duties and responsibilities was characteristic of firms in the middle ranges while flexible organisation with a high degree of delegation, both of authority and of the responsibility for decision making and with permissive and participating management, was characteristic of firms at the extremes. There was less organisation consciousness, fewer specialists and less line-staff type organisation at the extremes, and it was extremely difficult to distinguish between executive and advisory responsibility.

In both process production and unit production, stress was laid on the importance of line managers being technically competent. The technical competence required was however of a different kind in the two types of production. In process production it was intellectual, based on qualifications and knowledge, whereas in unit production it was intuitive based on long experience and know how.

Another thing that the two groups of firms at the extremes of the scale had in common was that they tended to be homogeneous in organisational and behavioural patterns. The physical work flow and the nature of the manufacturing operations appeared to place considerable restrictions on organisational choice. Between these two extremes however, in the batch production area, the physical work flow did not impose such rigid restrictions, with the result that technology did not as much determine organisation as define the limits within which it could be determined. The separation of production administration from production operations, the rationalisation of production methods and the attempts to push back the physical limitations of production resulted in the emergence of a control

---

[4] A new concept for classifying industrial organization was developed by Burns (see Tom Burns, *Management in the Electronics Industry: A Study of Eight English Companies,* Social Science Research Centre, University of Edinburgh, 1958) and subsequently applied to the survey data. His empirical investigations suggested that firms follow two fundamentally different organizational procedures, one resulting in the establishment of a "mechanistic" system and the other an "organic" system. "Mechanistic" systems are characterized by rigid breakdown into functional specialisms, precise definition of duties, responsibilities and power, and a well developed command hierarchy through which information filters up and decisions and instructions flow down. "Organic" systems are more adaptable; jobs lose much of their formal definition, and communications up and down the hierarchy are more in the nature of consultation than of the passing up of information and the receiving of orders. In this type of situation the chief executive is not regarded as omniscient. Woodward, *op. cit.,* p. 23.

system that depended in part on top management policy and in part on the physical work flow. In batch production therefore, the management process is not as much a function of the technology as of the control system which in turn depends on both technology and on sociological and economic factors.

It should be pointed out that the work done so far has identified association, and not necessarily causation. It has indicated that in a socio-technical system, there is an interrelation between the social factors and the technical factors, without specifying the cause and effect relationship. This is likely to be clarified as the theoretical framework is developed more fully and in greater depth and detail.

It must also be pointed out that the basis on which organisational patterns have been said to be appropriate or inappropriate to the firm's technology, is the extent to which the firm has or has not been economically successful—in terms of profit, for example, and rate of growth. No account has been taken of "social success" as well as economic success—the extent to which a firm's organisation was appropriate to its technology, in terms of the social satisfactions and dissatisfactions it provided.

THE IMPLICATIONS OF THIS ANALYSIS FOR TECHNICAL CHANGE

As implied above, the attempts made in these studies to measure and quantify both technology and organisation were crude and superficial, but though they did not produce anything approaching a general law about the relationship of technology to organisation and behaviour, they did encourage the belief that the concept of the socio-technical system need not remain forever an abstraction. They also suggested that the possibility of planning organisational change simultaneously with technical change was not entirely a pipe dream. The field work of these studies was done in a part of England where newer and developing industries predominated. It was also coincident with a speeding up of the pace of technical change.

Where changes were encountered during the research, it was found that they had come about in one of two ways. Some began with a policy decision to modify objectives which made possible a different or more advanced system of production. Others came about as a result of technical or administrative developments making it possible to achieve the same objectives in a newer and more effective way. Among changes of the first kind were those that followed decisions to standardise either production itself or component manufacture. There were, too, the changes that had taken place in the pharmaceutical industry in response to an increased demand for prepared and packaged drugs as an alternative to the making up of prescriptions at the chemist's shop. Other changes had resulted in oil refining from the government decision that crude oil should be distilled in this country as a matter of policy.

The changes leading to a more effective pursuit of original objectives were of two main kinds, those resulting from a radical re-thinking of the manufacturing operations, the outcome being a more elaborate control system and a more formal structuring of the decision-making process, and those which were entirely technical. Many but not all of the latter were associated with one of the three main streams of engineering progress covered by the term automation. In one firm the two kinds of development had come together in the installation of a computer for production programming; the computer itself being the result of technical advance while its effective use depended on a complete re-thinking of the manufacturing operations and on analysis of all the contingencies that would have to be allowed for in its programming.

It soon became clear that in some cases technical changes fundamentally altered the system of production, the firm concerned moving out of one of the production categories already referred to and into another. In others the changes had relatively little effect on either the system of production or the management process. Moreover, the scale of the change did not necessarily indicate the extent of its effect. In an automobile manufacturing place the installation of a cylinder block transfer line accounted for only one per cent of total production operations in the firm concerned. Organisation and management were affected only marginally. On the other hand a new line for producing boiled sweets in a much smaller factory and representing a much smaller capital investment, brought about a fundamental change in the management process and the technology became continuous flow rather than batch production.

Like the scale of the change, the nature of the change was not necessarily an indication of its effect in changing the production system. Changes initiated by a radical re-thinking of the manufacturing operations, for example the installation of the computer already referred to, were not restricted in their application to only one production system, although the techniques to which they gave rise seemed particularly appropriate to the production of small- and medium-sized batches and to the type of line assembly that depends upon the integration of large numbers of component parts. Neither were changes initiated by technical developments restricted in their application. There were areas of production in which particular kinds of technical change were most easily and most often applied. Automatic control is obviously most appropriate to continuous flow production. Nevertheless there were firms operating in the unit and small batch production field where automatic devices had been introduced to control individual workers.

Where technical change did result in a change in the production system, the tendency was to move towards a newer and more complex system from unit and small batch to large batch and mass production and from large batch to continuous flow production.

It can be seen from this broad review of the kind of changes encountered during the South Essex studies that it is possible to categorise and classify not only technology but also technical changes.

If we relate the two systems of classification we have a predictive tool. This tool is still a primitive one, but even the arrowheads of ancient civilisations were effective in the circumstances in which they were applied. A series of questions can be asked about any technical changes planned. If the answers to these questions indicate that the change is likely to alter the production system in a radical way, the method of analysis already available for linking organisation and behaviour with the new system of production, will give an indication of what is likely to happen when the technical change is put into effect.

At the conclusion of the main phase of the South Essex studies, the opportunity arose to test out some of these predictions, and to see how far the actual organisational and behavioural results of a technical change lined up with the anticipated ones. As suggested above, one fact that had emerged from these studies was that as a firm moved up the technical scale towards continuous production, managers became increasingly the supervisors of the technology rather than the supervisors of people. Moreover, moving up to at least the mass production point on the scale, the management structure became increasingly complex. The separation of production administration from the supervision of production operations and the increasing use of specialists and functional managers created a new and more intricate pattern of interaction.

Among the firms originally studied were three engineering firms in which a change of this kind was taking place. All three were moving from small batch production to complete standardisation of components with subsequent diverse assembly. Approximately three months before the changes were actually put into effect a research worker spent a week with the production manager in each firm, observing and recording what he did and whom he contacted. The same thing was done approximately three months after the changes had taken place. The following table shows the patterns of interaction before and after the change.

Several points of interest emerge, and the changes proved to be much as had been predicted. Moreover, there is consistency from firm to firm; the figures show differences of degree but trends are similar. All three of the men concerned spent less time alone after the changes had taken place, and the average number of daily contacts increased. They spent more time in contact with their superiors and less with colleagues in other departments. They also had a lot less contact with their subordinates.

Patterns of interaction (production superintendents)

	Firm A/1		Firm A/2		Firm A/3	
	Before change	After change	Before change	After change	Before change	After change
1. (a) Percentage of time spent alone; in office, on machines, etc.	30	28	36	18	33	20
(b) Percentage of time spent in face to face or telephone communication with others	70	72	64	82	67	80
2. Percentage of interaction time (i.e., (b) above) spent with: (a) Superiors and equals inside the production function	30	58	34	47	24	54
(b) Subordinates in the production function *	26	16	24	14	33	16
(c) Staff from development and marketing functions or administration	44	26	42	39	43	30
3. Average number of daily contacts (telephone calls, discussions, meetings, etc.)	34	52	28	54	33	40

* **2. (b)** Included in these percentages is the time spent discussing subordinates' affairs with the staff of such departments as personnel, wages, accounts, and surgery.

Similar confirmations of anticipated results were found in relation to other technical changes which affected the total production system. Moves into the continuous process area of production facilitated almost automatically the building up of harmonious and contributive human relationships. It certainly seemed that the highly automated chemical plant had a number of advantages. The plant itself, and the process of decision-making prerequisite to its erection, provided a rational framework of discipline and control for people employed at every level.

Because most of the critical decisions had been made in advance—the plant capacity, product quality and cost of operation had been determined—there was less day-to-day pressure on people and a more marked distinction between crisis and policy decisions than there were in other types of production. Moreover, technical advance was associated with more sophisticated management; managers had a better educational background, formed a more socially homogeneous group and approached their problems more intellectually and less emotionally. There was a greater awareness of the nature of risk and uncertainty in the making of decisions.

In all, seven case studies were made of firms where technical changes had occurred of sufficient significance to change the character of the production system, and in every one of these, the actual effect on the management process was as had been anticipated.

Many problems still remain, however, that have to be overcome before the effects of planned technical change on the management process can be predicted with precision. In two areas in particular more work is required. First, a more precise instrument to measure technology is essential so that the many changes in technology which do not affect the production system in such a fundamental way as those already studied can be brought into the framework. Secondly, the problem already referred to of the heterogeneity in patterns of organization and behaviour in the batch area of technology and the relevance to them of the system of control, requires further investigation. Some progress has been made in both directions. . . .

TECHNOLOGY AND SOCIAL STRUCTURE

The fact that it was possible to demonstrate that there is a link between technology and organization has significance not only for the industrial manager but also for the social scientist. The concept of the sociotechnical system was of course already familiar to and accepted by social scientists, but progress in social science, unlike progress in social philosophy, proceeds by way of demonstration as much as by way of ideas. Thus the demonstration of the link could be a step forward in the pursuit of knowledge relating to the formulation of social structure and to the administrative process generally. For the social scientist the most interesting question raised by the survey is this: how far does technology influence the formulation of social structure inside an industrial setting?

Formal organization is not of course the whole of social structure. The social scientist sees an industrial or commercial enterprise as a social system within a social system; a small but complete society of individuals bound together into a functioning team operating against a wide social background. Social structure is the framework on which the system operates. The variables in the system include occupational structure, the enterprise consisting of members of different occupational groups which are linked with various social groups in the community; formal organization, i.e. the stabie and explicit pattern of prescribed relationships designed to enable those employed to work together in the achievement of objectives, and informal organization, i.e. the pattern of relationships which actually emerges from day-to-day operations.

Formal organization can arise imperceptibly and gradually from informal organization and spontaneous relationships, or it can be consciously planned without reference to informal organization. As already indicated, the basic idea underlying the development of scientific management is that formal organization in industry should be consciously planned. Indeed, the general trend in modern society is towards this kind of planning, with the result that firms who consciously plan their formal organizational structure tend to regard themselves as more progressive and up-to-date than firms that do not.

The link between technology and the occupational structure element in social structure is obvious, and research has shown that informal organization too is influenced by technology. But because conscious planning of formal organization has been based on principles and ideas that have become increasingly divorced from technical development, it has generally been assumed by social scientists that formal organization is the part of social structure least affected by technical considerations.

The information obtained from this survey demonstrates quite clearly, however, that in the firms in South Essex formal organization too is affected considerably by technical factors. The reason for this may be that conscious planning is not as commonplace as might be supposed; nor the only distinction between formal and informal organization as clear-cut. Approximately only half the firms studied showed any organization-consciousness, and in many of these its effects were limited to a few aspects of formal organization. The formalization of spontaneous relationships still seems to play an important part.

The approach to the study of organization suggested here, that is, the approach through empirical sociology, must be regarded at this stage as a basis for speculative thinking rather than as a guide to action. It does, however, provide a framework for further study.

The survey findings suggested that the link between technology and organization persists in spite of, rather than because of, conscious behaviour or deliberate policy, and in defiance of the tendency in management education to emphasize the independence of the administrative process from technical considerations. The examination of the situational demands arising from different kinds of manufacture might therefore lead to a deeper understanding of the administrative process.

If we could find answers to such questions as why unit articles can be produced successfully only where the lines of control are short, why mass production demands the definition of duties and responsibilities, and why the chief executive in a process production firm can successfully control more subordinates than his counterparts in other types of production, we would have come a long way towards the discovery of cause and effect relationship between systems of production and the forms of organization they demand. These cause and effect relationships might in turn provide us with a basis of reasoning in the field of management.

If it could be demonstrated not only that technology is limited and controlled by objectives, but also that technology itself limits and controls both organization and certain aspects of behaviour, Follett's [5] assertion that the principles and direction of human endeavour are the same no matter what its purpose is, would have to be regarded as true only at a very general and superficial level of analysis. The understanding of certain elementary principles of human behaviour is obviously helpful in any situation in which people have to form relationships. But although at one level of analysis all firms may appear to have similar organizational problems, at a deeper level constants may become variables, and the purpose towards which human endeavour is directed could ultimately prove to be one of the important determinants of the principles of that direction.

Finally, what implications would this new approach have for the selection and training of managers? It would immediately raise a doubt as to whether decisions relating to organizational structure can be made effectively except by people with a knowledge and appreciation of the requirements of its technology. This would mean that the possibility of developing general managerial competence, except in association with technical knowledge or skill, would be questionable.

At present much of the management education and training undertaken inside industry and the teaching institutions is based on the assumption that management skills can be isolated from any technical background: that there is, in fact, a management vocation. There is a fairly widespread belief that at a certain level of responsibility managers and administrators are interchangeable between one industry and another and even between industry and other institutions. It is true, of course, that some people can and do move around successfully in this way, but the fact that they tend to be the exceptionally able people with a wide range of knowledge and skill may obscure any difficulties inherent in the

[5] Mary Parker Follett, *Papers on Dynamic Administration,* Annual Conference of American Bureau of Personnel Management, 1924–28.

interchange. Talent of this kind may not be available in sufficient quantities to make possible the planning of all executive development along these lines.

Formal organization theory is impersonal in so far as it defines a number of positions or roles and the relationships between them without reference to the personalities of those occupying them. Each person employed by a firm occupies a definite position in this organization and the role and status thus conferred upon him determine to a considerable extent the actions he initiates and the results and responses he can expect.

Technology, because it influences the roles defined by formal organization, must therefore influence industrial behaviour, for how a person reacts depends as much on the demands of his role and the circumstances in which he finds himself, as on his personality. There can be occasions when the behaviour forced on him by his role is in conflict with his personality. If so, role considerations may lead him to alter or modify his personality, or to leave his employment and seek a more congenial job elsewhere.

. . . At one stage in the analysis of the survey data the research workers considered whether the differences between firms both in organization and achievement could be attributed to differences in the ability of their senior managers. [This was] rejected as a complete explanation. In considering the personality differences between managers, it did appear, however, that senior executives in the firms in each production category had characteristics in common. This might imply that one of the ways in which situational demands impose themselves is by bringing individuals to the top of the management ladder whose personal qualities best fit the technical background in which they have to operate.

In general, the senior executives of firms in the batch production categories, where efforts were continuously being made to push back the physical limitations of production, seemed to have more drive and push and to be more ambitious than their counterparts in unit production or process production. Whether this was the result of natural selection or conditioning it is, of course, impossible to find out through studies of this nature.

The research results suggested too that some technical environments impose greater strains than others on individuals at all levels of the hierarchy. Reference has already been made to the differences in communication behaviour. Both inter-managerial relationships and employee-employer relationships seemed to be better at the extremes of the scale than they were in the middle; pressure was greater in the middle and it seemed more important to build mechanisms into the organizational structure which would resolve the conflicts likely to occur.

Thus it seems that an analysis of situational demands could lead not only to the development of better techniques for appraising organizational structure and for conscious planning, but also to an increased understanding of the personal qualities and skills required in different industrial situations, and to improve methods of training directed towards giving those concerned a better understanding of the strains and stresses associated with the roles they are likely to occupy.

2. AEROSPACE SYSTEMS AND HUMAN PROBLEMS

From Aerospace Systems,[1] *Harvard Graduate School of Business Administration, copyright 1965 by the President and Fellows of Harvard College.*

In the fall of 1964 the casewriter from the Harvard Business School was sitting in the office of Dr. Roger Simon, the director of the Aerospace Systems Research Center, and since 1963 a corporate vice president and director. The Research Center was housed in a new modern $6 million structure perched on the wild burnt-brown hills overlooking the Pacific. The setting sun cast a hard yellow light on the hostile-looking country below and on the severe modern furniture inside. The atmosphere was filled with a sense of unreality. Where did the building end and the wild country begin? In the building the hum of the air-conditioner droned reassuringly. It was permanent after all; it was safe. The same sense of unreality came to the casewriter on hearing Dr. Simon's story. Was it real? Did huge companies actually engage in such far-out dreamlike enterprises?

Reality [Dr. Simon was saying] is the familiar. In 20 years we have changed from an aircraft firm actually concerned with the classical scientific disciplines—working with massive bodies, airplanes moving at low velocities—to a company which has a great deal of business in the technical non-classical domain, that is in the area of quantum mechanics and relativity.

Things like transistors and optical masers are quantum mechanical devices. Superconductivity is a quantum mechanical phenomenon. Nuclear power is both a relativistic and quantum mechanical phenomenon. Now we have an enormous segment of our business actually in the non-classical world. Yet the classical world is a world in which our intuition is trained. We as human beings live at low velocities and we are massive compared to a single atom. So here we have a paradox. The

[1] All names disguised. Case material of the Harvard Graduate School of Business Administration is prepared as a basis for class discussion. Cases are not designed to present illustrations of either effective or ineffective handling of administrative problems.

business man who has to live and develop an intuition in the classical world is now called upon to make business decisions in a non-classical world. How does he gain this intuition? He has to have a little part of his business which will literally live in that non-classical world. In one sense the Research Center is that part.

Only two years had passed since the Research Center became a separate division of Aerospace Systems. In spite of its tender age, it had fulfilled many of the hopes of its founders. Its success could be measured in two broad domains. The first concerned the internal function of the Research Center, the environment which had been developed, the morale of the staff, the degree of communication with the external community of science, and the new scientific knowledge which has been made available as a result of its activities. In these accomplishments the laboratory had achieved distinction. The second domain was concerned with the degree of communication between the Research Center and the operating divisions of the company. Here it had not been as successful. Al Douglas, the president of Aerospace Systems, commented about the interaction between the divisions and the Research Center:

The drive for interaction that the Research Center has comes from those people themselves. It comes from their integrity. I have never put the pressure on them to interact. If we have created what we set out to do, then the technological leadership that we need in our corporation for the future will be there. When the Research Center attracts a scientist of the first calibre this does not mean very much to the division because it is a step removed from their experience. A man like Alfred Miller, however, can galvanize a whole technical effort of a division. So this part for the future I am not concerned about. In 10 years the Research Center will not only be taken for granted but will be a model for the industry.

Casewriter: How do you see the role of the Research Center in the future?

Mr. Douglas: I see a much better coupling with the people in the corporation. The Research Center will have had some accomplishments in the field of science, accomplishments which will raise the technical competence of the divisions.

The Research Center attempted to connect with the rest of the corporation by means of three activities: (1) as consultant to the divisions in helping them with their research problems; (2) as an advisor to the corporate offices in helping them evaluate the scientific merits of divisional research activities; (3) as a source of technical management in the future. Although the Research Center offered the divisions a body of free in-house consultants, most of the eight divisions did not make use of this service nor did they accept the Research Center. Bruce Nelson, one of the associate directors, commented:

We relate better to some divisions than to others and this has to do, I think, with the amount of intelligence that the presidents of the divisions have. The two who seem more intelligent understand what we are about; the ones who are not intelligent, don't.

Casewriter: How about acceptance of the Research Center among middle management?

Nelson: The middle managers show the most resistance to the Research Center. The Research Center is becoming somewhat accepted at the very lowest levels, that is, the working scientists, because scientists by nature will want to interact with other scientists. Interestingly enough, those divisions which have better organized research labs and make better use of their research, are the ones which feel more in competition with us and with which we have more trouble relating. On the other hand, those divisions which have no scientific research relate with us more easily.

Top divisional management's lack of enthusiasm for the Research Center was explained to the casewriter as being due to the general feeling of competition that the divisions had with each other in fighting for corporate funds. The Research Center was also seen by the divisional top management as a symbol towards increased centralization and a consequent diminution of their traditional prerogatives.

The directorate of the Research Center attempted to improve relations with the divisions in a two-pronged attack on the highest and lowest levels. Divisional top management was put under some pressure by the corporate officers to accept the Research Center. Although the divisional presidents outwardly began to accept the presence of the Research Center, the feeling within their divisions was still one of resentment. One divisional middle manager recounted to the casewriter that this year the annual report of the Research Center was circulated with a note from the president to find three items in the report which could be useful. Last year, the note from the president read: "What do you think of this?" The lowest levels, i.e. the working scientists, were approached on the basis of scientific interaction by means of symposia, conferences, and the like. To this end, the Research Center had established a yearly in-house scientific conference at a country club. Carl Nadel told the casewriter: "I think we are beginning to achieve a sort of interaction that we have been trying to get. The first conference was rather stolid. The barriers started breaking down last year and I think this year we may have achieved a breakthrough."

The casewriter spent several days at the conference and observed an energetic attempt by the members of the Research Center to engage in scientific interaction with the divisional scientists. The following random observation is an example.

> *Alfred Miller to a divisional manager of research: We have been working on this problem at Zeta for eight years and we thought we had pretty much cleaned up the field; the rest would be second-rate science. However, if you people are interested, or if any use can be made of this, I would be very happy to go back and work out some more of the details. I am delighted whenever an application can be found for the discovery that we have made.*
>
> *Divisional manager to Miller: I don't know . . . maybe . . . I'll think about it.*

Another conversation noted by the casewriter at the scientific conference was between an MTS and a divisional research manager. The MTS explained the difficulty of the dual role that the Research Center scientist played—one, of being a consultant to the divisions, and two, of being a staff assistant to the corporate research office. On the one hand the scientist has to help the division people make better scientific proposals, and on the other hand he has to turn around and judge that proposal. In this particular case the MTS had helped the divisional people make a more scientifically sound proposal involving laser fusion. Then as a staff specialist for the corporation, he had to judge the scientific content of the whole proposal and judged it as being quite risky for the corporation. The MTS said that in the last analysis the only way out was complete honesty all the way around. The divisional manager agreed.

A method of improving interaction with the divisions was to invite divisional managers of research to the Research Center for a familiarization tour. These were not too frequent as divisional managers found it difficult for one reason or another to make the trip. In fact, many divisional directors of research had not seen the Research Center.

When the casewriter had been at the Research Center about a week, he was told by Mike Moody to be sure to attend a meeting in the director's office the next day. "We've got three guys from the Radar Division coming up. That's the first time we've been able to get any of them to come." The next day, the casewriter sat in Dr. Simon's office when the three men from the Radar Division came in. One of the men made excuses for the absence of their boss, the director of research. Representing the Research Center at the meeting were, besides Dr. Simon, Bruce Nelson and Lou Masters, the Research Center public relations man. Roger Simon began the meeting by giving his talk on the function of the Research Center and some of its history. The following are the case-writer's notes:

> Roger Simon: In establishing the Research Center I was confronted by Douglas with the proposition, "Why do we need a Research Center?" I had come from Zeta Labs and had worked with the Atomic Energy Division as their Director of Research and was at this time faced with that problem. I happened to write a document expressing my views on a Research Center at AS. This document still exists, but I admit that I have changed my mind since then. The question is, "What is the role of research in industry?" It is now clear in my mind that not all industry and not all companies need research. I have an example that I like to give here: Universal Motors. It is well known that Universal Motors research is in fact engineering development and a styling center, and that is all the research they have, yet they do make a lot of money. We come to the conclusion that laboratories are not a panacea for industry and we cannot make a stereotype lab successful in each company. Now we are all partly products of our parents and I guess we keep our parents' values to a certain extent throughout our lives, and even though I come from Zeta Labs I do not see Zeta Labs in the Research Center here at AS, although I am influenced by Zeta. When I came here we quickly determined that AS is a systems organization. I felt that we could not cover the complex span of technologies completely unless we went far back into basic disciplines. Rather than focus our attention on technologies, we selected to focus our attention on disciplines.

At this point, Mike Moody came in and was introduced.

> Moody: I have just started working for the Radar Division. Someone asked me to find an electrometer, and I found two. (There is laughter.)
>
> Simon: I've just been going over the standard story. For the disciplines are the alphabet which allow you to combine to make technological words. The question now becomes, "What disciplines to engage in." I might add that we are not a reform school because we are engaged in discipline.
>
> Dr. Charles (a division man): I wonder if you would define what you mean by "discipline." Do you mean for instance, mathematics?
>
> Simon: No. That's too broad for us. We mean something a little bit more specialized.
>
> Charles: You mean a sub-discipline?
>
> Simon: Yes.
>
> Charles: Even these sub-disciplines could be combined in different ways.
>
> Moody: Yes. You see we can't cover the technical span of the company unless we use building blocks. We are still considering what sub-disciplines we should concentrate on. The distinction between applied

and fundamental is not valid, we feel, because a man can be doing applied work which uses very fundamental approaches. The distinctions we use are disciplinary versus applied work. Anyway . . .

Simon: The disciplinary scientist here at the lab engages most of his time in what we consider an exercise to keep him at the forefront in the technology in which he is engaged, but this is only an exercise. The value of this man to the company is when he is asked to interact with a division, and we hope that we can get 20% of this man's time interacting with the divisions. Now this can't be too much more than that because we'll kill the goose that laid the golden egg. The work that he does here at the lab is seen by us mainly as maintaining his competence and his progress in this particular field.

Moody: Yes, and this interaction with the divisions is, of course, free.

Simon: It is free but so far it amounts to only 10% of his time, and we do hope for 20. Twenty percent of his time interacting as a consultant is a lot of time for a top man. During the interaction period there are no holds barred in considering the kind of assistance we should furnish. This should be consistent with what we are trying to do. Now since we are a systems company, we need continuous interaction. We want to help you with proposals; we want to work in-house projects. When by chance we run across some fallout we will be able to explore it, but hopefully in the divisions.

Dr. Simon continues to explain his concept of colonization. He gives the example of transistors. It seems roughly the same talk that he gave to the casewriter at dinner a few nights ago. He continues his example of colonization by pointing out that the Atomic Energy Division is waiting for a technological breakthrough before it can market nuclear reactors cheaply enough to make a higher margin of profit. It does not matter whether the discovery is proprietary or worldwide. He continues.

Simon: Technical management is one of the strengths of the company. In the future the needs of the company will be for a more scientific orientation in technical management, and I think we could supply some of this. Although the future managers of the company will still be engineers, they must be exposed more to science than they have in the past. Now they can't get this orientation from the universities, because the trouble with the university scientist is that he is predisposed against industry. . . .

Dr. Crowley (a division man): Can I interrupt here?

Dr. Simon: Yes, go ahead.

Dr. Crowley: In my opinion, the Research Center is a magnificent prophecy, but only that. It is something that the corporation needs to be a whole man, but as yet I don't see it working. I perceive three problems in our interfacing with the Research Center. First—How can we assist you in determining the disciplines which you should engage in?

Second—the service problem. How do we tell what our people can use?

Third—expanding the applied science effort in the corporation. If the Research Center is to work in AS, the next step is in the applied function which must be in the divisions.

Simon: The applied science problem is especially difficult in our situation because, unlike Zeta Labs, our frame of reference is shifting. At Zeta Labs people stay where they are and transfer knowledge without moving, but here people move with the knowledge. So, in the end, there will have to be a small group of applied scientists in the Research Center who will not move with the project and a much larger group of applied scientists in the divisions who will move with the project.

Dr. Crowley: Then what you are saying is that the coupling device will be between these two groups of applied people.

Moody: Yes. But the polarization, the attitude of these two groups is different. One is looking towards the fundamental side and the other is looking towards the product.

Nelson: They have different objectives. . . .

Moody: The interface between us and the divisions is exceedingly poor and we haven't yet learned how to bridge the gap. When we are onto something then we want to show feasibility—that's the next step. In fact, we have three such studies going on right now in the divisions. . . .

Simon: In labs as this one you don't want to say that the possible technical breakthrough justifies the existence of the lab. We have constructed the lab in such a way that the breakthrough is not a mission of the lab, but that the probability of a breakthrough is maximized. It costs us roughly a hundred thousand dollars a year per Ph. D. to run this lab. At a hundred thousand dollars per year, per man, we can't afford to have the pyramidal structure of directed research.

Dr. Simon continues to describe the structure of the lab and the motivation of scientists. . . . He tells a story which illustrates the difficulty in cracking the university supply of students. This particular story illustrates that it took almost two years of close collaboration with a professor before this man would let him see his best students.

Dr. Crowley: Perhaps we should use the same infiltration techniques. (Laughter.)

Moody: But here's the point. We are very anxious to recruit for you because we have these contacts with the universities.

Lou Masters (P. R. man): We haven't gotten to the plan that Dr. Crowley thought up—the question of interfacing.

Dr. Crowley: I think we should point out some of our applied people who should come to you for an orientation tour and even an exchange of compatible people.

Moody: Let me tell you what we are doing with the Electronic Systems Division.

Dr. Crowley: Yes, but that helps you more than it helps the divisions.

Moody: No, it works both ways. The divisional men can come up here and spend one or two days directly with the scientists, working in his lab, interacting. After that the men know each other and there should be very easy communication.

Simon: Most of us here come from AE so we have a very good relationship with them, but the relationship with the other divisions is not so easy. We would like to get one or two men from each division to come and work here or possibly to work out a loan arrangement.

Charles: Now if we send one of our guys up to you, how do we pay for him?

Moody: Well, we are budgeted for one man per year from the divisions. That's in our budget now.

Charles: If we send a man for a number of days, say four or five, the availability of such a fund would not help.

At this point the meeting breaks into two groups with one group discussing whether a scientist or a manager should be the first to come to the Research Center, and the other discussing the budget implications of sending a man from the divisions to the Research Center for a few days.

Moody (in a loud voice): Well, if it pinches the divisions financially to send a man up here even for a day, there is something wrong. This is something we have to get cleared up with the general office. If you have that kind of a rigid bind that you can't spend a day up here, then there is something wrong—it should be fixed up.

Dr. Franks (division man): Well, what budget line items do we charge the man's time to? We even have hours timed pretty closely and assigned to a particular project.

Moody: He's working here, but he's doing his job. What do you do when he goes to the library?
(To Simon): This reflects the thing that we got right away from Rocket Engines. They couldn't send a man to a seminar. Well, that was just an excuse. I'm sure that this is not the real problem.

Franks: Rocket's customer is the same as our customer, so that the control systems that our two divisions have are pretty much alike.

Moody: There is something wrong here.

Simon (interrupts): Mike, you can see that the customer controls the accounting system. Still, there must be some way in the corporation to absorb the cost of this interaction.

Moody: We shouldn't be charged for your man's time up here. This is really a question of the government creating a narrowing atmosphere to its system of contracts.

Mike Moody continues discussing the problem of the government in research, the government as a customer for research. . . .

Simon: We have to find some way around this obstacle.

There is some talk about how to schedule the rest of their time. Roger Simon decides to give them a brief talk on scientific accomplishments and activities of the lab, after which they will all go to lunch and then have a quick tour of the lab before departing. Simon goes to the board and lectures for about forty-five minutes on the activities in the laboratory.

The day following the meeting with the Radar people, the casewriter asked the Research Center participants for their views of the interaction.

> *Roger Simon: I didn't let them have their catharsis. They were prepared to argue the role of the Research Center with me but I didn't give them a chance. I think I gave them an idea of the kind of science we do here.*
>
> *Mike Moody: I don't think we got our point across. We just talk a different language than those guys. But I think that Roger has got to make himself an outline when he gives that talk. He was wandering all over the lot and I think he lost them.*
>
> *Bruce Nelson: I think Roger made a tactical error when he lectured them.*
>
> *Lou Masters: I thought it was an insult to the division men. Dr. Crowley and I spent two months setting this thing up, and they had come a great distance to talk, not to be talked to.*

Later, the casewriter asked Dr. Crowley his reactions.

> *Dr. Crowley: I don't know really. I have a capacity for turning off conversation. I was a little discouraged; I felt they were talking down to us.*

After the meeting with the Radar Division research managers, the casewriter was interested in getting more information about the divisional middle managers' feelings about the Research Center. He interviewed one middle manager in a division that had a good relationship with the Research Center and one in a division that did not. In the latter case, the manager said:

> *My own personal theory of the Research Center is as follows: As a scientific research organization they want and have tried to promote helping divisions. I wondered if they really should do this. It is just human nature that a man does not want to be helped until he is ready for it, and perhaps the Research Center should not try to help people until they ask for it.*

Now if they engaged in their disciplines instead of trying to interact so much, and as a result produced a good solid reputation, then they could let the divisions come to them for help. I think this would make things a lot easier. Where they have tried to force themselves on people their rate of acceptance has diminished, whereas where they have waited to be called in, their rate of acceptance has increased a great deal.

Casewriter: Could you give me an example of what you call forcing behavior?

Research Manager: Well, for instance, the views expressed by the Research Center personnel, particularly Roger Simon, to our own management—that is one example. And there have been quite a number of complaints by the Research Center to corporate officers on the lack of cooperation and this always feeds back and creates a very bad feeling. But let's say this—in my opinion, the complaints to the corporate office were justified, but they were not diplomatically handled.

The Research Center is seen as competing with the scientists in the divisions on the same project for the same research funds. This is reinforced by the attitude of the Research Center in its long-range goal of being the window outside for the corporation. This excludes the division and subdivision scientists from what they consider a cherished activity. The second reason is that Simon has stated that the Research Center will be the source of management for the divisions in the future. The source of divisional scientific management in the past has been these self-same scientists. The third reason is the continual playing up of the Research Center personnel as the world's or the country's outstanding scientists in their fields. The fourth reason is an attempt to emulate the Zeta Laboratory organization within the AS system. There seems to be a lack of recognition on the part of the directors of the Research Center to the fact that AS is different than the Zeta system and therefore needs a different approach to solving a centralized science lab.

A further weakness in the Research Center is the large number of personnel from one division, AE, and a lot of personal ties to that one division. Now when the Research Center was announced many people in all of the divisions wanted to go but they were not asked and furthermore the divisional management did not want to let them go. So it was not a case of many were asked and few were chosen—but that few were chosen. And this created some bad feeling in the divisions also. If the approach had been to select scientists from all of AS, the scientists from all the divisions would have considered it a great honor to have been chosen. At the same time good personal relations between the Research Center and the divisional managements would have been established. As things stand now, if Douglas should retire, things could get very tough for the Research Center.

The divisional research manager who was considered to have good relations with the Research Center told the casewriter:

I have developed a rapport with Roger in one form—I have one little game that we play with each other. I am sure you must be aware of it: I don't refer to what we are doing as science—we are engineers. As long as we don't call ourselves scientists, Roger and I get along fine! I am sure that he plays an appropriate game with me. We have our own little ways. Roger and I of course are on a management kick.

You have heard Roger's talk, or maybe you have read a transcript of it. Roger gave a talk here—he gave a talk at one of our president's policy level staff meetings—they meet once a month—it is attended not only by the immediate vice presidents but also by the second tier of management, the directors like myself, and at one of these meetings he had invited Roger to talk. And Roger said that all of the first-rate scientists go to the universities; the second-rate scientists—you are lucky if you can attract them to places like the Research Center—and the rest of them, they end up going into industry. Not well calculated to make you feel very good! I have my Phi Beta Kappa key too, and I have about eight or nine guys that also have them. You don't walk around dangling this but we all publish. But immediately these people who are engineers or scientists have their backs up and by the same token the management could feel a little bit happier about the whole thing because the next thing that he talked about was that when the scientist gets older and into his thirties and becomes sterile—then he has the company approach and he goes into management for the division. Not only do you hit every guy like me in the rear end who are the engineers and applied scientists in the various divisions, but you also serve notice to all those who came up through the business route that "fellows, you are dated!"

In an attempt to improve the link with the divisions, the directorate of the Research Center was in sympathy with a system developed at Bell Labs.[2] The Bell experience suggests that spatial distance acts to reduce feed-back. Therefore, organizations should carefully plan where they want to make geographical cuts. To encourage the forward flow of information across a geographical separation, an organization must create an administrative bond. The resulting rule is that nowhere along the process should there be both a geographical and administrative cut. At Bell Labs, basic research is connected to applied research by a spatial bond, i.e. proximity, but feed-back is reduced by an organizational barrier. Applied research is connected to engineering development by an organizational bond but separated by a spatial barrier. In using this model, Mike Moody told the casewriter:

Douglas, not being a scientist, did not think of all these ins and outs of connecting the lab to the corporation and Roger didn't either. The cor-

---

[2] Described by Jack Morton in the May, 1964, issue of *International Science and Technology.*

poration has traditionally begun to process its knowledge at the engineering development level. Now suddenly, it has begun to add the very front end, disciplinary science, without the connecting link of applied research, and developmental research. There is a geographical and an administrative separation between the Research Center and the divisions. We are now slowly trying to build in the connections.

The corporate vice president for R&D, Howard Adler, was seen by the Research Center as an administrative link to the divisions. Dr. Adler and his group administered the corporate R&D funds and thus had an influence on the R&D activities in the corporation. Dr. Adler, in filling this new position, had the support of Roger Simon. Since the Research Center acted as advisor to Dr. Adler's office on questions requiring scientific evaluations, the Research Center had, in effect, an indirect influence over those divisional research efforts that were supported by corporate funds.

A second plan to create a link was to establish a centralized applied research laboratory. There was considerable disagreement about the implementation of such a lab, even among the Research Center directorate. Carl Nadel said:

I think if we try to do this we are going to find opposition that we won't be able to overcome. I am not even completely convinced that in the type of organization that we have at AS that we really want to do this. It may not be worth the strain and effort that it would require to change.

Roger Simon, however, agreed with Mike Moody that such a lab was a necessity:

It is our contention that we keep insisting to Howard Adler that the company must work towards a consolidation of at least the essential portion of the applied research in the geographical location of the Research Center. From my point of view, that means including it as part of the Research Center, perhaps in another building. However, the divisional presidents will continue to hold the line on this for some time. Yet you could do more research with half as many people and a third as much equipment if it were all brought together in one location. Of course in an organization where competition is the rule, this immediately implies empire-building. I personally don't feel that myself or Mike are interested in building an empire, except an empire of ideas; we just would like to see it work properly. I can't see any other way to have it work.

Another plan for improving interface with the divisions was to staff divisional research with experienced Research Center men. During the casewriter's stay, the Research Center and the Radar Division were forming plans to send Mike Moody to help the president of the division organize his science effort. The plans were for Mike to spend four days in the division and one at the RC. He said:

I think that if someone goes down there with my background and keeps out of the paper shuffling act, leaves the people alone, leaves the whole act alone, just goes in there and analyzes it from the technician right up to the president, and figures out where the money is coming from, how it is being used, who is doing what and when, we may get somewhere. We will change a little here and we will change a little there. We won't shake up the boat. The president agreed with me. He said—he thought that it would take about four years. That doesn't mean that you solve everything in four years; that means you achieve a reasonable share of your objective. As you go on you learn more.

In his final interview with Roger Simon the casewriter asked him to explain his future time schedule for the Research Center. Dr. Simon said:

I think the Research Center has to be far more functional to a large cross section of the company within five years. I would be willing to move more slowly if I knew that we could survive, but I can think of several labs, established with some fanfare whose mean life span was five years. I don't see any reason why our organization should be any different. So that's one limitation; how long can you go on without becoming maximally functional? The other limitation is, how long does it take to institute fairly large changes? In this I use my intuition.

Deciding to push for interaction now, instead of spending all of our time working at science, is based on my desire to train our people to look towards the company. We have competent scientists, but having competent scientists does not solve the problem. There is another danger in waiting. Custom in the Aerospace industry seems to be that when a division is formed it becomes a separate company unto itself. Some labs have elected eventually to go into business to support themselves and have done rather well with it. We could do that, but our original purpose would not have been filled.

The casewriter recalled his interview with Al Douglas, president of AS, who explained that he planned to retire in three or four years and went on to say: "Perhaps ten years from now, the Research Center will be known as Douglas' folly, but I don't think so."

3. TAILORING MANAGEMENT ORGANIZATION TO THE NEW TECHNOLOGIES

From Jay W. Lorsch and Paul R. Lawrence, "Organizing for Product Innovation," Harvard Business Review, vol. 43, no. 1, pp. 109–120, January–February, 1965.[1]

INTRODUCTORY NOTE

To know how to create new or to tailor old organizations to different technologies and markets in a period of rapid change is an increasingly urgent problem for management. Lawrence and Lorsch of the Harvard Business School have done organizational research in several industries with different rates of technological change affecting both products and processes. The full findings of this research, based upon three years of field study and analysis, have been published by the Harvard University Press under the title *Organization and Environment*. The selection here reprinted deals with one basic problem in the general field of finding appropriate organizational devices for an age of rapid product innovations. Put in the simplest terms, it is the problem of relating "the generalist to the specialist." Or translated into managerial language, the problem of prompt and effective collaboration between specialists: specialists in research, specialists in production, and specialists in marketing or selling. Top management must, of course, take an overall generalist's view. The reason why the problem grows more urgent is that each year not only does the training and thinking of scientists and engineers grow more sophisticated and specialized, but with the coming of data processing and automation on the one hand, and new selling media on the other, new specializations characterize the occupations of production managers and of market specialists as well. Managements' problems are complicated by the rapid changes occurring in each area of specialization. We give first a brief condensation of the research written by the authors, and then a selection from the research report itself.

In this article we shall report the results of a pilot study on the problem of obtaining collaboration and coordination between research, sales, and production specialists involved in product innovation in two organizations producing basic plastic products. In presenting the findings we shall emphasize these points:

(1) The research, sales, and production specialists working on different tasks connected with product innovation develop different viewpoints and

[1] Authors' note: Acknowledgment is due to the managements of the two companies that participated in this study. Support for this research was provided by the Division of Research, Harvard Business School.

methods of operation and tend to work best in different kinds of organizational structures. This specialization and the differences associated with it are important for the effective operation of the separate sales, research, and production units, but they also contribute to the disagreements and differences of opinion between these departments which inevitably occur around the product-innovation process.

(2) *Successful product innovation depends not only on this specialization but also on the development of methods of coordination which enable executives with diverse points of view to resolve their disagreements and achieve a unity of effort.*

(3) *One method of obtaining effective coordination is to establish a separate organizational unit which has as its primary task coordinating the activities of sales, production, and research. Such a unit is most effective when its members have a balanced point of view which enables them to work effectively with each of the specialist groups. By this we mean that the coordinators do not consistently favor the viewpoints of salesmen or researchers or production men but understand the interest of all three groups and can work back and forth effectively among them.*

(4) *A second method of improving collaboration is to use teams or committees in which the members have learned to fight constructively with each other, confronting their differences and resolving them rather than avoiding them. The members must have authority to make decisions —and they must not be too high up in the organization. Effective coordination seems to result when they are at a sufficiently low level in the company structure to have detailed technical and/or market knowledge bearing on the conflicts they try to resolve.*   The Authors

How can we get our research people to be more responsive to the needs of the market?

What can we do to get our salesmen more involved in selling new products and seeking new applications?

Why are our production people so conservative when it comes to introducing new products?

How can we get sales, research, and production people to pull in the same direction on product development?

Questions such as these have become of increasing concern to executives in companies operating in the many industries characterized by rapid technological and market change, in which new and improved products are the key to corporate success. Several years ago we were all concerned with obtaining effective research organizations. It was generally believed that if a climate could be developed in which talented scientists and engineers could work creatively, we would be assured of a constant flow of product improvements and new products. As companies have become successful in developing more effective research organizations, however, it has become increasingly apparent that creative, innovative researchers are not enough by themselves. What is needed, as the questions above indicate, is an organization which provides collaboration between scientific innovators and sales and production specialists, so that:

— The skills of the innovators can be directed at market needs and technological problems.

— Sales and production specialists can be actively involved in the commercialization of ideas developed in the laboratory.

— And, as a result, ideas can be transferred smoothly from laboratory prototype to commercial reality.

HOW COMPANIES INNOVATE

We can begin our discussion of the problems of organizing for innovation by briefly examining the essential functions of any organization. Basically, an organization, whether it be the product division of a diversified chemical company or a corner drug store, provides a means by which more than one person can work together to perform a task that one individual could not perform alone. This means each individual or unit of the larger organization will be performing some specialized portion of the organization's task.

The first function of an organization, then, is to divide the total task into specialized pieces. The organization's second function is to provide a means by which units working on different parts of the total task may coordinate their activities to come out with a unified effort. While these processes of specialization and coordination are essential in any organization, they are particularly crucial for companies competing in developing new products.

Perhaps the best way to understand the specialization and coordination required in the innovation process is to describe the steps involved in developing products in the two plastics companies we studied. These were prominent companies in their industry, chosen to show similarities and contrasts in their organizational approach to product innovation. To protect their identity, we shall refer to them as the "Rhody" and "Crown" companies. It should be stressed that the two companies sold their products for industrial applications and there was, therefore, a constant demand not only for major new products but also for a flow of modifications in properties and processes that could improve the performance of old products and yield new applications for them. In our description of the innovation process we will be referring to the steps required for both types of innovation.

Required collaboration

. . . As we have already indicated, there are three major groups of specialists in each organization. Sales, production, and research specialists are each coping with a different sector of the organization's environment, and each should have a different portion of the total skills and knowledge required to discover a product idea and convert it into a tangible product:

The sales department in dealing with the market environment should be in a position to extract information about market trends and customer needs.

The research department in dealing with the scientific environment should be able to provide data about the technical and scientific feasibility of any new product development.

The production department should have a store of knowledge about the limits of plant processes from the production environment.

Information from the sales department about customer needs and from production about processing limits has to be passed on to the research unit so that this information can be assimilated with the scientific feasibility of developing or modifying a product. Within the limits set by the needs of the customer and the capacities of the production process, the research units are then required to come up with a new development. If they succeed, it is then necessary to transfer information back to the sales department about product characteristics and to the production department about process specifications. With this information sales should be in a position to make and implement market plans, and production should have the data for planning and executing its task of manufacturing the product.

In short, product innovation requires close coordination between research and sales, on the one hand, and between research and production, on the other. This coordination is necessary not only to provide the two-way flow of technical information described earlier, but also to develop mutual trust and confidence between the members of the units which are required to collaborate in product development. Sales personnel must have confidence in research's knowledge of science, while research scientists must have confidence in sales' appraisal of the market. Similarly, there must be mutual confidence between research and production about production's ability to operate the process efficiently according to specifications and about research's capacity to develop a process that can be operated efficiently.

Product innovation, then, requires close collaboration between the sales and research units and the production and research units if the specialists involved are effectively to bring their separate skills to bear on a successful product development. However, the complexity and uncertainty of the factors which must be dealt with (at least in companies developing a multiplicity of new products) make it necessary for this coordination to take place at the *lower* levels of the organization. Executives in both Rhody and Crown indicate that it is difficult for managers at the upper levels of the organization to keep in touch with the multitude of rapidly changing factors which must be considered in the day-to-day process of developing many new products. Only the specialists on the firing line have the detailed knowledge of markets and technologies to make the frequent day-to-day decisions which the innovation process requires.

So far we have presented only a description of what *should* happen in both organizations if innovation is to be successfully accomplished. But our interests are in investigating not only what should happen but also, and more importantly, what *actually* happens in each organization as a result of the processes of specialization and coordination required for product innovation. We want to find out in what ways the groups of specialists working on diverse tasks in the two companies are different in their ways of thinking, in the ground rules they work by, and in terms of the organizational structures in which they work.

DIMENSIONS OF SPECIALIZATION

When we undertook our study, we decided to find out first how groups of specialists actually were differentiated. We expected the differences to be related to the problems of obtaining coordination between units. . . . Departmental differences were classified in terms of four main dimensions: (a) degree of departmental structure, (b) members' orientation toward time, (c) members' orientation toward others, and (d) members' orientation toward the environment.

Each of the differences between departments was seen to be a function of the characteristics of the environmental sector (market, science, or plant) with which a unit is coping in performing its task. Groups, such as production units, which have a very certain environment (as measured by the certainty of information at a given time, the rate of change in the environment, and the time range of the task) are highly structured. Because they are working with a highly stable environment, they tend to develop explicit routines and highly programmed ways of operating, adopt a directive interpersonal style, and also find a short-range time orientation useful for the performance of their task.

On the other hand, units, such as research, which are coping with less certain environments tend to be less structured, are characterized by a more permissive interpersonal orientation, and have a longer time orientation. These characteristics are consistent with an uncertain, nonroutine task, since effective performance of such a task requires opportunity for open consultation among colleagues in seeking solutions to problems and freedom to consider and attempt different courses of action.

Principal patterns

How do the differences in orientation and structure characterize the departments in Rhody and Crown? . . . The data presented here are representative of the *general* pattern which exists in both organizations; some minor variations between the two organizations are not depicted.

Members of each department tend primarily to be oriented toward the sector of the environment with which their task involves them. Research people tend to be more oriented toward discovering new scientific knowledge, while sales people are more concerned with customer problems and market conditions, and production personnel indicate a primary concern with production costs and processing problems.

In time orientation, the research scientists tend to be more concerned with long-range matters which will not have an impact on company profits for several years in the future. Sales and production specialists are primarily concerned with the more immediate problems which affect the company's performance within the current year.

The interpersonal orientations of the members of the units in both companies are also different. Research and sales personnel tend to prefer more permissive interpersonal relationships, while production specialists indicate a preference for a more directive manner of working with their colleagues.

As for the degree of departmental structure, the research units have the lowest amount and the production units have the highest. The sales units, which seem to be performing a task of medium certainty, have a structure which falls between the extremes represented by research and production.

What we find in both companies, then, are units which are quite different from each other both in terms of members' orientations and the structure in which the members work. These differences in ways of thinking about the job and in ground rules and operating procedures mean that each of these groups tends to view the task of innovation somewhat differently.

Impact on ability

While we next want to examine the influence of these differences on the process of obtaining coordination, we should first emphasize a point which too often has been overlooked: The differences have a *positive* effect on the ability of each individual unit to perform its particular task. The common orientations and ground rules within a unit and a departmental structure which facilitate task performance direct the efforts of people in the unit to their segment of the organizational task and enhance their ability to carry out their mission. Because the units are performing different tasks, we have to expect that they will develop different departmental structures and that their members will be oriented differently. If attempts were made to standardize the structures of all units and to have all members of the organization oriented in the same direction, we would lose the benefits of specialization.

The two companies in our study recognize this fact to differing degrees. At Rhody the differences along the four dimensions tend to be greater than at Crown. Each department at Rhody not only has a structure conducive to the performance of its task, but also tends to be more highly concerned with a single task dimension or with a particular period of time than does the same unit at Crown. While in both organizations the specialization of units enables them to address their separate tasks, the units at Rhody, by virtue of their higher degree of specialization, often seem to be better able to perform their individual tasks.

ORGANIZATIONAL PARADOX

While specialized orientations and structures facilitate a unit's task performance, we would expect the patterns to be closely related to the problems of coordination in both firms. Because members of a given department hold common attitudes about what is important in their work and about dealing with each other, they are able to work effectively with each other. But to the extent that the ground rules and orientations held by members of one department are different from those held by members of another, we would expect the departments to have increased difficulty achieving the high degree of coordination required for effective innovation.

The data we collected through a questionnaire about the effectiveness of coordination between departments at Rhody and Crown confirm this expectation. When two units are similar in departmental structure and in the orientations of their members, we find that they have few problems in obtaining effective collaboration *with each other*. But when units tend to be on opposite poles along the four dimensions, we find that there are more problems in integrating their efforts. Within each organization there is clear evidence that the greater the differences in orientation and structure between any pair of units, the greater the problems of obtaining effective coordination.

Although this relationship holds within each company, we find an interesting paradox when the two organizations are compared. As already indicated, there is a higher degree of specialization and differentiation at Rhody than at Crown. Pairs of units which are required to collaborate at Rhody tend to be less similar than the comparable pairs of units at

Crown. Since units at Crown are more similar, this *should* mean that Crown encounters fewer problems of coordination. However, this does *not* turn out to be the case. Rhody appears to be achieving better integration than Crown, even though it also has a higher degree of differentiation. In short, within each organization there is a relationship between the effectiveness of coordination and the degree of differentiation, but the organization which has the highest degree of specialization also has the most effective collaboration.

The significance of this paradox grows if we recall that specialization is a two-sided coin. Specialization is useful because it is necessary for the performance of individual departments; on the other hand, it can have negative consequences in that it is at the root of the problems of achieving the coordination required for innovation. At Rhody we have a situation in which one organization is able to have its cake (in the form of specialization) and to eat it too (in the form of coordination).

Contrasting methods

Does the explanation reside in the methods used by the two organizations to facilitate coordination between units? We believe it does.

Attempts at devising methods to improve coordination between the specialized departments involved in product innovation are certainly not novel. New-product departments, or coordinating departments with other appellations, have been established in many organizations with the primary function of coordinating the activities of research, sales, and production specialists in the development of new products. Similarly, many firms have appointed liaison individuals who are responsible for linking two or more groups of functonal specialists. Another frequent device has been to develop short-term project teams with representatives from the several functional departments to work on a new product. Finally, many companies have relied on permanent cross-functional coordinating teams to deal with the continuing problems of innovation around a given group of products.

Both Rhody and Crown have developed the same types of devices:

1. In each company there is a coordinating department which has the primary task of coordinating or integrating the innovation activities of the research, production, and sales units.

2. Each company is making use of permanent cross-functional coordinating committees which have representatives from each of the basic departments and the coordinating department. The primary function of these committees is to serve as a setting in which coordination can take place.

Since both organizations are utilizing the same devices to achieve coordination, it is pertinent to ask whether there are differences in the functioning and effectiveness of these devices. The answer provided by our investigation is an emphatic *yes*.

We now turn to an examination of these differences, looking first at the coordinating departments, then at the committees.

COORDINATING DEPARTMENTS

In addition to seeking teamwork among research, production, and sales, the coordinating departments at Rhody and Crown perform certain other tasks. At Crown the department is also involved in market planning and the coordination of sales efforts. At Rhody the coordinating department is also involved in technical service and market-development activities. As might be expected, both departments have developed orientations and structural characteristics somewhat different from those of the other units in the companies.

Key to coordination

While various similarities exist between the two coordinating groups, there is also, as our measurements reveal, a major distinction:

At Rhody the coordinating department falls in a middle position on each of the four dimensions we have considered. That is, if we compare the department's degree of structure and its members' orientations with those of the sales, production, and research departments, it always has an intermediate value, never an extreme one. For instance, members of the coordinating department have a balanced orientation along the time dimension. They are equally concerned with the short-range problems of sales and production and the long-range matters with which research wrestles. Similarly, coordinating personnel have a balanced concern with production, scientific, and market environments. The degree of departmental structure and the interpersonal orientation of coordinating members also fall between the extremes of the other departments.

At Crown the coordinating department is in the middle along the structure and interpersonal dimensions but tends to be highly oriented toward short-range time concerns and toward the market enviornment. Personnel indicate a high concern with immediate sales problems, and less concern with longer-range matters or with research or production environments. On both the time and the environment dimensions, therefore, the coordinating department is not intermediate between the departments it is supposed to be linking.

The foregoing difference . . . appears to be related to differences in the effectiveness of the two units. Our questionnaires and interviews indicate that the coordinating department at Rhody is generally perceived by members of that organization to be doing an effective job of linking the basic departments. On the other hand, the coordinating department at Crown is not perceived to be as effective as most members of the Crown organization think it should be.

Observations by executives

The reactions of executives in the two companies pretty well explain for us why the intermediate position of the Rhody coordinating department is associated with effective coordination, while the imbalance in certain orientations of the Crown unit inhibits its performance. The following are a few typical comments from Rhody managers:

> *The most important thing is that we have the coordinating department with its contacts with the customers and its technically trained people who are in contact with research. They are the kingpins. They have a good feel for research's ability, and they know the needs of the market. They will work back and forth with research and the other units.*
>
> *Generally speaking, the feeling of close cooperation between the coordinating unit and sales is echoed in the field. The top salesmen all get along well with the coordinating guys. You take a good coordinating fellow and a good salesman and that makes a powerful team. In our business the boys upstairs in the coordinating unit are top notch. They know what the lab can do, and they know the salesman's problems.*

But at Crown the comments of executives have a different tone:

> *My biggest criticism of our situation is that the coordinating department isn't a good enough mechanism to link the research activities to the customer. We need a better marketing strategy on certain products and some long-term plans. The lack of planning in the coordinating department is deplorable. One of our troubles is that the coordinating people are so tied up in day-to-day detail that they can't look to the future. They are still concerned with 1964 materials when they should be concerned with 1965 markets.*
>
> *Our problem is we can't clearly define the technical problems the customer is having. Theoretically the coordinating men should be able to handle this for research because they know the customer best. But they are so involved in present business that it takes all their time. They have a budget they have to live up to, and the best way to make money is to sell existing products. They know that selling existing products is more profitable than selling new products, so they keep on selling existing products to live up to the expectations of the budget.*

In other words, we have a marked difference in reaction. What managers at Rhody are stressing is that the coordinating unit in their organization is effective because it has a familiarity with the problems, orientations, and ways of operating of the basic units it connects. At Crown the primary complaints about that organization's less-effective coordinating unit are that its members tend be too oriented toward immediate sales matters.

The situation in these two organizations seems to indicate that for a coordinating department to be effective in linking the several specialized departments, it must be intermediate between any two along each of the several dimensions of orientation and structure. When a coordinating department is in this position, its members have more in common with members of the other units. Coordinating personnel tend to think and act in ways which are more understandable and agreeable to members of the other departments—and this facilitates collaboration. If members of the coordinating department have orientations and ground rules which are more suited to one specialized unit, as is the situation at Crown, their ways of thinking will necessarily be different from the other departments —and this situation will impair their effectiveness as coordinators.

CROSS-FUNCTIONAL GROUPS

Even in an organization like Rhody, where the coordinating unit is doing an effective job of facilitating cooperation between the specialized units, certain disagreements between the various specialist units seem to be inevitable. Management's problem is to provide a setting in which attempts at resolving these disagreements can be made effectively. Both organizations in this study have turned to permanent cross-functional coordinating committees as devices for providing a setting in which to work at achieving coordination between units.

In investigating the functioning of these committees in the two organizations, we again want to obtain an assessment of their effectiveness as well as some understanding of the factors which might be related to their performance. If we listen to some of the comments made by members of both organizations, the differences between the devices in the two companies become apparent.

At the Rhody company, managers make comments such as these about the cross-functional teams:

Our problems get thrashed out in committee. We work them over until everybody agrees this is the best effort you can make. We may decide this isn't good enough; then we may decide to ask for more people, more plant, and so forth. We all sometimes have to take a modification and be realistic and say this is the best we can do.

I may want us to do some work on a particular new product. The coordinating guy may say, 'Let's get the customer to change his process instead.' A research guy may say we need both. It is the way we do it that becomes argumentative and rightfully so. These things take several meet-ings to work out, but we are never really stalemated. We have decided in our·committee that we won't stalemate. There is more than one way to our ends. If I don't agree with the others, then I abdicate my position—some-times gracefully and sometimes not.

We had a disagreement about releasing confidential information to a customer and had quite a discussion about it. This was only the second time we had gotten so formal as to have a vote. I was outvoted three to one, but that afternoon I was the one who had to call the customer and give him the information as we had decided.

Since we have had these committees, we are working more closely with other groups. It is really working out. In the past, production was reluctant to give us information, and they wanted to keep the prerogative of making process changes. Since this committee has been operating, there has been a greater exchange of information. . . .

At Crown the executives speak differently about their experiences with cross-functional committees:

Unfortunately, the committees are not decision-making groups as much as I would like. Generally there is a reporting session. We don't have time going over all these things to make some of the decisions which need to be made. I would like to see more hashing out of the problems and making of decisions. Of course we do make decisions every day between us.

If I want something very badly and I am confronted by a roadblock, I go to top management to get the decision made. If the research mana-gers are willing to go ahead, there is no problem. If there is a conflict, then I would go to their boss.

I think these meetings only intensify the arguments. I haven't learned much that I didn't know already before I got to the meeting. It used to be that we had some knock-'em down, drag-out fights, but then we would get things settled. But this doesn't take place anymore, so there isn't any place for us to resolve our difficulties.

These and similar comments indicate that members of the Rhody organization find the cross-functional committees an important aid in achieving collaboration, while members of the Crown organization do not. They also indicate, as do our observations of meetings of these com-mittees in both organizations, that there are at least two important differ-ences between the functioning of these committees in the two organiza-tions. Before going into these contrasts, however, we must first point to an important distinction in the organizational structures of the two com-panies.

The Crown organization tends to have a higher degree of structure (tighter spans of control, more specific rules and procedures, and so forth) in *all* its parts than does the Rhody organization. One important aspect of this difference is that the level at which decisions about product innovation are supposed to be made is much lower in the organizational hierarchy at Rhody than at Crown.

Decision authority

The significance of this distinction becomes apparent if we turn to look at the teams at Rhody. In this organization team members are in most cases first-line supervisors who (being right down at the working level) have the detailed market and technical knowledge required to make decisions. They are the only persons who attend the meetings, and they usually have the formal authority to make decisions.

Our observation of meetings at Rhody, along with comments made by company executives, indicate that there are ground rules or norms operating in cross-functional committees which sanction the open confrontation of disagreement between members. Members of the committees tend to recognize their differences and seek ways of resolving them within the constraints of the situation with which they are dealing. This working through of disagreements often takes a great deal of emotional and intellectual effort, but members of the committees at Rhody tend to persevere until some resolution is reached. After decisions are made, the members of the committees are highly committed to them. As we learned from one executive, even though a member is not in initial agreement with the decision taken, he is expected to—and he does—carry out the actions worked out in the meetings.

In contrast with the situation at Rhody, we find at Crown (as we would expect from the greater degree of structure throughout this company) that members of the committees are at a higher level than their counterparts at Rhody, but even these managers often do not have the authority to make decisions. Furthermore, because they are at a higher level, they usually do not have either the technical or market knowledge required to make the detailed decisions necessary to develop products.

As a consequence of this situation, members of the Crown committees often bring both their superiors and their subordinates to the meetings with them—the superiors in order to provide someone who has the authority to make decisions, the subordinates so that someone is present who has the detailed technical and market knowledge to draw on for decisions. Bringing in all these participants results in meetings two or three times as large as those at Rhody.

Resolving conflict

Our observations of meetings at Crown and the comments of executives indicate that there are other shortcomings in the Crown committees. The norms of behavior in these groups sanction withdrawal from disagreement and conflict. Whenever there is a disagreement, the members tend to avoid discussing the matter, hoping it will magically go away. If this doesn't place the problem out of sight, they find another avenue of avoidance by passing it on to their superiors. As a consequence, many decisions which should be made at Crown seem to get dropped. They are not picked up again until they have festered for so long that somebody *has* to deal with them—and it is often too late by that time.

There will always be disagreements between members of departments which have highly different orientations and concerns. The problem facing members of coordinating committees is to learn to fight together constructively so that they can resolve these differences. At Rhody members of the cross-functional teams have developed this ability. They work at resolving conflict at their own level. They do not withdraw from disputes, nor do they try to smooth over their differences or arrive at some easy compromise. Rather, they seem willing to argue the issues involved until some understanding is reached about the optimal solution in a given situation.

In essence, the committees at Rhody have developed the ability to confront their differences openly and search persistently for solutions which will provide effective collaboration. At Crown, on the other hand, the committees avoid fights and forfeit the opportunity to achieve the coordination required for innovation.

CONCLUSION

The foregoing comparisons seem to provide an answer to the paradox of the Rhody organization achieving both greater specialization and more effective coordination than the Crown company does. The effective coordinating unit and cross-functional coordinating committees allow members at Rhody to concentrate on their specialties and still achieve a unity of effort. Sales, research, and production specialists are each able to address their separate departmental tasks and work in a climate which is conducive to good performance. At the same time, the men in the coordinating department, who have a balanced orientation toward the concerns of the three departments of specialists, help the three units to achieve a unity of effort. The cross-functional committees also provide a means by which the specialist groups and the coordinators can work through their differences and arrive at the best common approach.

At Crown, in spite of the fact that the specialist departments are more similar in orientation and structure than are the units at Rhody, there is more difficulty in obtaining unity of effort between them. Since the coordinators are overly concerned with short-term matters and sales problems, they do not effectively perform their function of linking the three groups of specialists. The cross-functional committees do not contribute much to coordination between these departments, either. They do not provide a setting in which problems can be solved, since authority to make decisions often resides in the higher levels of the organization and since norms have developed within the committees which encourage members to avoid conflict and pass it on to their superiors.

But what about the results the two companies have achieved in the market place? We have been asserting that both a high degree of specialization and effective coordination are important in achieving product innovation in this situation, but we have not presented any evidence that Rhody, with its greater specialization and more effective coordination, is in fact doing a better job of product innovation than is Crown. The following figures do show that the Rhody organization *is* achieving a higher level of innovation than Crown:

At Rhody, new products developed in the last five years have accounted for 59% of sales.

At Crown, the figure is only 20%, or just about one-third of Rhody's.

Part of this difference may have been due to some variation in market and technical factors confronting the two organizations. However, since these two organizations have been operating in the same industry and have been confronted by similar market conditions and technical problems, and because of the different levels of coordination and specialization achieved in each company, it seems safe to conclude that there is indeed a relationship between innovation performance and the internal organizational factors we have been discussing.

Management challenge

While this discussion has been based on an examination of two organizations in the plastics industry, there is no question that the requirements for specialization and coordination are just as urgent in other industries confronted with the need for product innovation. It seems safe to generalize that, whatever the field or function, managers interested in improving their record with new products must recognize two essential organizational ingredients of success:

1. Specialists who are clearly oriented toward their individual tasks and who work in organizational structures which are conducive to task performance.

2. Effective means of coordination which permit specialists with diverse knowledge and orientations to work together. (There will be disagreements and conflicts among these specialists, but the organization must provide a means to resolve the conflicts in such a way that the full

energy of research, sales, and production people can be brought to bear on innovation.)

Our discussion has focused on two devices to achieve this coordination —*coordinating departments* whose members have a balanced point of view enabling them to work effectively among the several specialist groups, and *cross-functional coordinating committees* in which members have learned to confront their differences and fight over them constructively so they can reach an optimal resolution. But other means of coordination are also available. The challenge confronting managers responsible for organizing for innovations is to work at developing means of coordination which permit effective specialization *and* effective coordination. This is the combination that is needed to produce the constant flow of innovations necessary for corporate growth in changing markets.

4.   COORDINATION: A KEY PROBLEM IN MANUFACTURING COMPLEX PRODUCTS

By Charles R. Walker, written for this book.

On the frontiers of the new technologies, IBM's experience, not only in product but in methods of manufacture, illustrates many typical managerial problems of today and tomorrow. Coordination, on a company-wide and multi-national scale, is what the president of IBM, T. V. Learson, told the author is the greatest immediate problem in satisfying the market requirements for IBM's System 360. He hopes and expects that the computer itself—after being fully programmed by systems experts to cope with the intricacies of the manufacturing process—will increasingly take over the details. "You can illustrate the problem," he continued, "by looking at the impact of just one order on the whole manufacturing work-flow."

With the help of a number of IBM people, an order was exploded for the author, that is, split into manufacturing segments. A summary of the breakdown is given here. Five points are particularly arresting for managements of today and tomorrow:

The new technologies of communication—"computers talking to computers," for example, over great distances—are already making possible a "functional distribution" of segments of the manufacturing process in different plants, cities, and countries around the world.

As a result, although the process is not yet complete, the computer has already taken over a substantial part of President Learson's coordination problem.

It is clear that change is a *constant* at most steps in the manufacturing process, change stemming from new and better methods by the company's own engineers, change from fresh demands, even last-minute ones, from the customers.

Although the point is not fully articulated in what follows, a new amalgam is emerging of opposite trends: the trend toward a more perfect standardization in the manufacturing process, as in the making of the circuit modules basic to all the new IBM computers; and, on the other hand, the trend toward individual differences—in short, toward customization of the final products.

Finally, the reader will notice not only that there is an enormous amount of product testing at all stages of manufacture but that little of it could be performed economicaly, if at all, without the computer itself and other automatic machinery.

The XYZ Company of San Francisco, California, has ordered an IBM System/360 Model 30. A regional manufacturer of household goods, the XYZ Company has its main plant in the bay area, a smaller plant in Los Angeles, and warehouses in between. The Model 30 will be used for manufacturing scheduling and inventory control, as well as for design and distribution of goods.

Like an automobile, a computer can be ordered with features, so that virtually every order is customized. As a result, it takes the efforts of many IBM locations, and hundreds of people, departments, and vendors, plus the use of computers for planning, order processing, controlling, scheduling, and other tasks.

A computing system, in addition to the central processing unit, could include input/output equipment from the following IBM manufacturing plants: tape drives from Boulder, Colo.; direct access devices from San Jose, Calif.; typewriter-printers and control units which control this equipment from Raleigh, N.C.; graphic display units from Kingston, N.Y.; card reader punches from Rochester, Minn.; printers from Endicott, N.Y.; and paper tape readers and controls from as far away as IBM France. The circuit modules—the basic building blocks of a computer—come from East Fishkill, N.Y., and Burlington, Vt. The circuitry switches, amplifies, and controls electronic signals to perform the computer's mathematical operations.

The Model 30 ordered by the XYZ Company is manufactured and assembled in the following locations: the 2030 central processing unit, the 1403 printer, and the 2821 control unit which controls the card reader punch and printer, in Endicott; the 2821 direct access storage facility, which is a file with nine interchangeable disk packs, and 2821 storage control unit in San Jose; the 2250 graphic display unit, featuring a television-like cathode ray tube screen, in Kingston; and the 2540 card reader punch in Rochester. (During the manufacturing cycle of this Model 30, the order will be changed at the customer's request to include several 1052 printer keyboard terminals from Raleigh.) This represents the hardware of the system, but there is a commitment to supply programming support as well—application and operating programs.

COMPUTERS TO HELP MAKE COMPUTERS

Getting this computing system to the customer in San Francisco from these five IBM plants takes planning and scheduling in areas such as manufacturing, final testing and shipping. The peripheral equipment of the total computing system must be shipped from separate IBM plants to arrive at the customer's location at the same time as the central processor so customer engineers can install the system without having to wait for delivery of a certain "box." The transportation problem is obvious in this case—the direct access storage facility and storage control unit have to be shipped only a few miles from San Jose to San Francisco, while the central processor, printer, and control unit must be delivered from Endicott. N.Y., 3,000 miles away.

To help solve this problem, each plant has *some type of automated system* to meet its own particular needs for order processing and scheduling. In Endicott, for example, a "real-time" computing system provides an up-to-the-minute record of the XYZ Company's—and every customer's—central processor four months prior to shipment. Soon each plant in IBM's Systems Manufacturing Division will be part of a division-wide order processing system called CCOP (Consolidated Customer Order Processing).

CCOP is a massive "store and forward" message control system linking the plant order departments, processing customer orders throughout the manufacturing division. This order processing system covers the entire backlog of IBM orders, and consolidates the backlog into one data bank for the Systems Manufacturing Division.

One of CCOP's most important functions will be to audit the validity of each IBM system order. As of now the plant of system control—in this case, Endicott—performs this audit, both at the system and individual machine level.

In addition, CCOP sends orders and transactions to the right location at the right time, formally records all order related transactions, performs message switching, acts as the "file cabinet" to order data for retrieval purposes, and produces all "national" reports.

CCOP processing is done on three 7010 computing systems at the division's headquarters at Harrison, N.Y., with transmission to and from the locations via 7711 high speed data communication units. CCOP also will link regional sales and World Trade area offices into the manufacturing loop.

THE XYZ COMPANY'S MODEL 30

After the XYZ Company signs the order for a Model 30, the paperwork is sent to the local branch office Data Processing Orders and Movements department. Specifications are completed and a customer number is assigned. The branch manager reviews the order, and forwards it to the regional office Sales Order Control department.

There the plant order and system numbers are assigned, and the plant of order control is identified. In this case, Endicott has system responsibility for the System/360 Model 30.

The regional office logs the order and its Product Scheduling department assigns a delivery date. Further review is made in the region if the order calls for special equipment, an unusual configuration, or for other special treatment. The order then goes back to Sales Order Control where it becomes part of the IBM backlog of orders. A record of the XYZ Company's order is then processed through a computer at Western Region and is sent to Data Processing Division headquarters at White Plains, N.Y., and to the Systems Manufacturing Division headquarters at Harrison, N.Y. (The Data Processing Division represents IBM's sales force while the Systems Manufacturing Division is responsible for the production of System/360, other IBM computers and peripheral equipment.)

Once Endicott receives the order from the division headquarters at Harrison, it reviews it further to make sure the system will do what the customer wants it to do. For example, does the order include enough control units to operate all the input/output equipment?

ENDICOTT PLANT OF ORDER CONTROL

As the plant of order control, it is Endicott's responsibility to notify the peripheral equipment manufacturing plants what input/output units are needed, and when. It is also Endicott's responsibility to decide whether to "plant merge" or "field merge" the system. ("Field merge" brings together the entire system for the first time at the customer's location. Under plant merge, all the input/output equipment is shipped to Endicott before the system is delivered to the customer.) The XYZ Company's system will be field merged.

It is at this point that Endicott notifies Kingston, Rochester, and San Jose what equipment is needed from them. But it is up to them to determine when to start actual production. They receive a field merge date from Endicott and plan their production, test and shipping schedules accordingly.

VENDORS

While several IBM plants are involved in the manufacture of a computer system, IBM also relies on thousands of vendors to supply parts and services to these plants. Vendor parts are furnished in economic purchase order quantities calculated by computer, after requirements are obtained from master schedules based on manufacturing forecasts.

MOST ORDERS CHANGE

During assembly of computer systems, changes are often made in the order. As a practice, IBM reconfirms with the customer 120 days before scheduled shipment to determine if there are to be any changes. Or the customer may initiate changes on his own. If a change is significant enough to delay the delivery of a particular system, the inventory of input/output equipment in many cases can be used on other orders.

At Endicott, when the time approaches to begin assembly of this particular System/360 Model 30, the Interplant and Customer Expediting department releases the order to the Machine Level Control Center. The Control Center keeps tabs on it through the Assembly Control System, which is a series of computer programs using master production schedules to assign start-to-build dates for specific customer systems and to produce related progress and status reports for the products produced in Endicott.

Input from the Interplant and Customer Expediting department lists the peripheral equipment manufactured at other IBM plants for this or any particular Model 30.

MACHINE LEVEL CONTROL SYSTEM

The Machine Level Control System maintains and processes a record for each machine's top bill of material configuration, location, engineering change levels, and related documentation, during manufacture and after customer delivery. It maintains the 2030 central processor records in "real-time," providing an up-to-the-minute report on each central processor in Endicott. This real-time approach is particularly valuable for keeping updated on engineering changes and late customer alterations. Through the real-time system, for example, the Machine Level Control System can retrieve information about every processor in the assembly line needing a certain engineering change. Real-time information is kept on direct access files which can be interrogated at any time providing instant information via IBM Tele-processing terminals.

Any alterations to a customer's order after starting assembly of the machine are controlled through the Endicott Order department. Test and assembly department technicians are notified of alterations so they may incorporate them without affecting the customer's delivery schedule. If necessary, the Endicott plant frequently can alter machines up to the day of shipment.

COSMOS

Before assemblers start on this Model 30, however, Endicott uses its COSMOS system (Computer Oriented System for Machine Order Synthesis) to automatically convert the device code, or sales feature code, to top bills of materials for the manufacturing process. (This operation ultimately will be placed within CCOP.)

ASSEMBLY STARTS

The Assembly Control System is used to notify Endicott's assembly departments, Units Assembly and Final Assembly, that it is time to start assembly on this particular central processor. Operators assemble hardware and electrical sub-assemblies on to the frame "power tower"—the Kingston-built power supplies for the Model 30; feature the frame and power assembly; install connections for all input/output gear; connect the Burlington-built CCROS (Card Capacitor Read-Only Storage) and the Boulder-built Read-Write Memory unit to the processor frame; and perform other assembly operations involving cables, wires, and solid logic technology cards and boards.

After this, the central processor is ready for its initial "power-up" check. Testers check various fan units, air blowers and voltage distribution to all points. In addition, all terminal blocks, the six DC voltage supply units, and AC voltage scattered throughout the machine are tested.

Next comes inspection by the Assembly and Test Quality department and by Quality Assurance before the central processor goes to Final Test.

At this arbitrary point, the order of the XYZ Company has been changed to include 1952 terminal/consoles from Raleigh. Now Raleigh will become part of the manufacturing cycle.

TESTING

Meanwhile, the central processor is in Endicott's Final Test area, where IBM engineers and technicians see that the system will perform for the customer as he expects it to. The machine is tested thoroughly—from A to Z and back to A again.

In yet another test, the machine is turned over to Quality Assurance, where functional checks, visual inspection and documentation checks are made. Quality Assurance also generates reports for management on the performance of the machine in the field.

From Quality Assurance, the machine is moved to the Audit department, where it is monitored for such things as engineering change compatibility. If there are no inconsistencies, the machine is ready for shipment.

However, a step or two must be retraced here. Not all systems, once they leave Final Test, are sent to the Audit department.

CUSTOM SYSTEMS MANUFACTURING

Specially ordered systems go to Custom Systems Manufacturing. If a customer had ordered non-standard features, for example, the 2030 central processing unit would have been delivered to this department. The 2030 is handled separately because each is individually engineered.

SYSTEMS TEST

Another area, Systems Test, may get involved, but not with the central processor, This is a special purpose area which is concerned only with input/output equipment that is standard on the Model 30. If a product is not field mergeable, for example, the input/output gear goes there, and is tested using a 2030 central processor. Problems are corrected, if there are any, before shipping.

Following these tests, Quality Assurance once again makes a functional check of equipment. Any equipment shipped to Endicott from other manufacturing plants has to be checked out by Quality Assurance before it goes back out.

Once all these assembly and test functions are complete, the Model 30 is ready for shipment.

PRODUCTION AT OTHER LOCATIONS

While assembly and test are going on in Endicott, parallel production operations are being performed at other IBM manufacturing plants on the peripheral equipment that ultimately will become part of this System/360 Model 30 at San Francisco.

Kingston, for example, is assembling and testing the 2250 graphic display unit. Raleigh is busy getting the 1052 printer-keyboard terminals ready for shipment, and San Jose is performing similar operations on its 2314 direct access storage facility and 2841 storage control unit.

KINGSTON

(When negotiations were held with the XYZ Company leading up to the order for the Model 30, the branch office sales representative and the customer agreed upon the Kingston-produced 2250 graphic display unit as part of the system configuration. The regional office received the order and prepared an IAC (Installation-Alteration-Cancellation) form for review and approval. A contract was sent to the sales representative for the customer's agreement and an order was processed.)

When the time approaches to begin assembly of the 2250, the system house receives the IAC (in this case, it is Endicott); it is analyzed and processed by computer into a bill of material structure so it can be manufactured. An equipment order is processed to the plant of manufacture (2250-Kingston) specifying in a bill of material format those features the customer desires on the 2250.

The equipment order goes to the Order and Scheduling departments in the Production Control area in the Kingston plant and is reviewed to make sure that the sub-assemblies, build, test, quality control acceptances, and clean-pack and ship areas, will meet the customer's shipping date. Then the unit is scheduled for manufacturing. After approval of the equipment order, Production Control uses a computer to process complete bills of materials, which are then sent to the manufacturing floor.

If the customer later makes an alteration in the configuration, an IAC form is again processed through the branch office, regional office, and Endicott altering the original order at Kingston. The alteration is reviewed to ascertain if the original ship date can be maintained, and the customer may be advised accordingly.

Upon receipt of the necessary hardware from stock, manufacturing personnel begin building the sub-assemblies which consist of the gates, control panel, power supplies and boards. The power supplies and boards are pre-tested before they are sent to unit build. In unit build all the sub-assemblies required, internal hardware and desk top are integrated into the frame to make the completed 2250.

UNIT TEST

The unit is then processed through unit test where testers attach it to a channel simulator. This simulator has the ability to exercise the data and control circuitry similar to a computer channel. After the unit has passed successfully basic simulator tests, it is attached to a System/360 Model 65 for its final testing and functional acceptance by Quality Control. When quality acceptance is completed successfully, the unit is covered and sent to the clean, pack and ship areas for shipment.

The 2250 includes an input/output interface and may be attached to any central processor unit in System/360 Model 30 and higher models by means of a selector or multiplexor channel. The computer can generate complex images consisting of both alphameric and graphical information by addressing the appropriate points on the cathode ray tube.

In Kingston, Quality Control inspections continually monitor the unit to assure IBM quality standards from sub-assembly to shipment. Engineering changes are continuously reviewed by Manufacturing Engineering to ascertain that the test procedure now in use remains valid. The test procedure and test programs will be updated and/or modified as necessary to assure that the 2250 will function at optimum operating conditions.

Manufacturing cannot ship a unit until it has Product Test support and approval. This test is usually performed and support obtained prior to the first customer shipment in this family of units.

When support has been obtained for field merging, the completed unit is shipped to the customer for installation by customer engineers instead of going through a systems test at the system house, in this case, Endicott.

CCOP

Kingston is already on CCOP, and uses a System/360 Model 50 to run CCOP reports in support of order processing operations. Before CCOP, Kingston used a 7010 computing system for its own order processing.

While production continues at Endicott and Kingston, similar operations are being performed at other IBM plants producing equipment for the XYZ Company's system.

RALEIGH

The original order did not call for any equipment from Raleigh, but later the customer decided to add 1052 printer keyboard terminals to his Model 30. The scheduled delivery date for the system is negotiated with Raleigh, and if Raleigh can meet the central processing unit delivery date, no reschedule is necessary.

Otherwise, the central processor is applied to another order and a reschedule of the system is given to the XYZ Company.

When the order alteration is made, Endicott notifies the Raleigh Order Control department, which in turn initiates the necessary paperwork for the production cycle. Raleigh does not have its own Assembly Control System, but uses Endicott's instead via Tele-processing. It uses a 7711 data communications unit for data link with Endicott's 7010 computing system. Endicott does the computing, but Raleigh does its own printout.

Under CCOP, Raleigh will use two 1410s and eventually a System/360 Model 40 for its order processing.

SAN JOSE

San Jose, like Raleigh, uses Endicott's Assembly Control System to process input/output equipment orders. Through Tele-processing, Endicott informs San Jose of what equipment is needed for the customer's configuration. San Jose's Control Center then releases the order to its manufacturing area allowing sufficient time for the equipment to meet the plant merge or field merge date.

Endicott's Assembly Control System also provides San Jose with a daily activity report, as well as a weekly listing, on the status of the customer's system. Any change is made by telephone or by wire and is reflected in the daily activity report.

A control center technician located in each manufacturing department keeps tabs on the status of the equipment as it moves through the manufacturing line.

When manufacturing and testing are complete, all field-merge equipment may be temporarily stored in San Jose's warehouse until the plant of systems control, in this case, Endicott, notifies it by telephone and confirms by wire the estimated time of arrival of the system at the customer's location. All equipment is supposed to arrive at the customer in the same calendar week.

READY FOR SHIPMENT

When all assembly and test are completed on the central processor and on the input/output equipment, the manufacturing plants ship their machines to arrive at the customer on delivery date. There Field Engineering Division customer engineers install the equipment while Data Processing Division systems engineers make certain the system will do what it is supposed to do.

5. BUREAUCRACY AND THE FUTURE OF INDUSTRIAL ORGANIZATIONS: A FORECAST

From Warren G. Bennis, Changing Organizations, Part I, "Evolutionary Trends in Organizational Development," McGraw-Hill Book Company, 1966, pp. 4–14; first published in Trans-action Magazine, July, 1965. .

BUREAUCRACY AND ITS DISCONTENTS

Corsica, according to Gibbon, is much easier to deplore than to describe. The same holds true for bureaucracy. Basically, though, it is simple: bureaucracy is a social invention which relies exclusively on the power to influence through reason and law. Max Weber, the German sociologist who conceptualized the idea of bureaucracy around the turn of the century, once likened the bureaucratic mechanism to a judge qua computer: "Bureaucracy is like a modern judge who is a vending machine into which the pleadings are inserted together with the fee and which then disgorges the judgment together with its reasons mechanically derived from the code." [1]

The bureaucratic "machine model" Weber outlined was developed as a reaction against the personal subjugation, nepotism, cruelty, emotional vicissitudes, and subjective judgment which passed for managerial practices in the early days of the Industrial Revolution. Man's true hope, it was thought, was his ability to rationalize and calculate—to use his head as well as his hands and heart. Thus, in this system roles are institutionalized and reinforced by legal tradition rather than by the "cult of personality"; rationality and predictability were sought for in order to eliminate chaos and unanticipated consequences; technical competence rather than arbitrary or "iron" whims was emphasized. These are oversimplifications, to be sure, but contemporary students of organizations would tend to agree with them. In fact, there is a general consensus that bureaucracy can be dimensionalized in the following way:

1. A divison of labor based on functional specialization
2. A well-defined hierarchy of authority
3. A system of rules covering the rights and duties of employees
4. A system of procedures for dealing with work situations
5. Impersonality of interpersonal relations
6. Promotion and selection based on technical competence [2]

These six dimensions describe the basic underpinnings of bureaucracy, the pyramidal organization which dominates so much of our thinking and planning related to organizational behavior.

It does not take a great critical imagination to detect the flaws and problems in the bureaucratic model. We have all *experienced* them: bosses without technical competence and underlings with it; arbitrary and zany rules; an underworld (or informal) organization which subverts or even replaces the formal apparatus; confusion and conflict among roles; and cruel treatment of subordinates, based not upon rational or legal grounds, but upon inhumane grounds. Unanticipated consequences abound and provide a mine of material for those comics, like Chaplin or Tati, who can capture with a smile or a shrug the absurdity of authority systems based on pseudologic and inappropriate rules.

Almost everybody, including many students of organizational behavior, approaches bureaucracy with a chip on his shoulder. It has been criticized for its theoretical confusion and contradictions, for moral and ethical reasons, on practical grounds such as its inefficiency, for its methodological weaknesses, and for containing too many implicit values or for containing too few. I have recently cataloged the criticisms of bureaucracy, and they outnumber and outdo the Ninety-five Theses tacked on the church door at Wittenberg in attacking another bureaucracy. For example:

1. Bureaucracy does not adequately allow for personal growth and the development of mature personalities.

2. It develops conformity and "group-think."

3. It does not take into account the "informal organization" and the emergent and unanticipated problems.

4. Its systems of control and authority are hopelessly outdated.

5. It has no adequate juridical process.

6. It does not possess adequate means for resolving differences and conflicts among ranks and, most particularly, among functional groups.

7. Communication (and innovative ideas) are thwarted or distorted because of hierarchical divisions.

8. The full human resources of bureaucracy are not being utilized because of mistrust, fear of reprisals, etc.

9. It cannot assimilate the influx of new technology or scientists entering the organization.

10. It will modify the personality structure such that man will become and reflect the dull, gray, conditioned "organization man."

Max Weber himself, the developer of the theory of bureaucracy, came around to condemning the apparatus he helped immortalize. While he felt that bureaucracy was inescapable, he also thought it might strangle the spirit of capitalism or the entrepreneurial attitude, a theme which Schumpeter later on developed. And in a debate on bureaucracy he once said, more in sorrow than in anger:

It is horrible to think that the world could one day be filled with nothing but those little cogs, little men clinging to little jobs and striving towards bigger ones—a state of affairs which is to be seen once more, as in the Egyptian records, playing an ever-increasing part in the spirit of our present administrative system, and especially of its offspring, the students. This passion for bureaucracy . . . is enough to drive one to despair. It is as if in politics . . . we were deliberately to become men who need "order" and nothing but order, who become nervous and cowardly if for one moment this order wavers, and helpless if they are torn away from their total incorporation in it. That the world should know no men but these: it is such an evolution that we are already caught up in, and the great question is therefore not how we can promote and hasten it, but what can we oppose to this machinery in order to keep a portion of mankind free from this parcelling-out of the soul from this supreme mastery of the bureaucratic way of life. [3]

I think it would be fair to say that a good deal of the work on organizational behavior over the past two decades has been a footnote to the bureaucratic "backlash" which aroused Weber's passion: saving mankind's soul "from the supreme mastery of the bureaucratic way of life." At least, very few of us have been indifferent to the fact that the bureaucratic mechanism is a social instrument in the service of repression; that it treats man's ego and social needs as a constant, or as nonexistent or inert; that these confined and constricted needs insinuate themselves into the social processes of organizations in strange, unintended ways; and that those very matters which Weber claimed escaped calculation— love, power, hate—not only are calculable and powerful in their effects but must be reckoned with.

MODIFICATIONS OF BUREAUCRACY

In what ways has the system of bureaucracy been modified in order that it may cope more successfully with the problems that beset it? Before answering that, we have to say something about the nature or organizations, *all* organizations, from mass-production leviathans all the way to service industries such as the university or hospital. Organizations are primarily complex goal-seeking units. In order to survive, they must also accomplish the secondary tasks of (1) maintaining the internal system and coordinating the "human side of enterprise"—a process of mutual compliance here called "reciprocity"—and (2) adapting to and shaping the external environment—here called "adaptability." These two organizational dilemmas can help us organize the pivotal ways the bureaucratic mechanism has been altered—and found wanting.

Resolutions of the reciprocity dilemma

Reciprocity has to do primarily with the processes which can mediate conflict between the goals of management and the individual goals of the workers. Over the past several decades, a number of interesting theoretical and practical resolutions have been made which truly allow for conflict and mediation of interest. They revise, if not transform, the very nature of the bureaucratic mechanism by explicit recognition of the inescapable tension between individual and organizational goals. These theories can be called, variously, "exchange," "group," "value," "structural," or "situational," depending on what variable of the situation one wishes to modify.

The exchange theories postulate that wages, incomes, and services are given to the individual for an equal payment to the organization in work. If the inducements are not adequate, the individual may withdraw and work elsewhere. This concept may be elaborated by increasing the payments to include motivational units. That is to say, the organization provides a psychological anchor in times of rapid social change and a hedge against personal loss, as well as position, growth and mastery, success experience, and so forth, in exchange for energy, work, and commitment.

I shall discuss this idea of payment in motivational units further, as it is a rather recent one to gain acceptance. Management tends to interpret motivation by economic theory. Man is logical; man acts in the manner which serves his self-interest; man is competitive. Elton Mayo and his associates were among the first to see human affiliation as a motivating force, to consider industrial organization a social system as well as an economic-technical system. They judge a manager in terms of his ability to sustain cooperation. In fact, once a cohesive, primary work group is seen as a motivating force, a managerial elite may become obsolete, and the work group itself become the decision maker. This allows decisions to be made at the most relevant point of the organizational social space, where the data are most available.

Before this is possible, some believe that the impersonal value system of bureaucracy must be modified. In this case the manager plays an important role as the instrument of change, as an interpersonal specialist. He must instill values which permit and reinforce expression of feeling, experimentalism and norms of individuality, trust, and concern. Management, according to Blake, is successful as it maximizes "concern for people"—along with "concern for production."

Others believe that a new conception of the structure of bureaucracy will create more relevant attitudes toward the function of management than formal role specifications do. If the systems are seen as organic rather than mechanistic, as adapting spontaneously to the needs of the system, then decisions will be made at the critical point, and roles and jobs will devolve to the "natural" incumbent. The shift would probably be from the individual to cooperative group effort, from delegated to shared responsibility, from centralized to decentralized authority, from obedience to confidence, and from antagonistic arbitration to problem solving. Management which is centered around problem solving, which assumes or relaxes authority according to task demands, has most concerned some theorists. They are as concerned with organizational success and productivity as with the social system.

However, on all sides we find a growing belief that the effectiveness of bureaucracy should be evaluated on human as well as economic criteria. Social satisfaction and personal growth of employees must be considered, as well as the productivity and profit of the organization.

The criticism and revisions of the *status quo* tend to concentrate on the internal system and its human components. But although it appears on the surface that the case against bureaucracy has to do with its ethical-moral posture and the social fabric, the real *coup de grâce* has come from the environment. While various proponents of "good human relation" have been fighting bureaucracy on humanistic grounds and for Christian values, bureaucracy seems most likely to founder on its inability to adapt to rapid change in the environment.

The problem of adaptability

Bureaucracy thrives in a highly competitive, undifferentiated, and stable environment, such as the climate of its youth, the Industrial Revolution. A pyramidal structure of authority, with power concentrated in the hands of few with the knowledge and resources to control an entire enterprise was, and is, an eminently suitable social arrangement for routinized tasks.

However, the environment has changed in just those ways which make the mechanism most problematical. Stability has vanished. As Ellis Johnson said: ". . . the once-reliable constants have now become 'galloping' variables. . . ." [4] One factor accelerating change is the growth of science, research and development activities, and intellectual technology. Another is the increase of transactions with social institutions and the importance of the latter in conducting the enterprise—including government, distributors and consumers, shareholders, competitors, raw-material and power suppliers, sources of employees (particularly managers), trade unions, and groups within the firms. There is, as well, more interdependence between the economic and other facets of society, resulting in complications of legislation and public regulation. Thirdly, and significantly, competition between firms diminishes as their fates intertwine and become positively correlated.

My argument so far, to summarize quickly, is that the first assault on bureaucracy arose from its incapacity to manage the tension between individual and management goals. However, this conflict is somewhat mediated by the growth of an ethic of productivity which includes personal growth and/or satisfaction. The second and more major shock to bureaucracy has been caused by the scientific and technological revolution. It is the requirement of adaptability to the environment which leads to the predicted demise of bureaucracy and to the collapse of management as we know it now.

A forecast for the future

A forecast falls somewhere between a prediction and a prophecy. It lacks the divine guidance of the latter and the empirical foundation of the former. On thin empirical ice, I want to set forth some of the conditions that will dictate organizational life in the next twenty-five to fifty years.

1 The environment. Those factors already mentioned will continue in force and will increase. That is, rapid technological change and diversification will lead to interpenetration of the government and legal and economic policies in business. Partnerships between industry and government (like Telstar) will be typical, and because of the immensity and expense of the projects, there will be fewer identical units competing for the same buyers and sellers. Or, in reverse, imperfect competition leads to an oligopolistic and government-business-controlled economy. The three main features of the environment will be interdependence rather than competition, turbulence rather than stability, and large rather than small enterprises.

2 Aggregate population characteristics. We are living in what Peter Drucker calls the "educated society," and I think this is the most distinctive characteristic of our times. Within fifteen years, two-thirds of our population (living in metropolitan areas) will attend college. Adult education programs, especially the management development courses of such universities as M.I.T., Harvard, and Stanford, are expanding and adding intellectual breadth. All this, of course, is not just "nice," but necessary. As Secretary of Labor Wirtz recently pointed out, computers can do the work of most high school graduates—more cheaply and effectively. Fifty years ago, education was called "nonwork," and intellectuals on the payroll (and many staff) were considered "overhead." Today, the survival of the firm depends, more than ever before, on the proper exploitation of brainpower.

One other characteristic of the population which will aid our understanding of organizations of the future is increasing job mobility. The lowered expense and ease of transportation, coupled with the real needs of a dynamic environment, will change drastically the idea of "owning" a job—and of "having roots," for that matter. Participants will be shifted from job to job even from employer to employer with much less fuss than we are accustomed to.

3 Work-relevant values. The increased level of education and mobility will change the values we hold vis-à-vis work. People will be more intellectually committed to their jobs and will probably require more involvement, participation, and autonomy in their work. [This turn of events is due to a composite of the following factors: (1) There is a positive correlation between education and need for autonomy; (2) job mobility places workers in a position of greater influence in the system; and (3) job requirements call for more responsibility and discretion.]

Also, people will tend to be more "other-directed" in their dealings with others. McClelland's data suggest that as industrialization increases, other-directedness increases; [5] so we will tend to rely more heavily than we do even now on temporary social arrangements, on our immediate and constantly changing colleagues.

4 Tasks and goals of the firm. The tasks of the firm will be more technical, complicated, and unprogrammed. They will rely more on intellect than on muscles. And they will be too complicated for one person to handle or for individual supervision. Essentially, they will call for the collaboration of specialists in a project form of organization.

Similarly there will be a complication of goals. "Increased profits" and "raised productivity" will sound like oversimplifications and clichés. Business will concern itself with its adaptive or innovative-creative capacity. In addition, *meta*-goals will have to be articulated and developed; that is, supra-goals which shape and provide the foundation for the goal structure. For example, one *meta*-goal might be a system for detecting new and changing goals; another could be a system for deciding priorities among goals.

Finally, there will be more conflict, more contradiction among effectiveness criteria, just as in hospitals and universities today there is conflict between teaching and research. The reason for this is the number of professionals involved, who tend to identify as much with the supra-goals of their profession as with those of their immediate employer. University professors are a case in point. More and more of their income comes from outside sources, such as private or public foundations and consultant work. They tend not to make good "company men" because they are divided in their loyalty to professional values and organizational demands. Role conflict and ambiguity are both causes and consequences of goal conflict.

5 *Organizational structure.* The social structure in organizations of the future will have some unique characteristics. The key word will be "temporary"; there will be adaptive, rapidly changing *temporary systems.*[6] These will be organized around *problems-to-be-solved.* The problems will be solved by groups of relative *strangers* who represent a set of diverse professional skills. The groups will be conducted on *organic* rather than mechanical models; they will evolve in response to the problem rather than programmed role expectations. The function of the "executive" thus becomes *coordinator,* or "linking pin" between various project groups. He must be a man who can speak the diverse languages of research and who can relay information and mediate among the groups. *People will be differentiated not vertically according to rank and role but flexibly according to skill and professional training.*

Adaptive, temporary systems of diverse specialists, solving problems, linked together by coordinating and task-evaluative specialists, in organic flux, will gradually replace bureaucracy as we know it. As no catchy phrase comes to mind, let us call this an "organic-adaptive" structure.

As an aside, what will happen to the rest of society, to the manual laborers, to the less educated, to those who desire to work in conditions of high authority, and so forth? Many such jobs will disappear; automatic jobs will be automated. However, there will be a corresponding growth in the service-type of occupation, such as the "War on Poverty" and the Peace Corps programs. In times of change, where there is a discrepancy between cultures, industrialization, and especially urbanization, society becomes the client for skill in human interaction. Let us hypothesize that approximately 40 per cent of the population would be involved in jobs of this nature and 40 per cent in technological jobs, making an *organic-adaptive* majority, with, say, a 20 per cent bureaucratic minority.

6 Motivation in organic-adaptive structures. The organic-adaptive structure should increase motivation and thereby effectiveness because of the satisfactions intrinsic to the task. There is a congruence between the educated individual's need for meaningful, satisfactory, and creative tasks and flexible structure or autonomy. . . . There will be, as well, reduced commitment to work groups. These groups, as I have already mentioned, will be transient and changing. While skills in human interaction will become more important because of the necessity of collaboration in complex tasks, there will be a concomitant reduction in group cohesiveness. I would predict that in the organic-adaptive system, people will have to learn to develop quick and intense relationships on the job and to endure their loss.

In general I do not agree with the emphasis of Kerr et al. on the "new bohemianism," whereby leisure—not work—becomes the emotional-creative sphere of life, or with Leavitt, who holds similar views. They assume a technological slowdown and leveling off and a stabilizing of social mobility. This may be a society of the future, but long before then we will have the challenge of creating that push-button society and a corresponding need for service-type organizations with the organic-adaptive structure.

Jobs in the next century should become *more*, rather than less, involving; man is a problem-solving animal, and the tasks of the future guarantee a full agenda of problems. In addition, the adaptive process itself may become captivating to many. At the same time, I think the future I describe is far from a utopian or a necessarily "happy" one. Coping with rapid change, living in temporary systems, and setting up (in quickstep time) meaningful relations—and then breaking them—all augur strains and tensions. Learning how to live with ambiguity and to be self-directing will be the task of education and the goal of maturity.

NOTES

1. R. Bendix, *Max Weber: An Intellectual Portrait*, Doubleday & Company, Inc., Garden City, N.Y., 1960, p. 421.

2. R. H. Hall, "The Concept of Bureaucracy: An Empirical Assessment," *The American Journal of Sociology*, vol. 69, p. 33, 1963.

3. Bendix, *op. cit.* pp. 455–456.
4. E. A. Johnson, "Introduction," in McClosky and Trefethen (eds.), *Operations Research for Management,* The Johns Hopkins Press, Baltimore, Md., 1954, p. xii.
5. D. McClelland, *The Achieving Society,* D. Van Nostrand Company, Inc., Princeton, N.J., 1961.
6. M. B. Miles, "On Temporary Systems," in M. B. Miles (ed.), *Innovation in Education,* Bureau of Publications, Teachers College, Columbia University, New York, 1964, pp. 437–490.

NOTE BY THE AUTHOR

The preceding chapter on The New Technologies and Management has taken a broad view of the impact of many of the new technologies in our age of acceleration. But both for students and for practicing managers, the role of the computer in today's and tomorrow's economy occupies a special place. The author therefore urges the interested reader to supplement the four selections in this chapter by consulting a book published by the M.I.T. Press in 1967, edited by Charles A. Myers, entitled *The Impact of the Computer on Management.* The book is based on a series of papers by experts during a conference at MIT; it reprints the papers themselves and also the tape recordings of discussions that followed. Conferees represented varied disciplines: industrial relations, economics, psychology, operations research, accounting, and control. All of them, however, focused upon the impact of computers on *management,* and in the main discussed the following questions:

1. Are organization structures becoming more centralized as a result of computers?

2. Are these organizational changes a necessary result of computer technology, or are other factors more important?

3. What is the significance of the centralization of the data-processing, or information-technology, function?

4. How has the nature of managerial work changed? Will it change further as certain types or levels of management work are subject to computer systems?

5. How will higher levels of management be affected?

The very nature of these questions emphasizes the transitional character of managerial structure today, and the reader will find the book full of challenging speculations and insights as well as reports of partially completed research in the field. To one of the latter especially his attention is directed: "The Impact of Computerized Programs on Managers and Organizations: A Case Study in an Integrated Manufacturing Company." Professor Myers, editor of the book, states that it is "a case study by

Professor Edgar F. Huse of Boston College on some of the human problems associated with the introduction of a computerized information system in a large integrated manufacturing company. Since the papers [reprinted from the conference] *deal very little with these human aspects,* the case study adds to our knowledge of the problems of implementation of computerized systems." (Italics supplied.)

It is to be hoped that in the immediate future there will be many similar research projects on *"the human problems associated with the introduction of computerized information systems into industrial organizations."*

the new technologies and labor

INTRODUCTION

tHE first selection is by A. H. Raskin of the *New York Times* editorial staff, for many years its labor reporter. It reviews a series of major strikes which have inflicted "greater punishment on the public than on the warring parties." Mr. Raskin's report, thoroughly documented and based on long experience, is also a considered and moving appeal for more inventiveness and imagination by labor leaders if unions are to survive in an age of technological revolution and increasing public employment.

The second selection reinforces Raskin's position but takes a more optimistic view of collective bargaining especially when the author cites examples of new and successful union-management agreements tailored to an age of rapid technological change.

The third selection, a paper by Neil Chamberlain given before an international conference on industrial relations, reaches deeper levels of analysis by probing for the root cause and justification for organized labor, either for today's or for tomorrow's world. Chamberlain finds them in a multidimensional need for security. He then suggests ways in which labor, through a process of education and re-education, can respond constructively to a changing world.

BIBLIOGRAPHY

"Automation and Job Evaluation Techniques," *Proceedings of the 16th Annual Meeting*, National Academy of Arbitrators, January, 1963.

Blauner, Robert: *Alienation and Freedom: The Factory Worker and His Industry*, The University of Chicago Press, Chicago, Ill., 1964.

Bright, James R.: *Automation and Management*, Graduate School of Business Administration, Harvard University, Boston, 1958.

————: "The Relationships of Increasing Automation and Skill Requirements," *The Employment Impact of Technological Change*, Appendix, vol. II, Report of the National Commission on Technology, Automation and Economic Progress, Government Printing Office, Washington, D.C., 1966.

Chamberlain, Neil: "What's Ahead for Labor?" *The Atlantic Monthly*, July, 1964.

————: "The Corporation as a College," *The Atlantic Monthly*, June, 1965.

Crispo, John H. G. (ed.): *Industrial Relations: Challenges and Responses*, University of Toronto Press, Toronto, Canada, 1966.

Davis, Louis E.: "The Effects of Automation on Job Design," *Industrial Relations*, vol. 2, no. 1, October, 1962.

———— "The Design of Jobs," *Industrial Relations*, vol. 6, no. 1, October, 1966.

Dubin, Robert: *Working Union-Management Relations; The Sociology of Industrial Relations*, Prentice-Hall, Inc., Englewood Cliffs, N.J., 1958.

Emery, F. E., and E. L. Trist: "The Causal Texture of Organizational Environments," Paper read at the International Congress of Psychology, Washington, D.C., September, 1963.

Healy, James J., and James A. Henderson: *Creative Collective Bargaining*, Prentice-Hall, Inc., Englewood Cliffs, N.J., 1965.

"Is the American System of Collective Bargaining Obsolete?" *Proceedings of 17th Annual Meeting*, Industrial Relations Research Association, December, 1964.

Jacobs, Paul: *Old Before Its Time: Collective Bargaining at 28*, Center for the Study of Democratic Institutions, Santa Barbara, Calif., 1963.

Kerr, Clark, John T. Dunlop, Frederick H. Harbison, and Charles A. Myers: *Industrialism and Industrial Man*, Harvard University Press, Cambridge, Mass., 1960.

Lipset, Seymour Martin, and Neil J. Smelser (eds.): *Social Structure and Social Mobility in Economic Development*, Aldine, Chicago, Ill., 1966.

Perlman, Selig: *A Theory of the Labor Movement*, new ed., Augustus M. Kelley, New York, 1949.

Raskin, A. H.: "Automation: Road to Lifetime Jobs?" *Saturday Review*, November, 1964.

————: "Making Strikes Obsolete," *The Atlantic Monthly*, June, 1966.

Report of the National Commission on Technology, Automation, and Economic Progress, *Technology and the American Economy*, vol. 1, Government Printing Office, Washington, D.C., February, 1966.

Selected Readings in Employment and Manpower, 6 vols., U.S. Senate Committee on Labor and Public Welfare, Subcommittee on Employment and Manpower, 88th Congress, 2d session, Government Printing Office, Washington, D.C., 1964–1965.

Silverman, William: "The Economic and Social Effects of Automation in an Organization," *The American Behavioral Scientist*, June, 1966.

Slichter, Sumner H.: *Union Policies and Industrial Management*, The Brookings Institution, Washington, D.C., 1941.
Tannenbaum, Frank: *A Philosophy of Labor*, Alfred A. Knopf, Inc., New York, 1951.
Trist, Eric L., and E. K. Bamforth: "Some Social and Psychological Consequences of the Long-Wall Method of Coal-Getting," *Human Relations*, 4, 1951.
Williams, Lawrence, and Floyd Mann: *Technological Change and Mental Health*, #270 Organizational Behavior Studies, Ann Arbor, Mich.

1.   MAKING STRIKES OBSOLETE

From A. H. Raskin, "Making Strikes Obsolete," The Atlantic Monthly, June, 1966, pp. 47–52.

Suddenly they all are gone—the pioneers who gave fresh direction to the American labor movement in the first feverish thrust of the New Deal. In the marble palaces they erected as monuments to labor's newfound eminence sits a new breed of union civil servants. It is a corps of organization men, bland, faithful, uninspired, drifting into an era of limitless technological change with compass points set in the Great Depression. In a society confident of everything except what reason it has for being, no element is more serene, more complacent, more satisfied of the eternal rectitude of its ancestral policies and practices.

The retirement of David Dubinsky as president of the International Ladies Garment Workers Union has removed from active leadership the last survivor of the insurrectionary band that met in the President Hotel in November, 1935, to create the original Committee for Industrial Organization. John L. Lewis, still majestic at eighty-six, watches lesser men struggle with the problems of degeneration that enshroud the wraith of his once indomitable United Mine Workers. Fourteen years dead is Philip Murray, the gentle Lewis lieutenant, who conquered the fortresses of the open shop in steel, then moved into the top spot in the CIO after his old chief had forfeited it in a vengeful bet against a Roosevelt third term. Gone, too, is Sidney Hillman, that unique blend of pragmatist, theoretician, and Talmudic scholar, whose legacy was an enduring mechanism for labor political action and a niche in history as the focus of FDR's admonition to "clear it with Sidney."

Now the twilight is descending on the "youngsters" in the second generation of New Deal union-builders, the men who led the picket crusades and the sit-down strikes in auto and rubber and textiles when the slogan was "President Roosevelt wants you to join the union" and millions rallied to the union cause. Only Walter P. Reuther, Joseph Curran, and

Harry Bridges are left. Michael J. Quill, whose ideal soapbox was the television screen, played his last scene in the flamboyance of a transit strike that paralyzed New York. James B. Carey, labor's perpetual schoolboy, engaging, energetic, and impossible, sputtered out in the humiliation of an election scandal.

They were a varied lot, these trailblazers, and most of them stayed too long. They were often vain, and even the most tractable among them was capable of incredible ruthlessness. But they had drive and a sense of purpose—so much so that they tended to identify the union with themselves. They were convinced that no one could do their job as well as they. And that is the tragedy of today's labor movement. Most of the pioneers fought as assiduously to stifle new leadership as they ever had against the bosses and their goons in the days when unions were on the march.

The accent has always been on one-party rule, with sycophants and yes-men more welcome than those with independent ideas, especially ideas that challenged the leadership. While corporations were combing the universities for bright young men and spending millions of dollars to foster originality in executive training programs, unions were contenting themselves with sporadic weekend institutes for business agents and shop stewards.

The scope of union activities keeps broadening. The head of a giant union must have some measure of charisma, but he needs even more an infinite range of specialized skills in personnel administration, the management of vast pension and welfare funds, industrial engineering, foreign trade, politics, community relations, law, and corporate structure. To all these have now been added the complexities presented by automation and the adjustments it entails for unions and workers. Yet the predominant union view remains that the most dependable leadership comes from the shop, with no need for formalized training. Reuther's United Automobile Workers stands almost alone in maintaining what amounts to a college for "graduate instruction" in unionism for all its organizers and secondary leaders. Its purpose is to stimulate them to bolder thinking about the total role of unions in industry and nation.

In general, however, labor seems thoroughly content with its old patterns; far from looking for fresh ideas, it abhors them. David J. McDonald lost his post as president of the million-member United Steelworkers of America last year chiefly because he had the temerity to update the creaky rituals of collective bargaining in steel. His fate will make other union presidents even more timorous about ever abandoning frozen practices.

McDonald took his cue from Arthur J. Goldberg, who served as the steel union's general counsel before his hop, skip, and jump into the Cabinet, the Supreme Court, and the United Nations. The 116-day steel strike of 1959, the sixth industry-wide shutdown since World War II, persuaded Goldberg that the old bargaining system had outlived its usefulness. He became the architect of a new approach based on year-round discussion of automation and other joint problems in an atmosphere free of strike deadlines. McDonald and the steel companies gave somewhat hesitant acquiescence, and a Human Relations Committee made up of four top representatives of the industry and the union was born.

It worked so well that most analysts began pointing to steel as a model of civilized industrial relations—an industry in which the tactics of siege and squeeze had been set aside in favor of no-crisis bargaining that protected the community as well as the parties. But the virtues of voluntary disarmament also proved its Achilles' heel. The committee worked in secrecy to allow its members freedom to exchange views without making eternal public obeisance to institutional shibboleths.

THE RUGGED OUSTS THE URBANE

The new technique produced agreements substantially more moderate than the rank and file had grown accustomed to in the years when every wage increase provided the springboard for an even bigger price increase. A side effect was to relegate to a role of total ineffectuality the 165-member wage Policy Committee, which theoretically represented the membership in all contract talks with the steel companies. The reality of this change was not great since the steel union had taken over from its foster parent, the United Mine Workers, a tradition of centralized leadership so complete that the Wage Policy Committee was never anything but a rubber stamp.

Nevertheless, the failure to go through the Kabuki routine of stylized consultation, coupled with the conspiratorial flavor of the top-level discussions and the relatively modest settlements, made the Human Relations Committee a sitting duck in the union's quadrennial elections a year ago. A group of anti-McDonald district directors engineered a palace revolution designed to "give the union back to the membership." They made the new bargaining setup and the increased authority it vested in the union's technical staff their prime target, and the members responded by throwing out McDonald and installing in his place the union's secretary-treasurer, I. W. Abel, a homespun man of the people, as rugged as his predecessor was urbane.

The new union administration promptly abolished the Human Relations Committee, although a subsidiary network of joint committees will be kept going to study such problems as apprenticeship, job classification, and medical care on a continuing basis. The first effect of the return to collective bludgeoning as a means of negotiating industry-wide wage agreements was that last year's contract talks wound up in the White House, the usual end of the road in precommittee days.

The degree to which the insurgent slate built its victorious campaign on the argument that the technicians had too much power sent a shudder through the professional staff of every major union in a period when there already was an insistent drift of intellectuals out of union posts. There is, of course, nothing new about the general disenchantment of intellectuals with a movement they once regarded as champion of the downtrodden and battler for individual liberty. But labor has retained inside its own house a dwindling company of brilliant staff people who continue to hope it will fulfill its proclaimed role as "the conscience of America."

Each year sees a few of the brightest stars in this collection disappear. They go into government, foundations, university faculties, and in an extremely limited number of cases, into industry. With them goes a little more of the chance that labor ever will pull out of its downhill slide and begin evolving imaginative new answers for its kaleidoscopic problems. The chief loss since the steel union election has been the decision of the most creative of all its technicians, Marvin J. Miller, to leave the union. He will take over a newly established post as executive director of the Major League Baseball Players Association, and his salary of $50,000 a year will be more than triple the $16,000 he got from the union. Few believe that the man who did most on the union side to assure the effectiveness of the Human Relations Committee could have been tempted away if he had felt the union's door was still open to experimentation and social inventiveness. In fairness to Abel, he did nothing to push Miller out; the question is whether anything could have made him stay after the know-nothing tone of the union campaign.

STANDSTILL IN NEW YORK

From the standpoint of the total community, however, the essential question is not who leads unions or whether unions can end their organizational torpor, but whether collective bargaining is an adequate instrument for protecting the public interest, not just the interests of labor and management.

The constant turmoil in railroads, shipping, newspapers, and other key industries, where stoppages often inflict greater punishment on the public than on the warring parties, provides one disturbing answer. But perhaps the most worrisome answer of all emerges from an evaluation of the strike that halted New York's subways and buses for the first twelve days of this year. It has particular significance, both because of its cruel consequences for millions of people in the largest of American cities and because of the menacing implications it holds for all cities now that the organization of teachers and other municipal employees ranks almost alone as an area of intense union concentration. [There followed in

Mr. Raskin's original article a narrative in great detail of the New York subway strike ending with a summary and appraisal as follows:]

Unquestionably, the absence of any estimate by neutral experts of what a fair settlement should contain was significant in bringing about the strike, in prolonging it, and in forcing up the cost to the city of the eventual settlement. When the TWU cut off the transportation lifeline, it still had on the negotiating table as its only formal position a demand for a package pay increase twenty times as large as the largest it had ever got before. This ludicrous demand would have provided an average *increase* of $7800 a year for each subway worker, more than doubling his annual earnings. Recommendations by the Lindsay mediation team would have provided the community with the kind of yardstick that was needed to convert hand-wringing and aimless expressions of outrage into a push for ending the tie-up on clear-cut and equitable terms. At last, with municipal suffering acute after a week and a half without subways, Lindsay overrode the reluctance of both union and mediators and demanded that his board make proposals for settling all the issues still unresolved. The trains were running again a few hours after it submitted its suggestions. . . .

MORE STRIKES AHEAD

In the general economy the advent of a period of gathering labor shortages after seven years of manpower surplus is likely to cause an upsurge of strikes. So is labor's coolness toward enforcement of the White House wage-price guideposts. To the extent that employers try to hold wages inside the 3.2 percent productivity fence, unions may call strikes for more, or find their members taking wildcat action on their own.

Troublesome as such strikes will prove in the months immediately ahead, the more fundamental long-range problem lies in the type of walkout that bedeviled General Motors and Ford when they negotiated their last national agreements two years ago. Thousands of local plant issues overwhelmed the bargainers and eclipsed in membership interest the impressive gains the UAW made on wages, pensions, and other major items. These local issues, ranging from rules governing smoking to holes in the paving on the employee parking lot, represent a back-to-the-womb development in mass unionism. They reflect the irritations and frustrations that caused workers to turn to unions in the thirties, and they stem from the worker's sense of obliteration in a society of union and corporate bigness.

The range of strike problems and the differing solutions that will be necessary to cope with them indicate the desirability of more priority for the search for answers. President Johnson gave assurance in his State of the Union message that he would recommend new measures to deal with emergency strikes. Governor Rockefeller and Mayor Lindsay are at work on plans for more dependable safeguards against civil service walkouts. Walter Reuther has put forward some ideas of his own for guaranteeing equity to public employees without muscle-flexing. But from most of labor's new leaders, just as was, traditionally, the answer from the old, comes the response: "Leave it all to collective bargaining. The less government does, the better." That response is not good enough—for unions, employers, or the country.

The first need is for less ritual and more inventiveness in the bargaining process itself. The idea of crisis-free negotiations on a continuing basis is not ripe for discard simply because of the abortive end of its initial application in steel. The important task is to piece out the elements of strength and weakness in the experience of the steel industry's Human Relations Committee so that future invocations of the same technique will not be vulnerable to demagogic attack.

THE KAISER PROFIT-SHARING PLAN

The best proof that this is no impossible undertaking exists in the record of a parallel experiment in the same industry, the long-range sharing committee that operates at the Kaiser Steel Corporation plant in Fontana, California. The committee also grew out of the long and costly 1959 strike, but it differed in two important respects from the Human Relations Committee. Instead of confining its membership to top leaders of the steel industry and the union, the Kaiser committee added to these three distinguished neutrals—Professor George W. Taylor of the Wharton School of Finance at the University of Pennsylvania, Professor John T. Dunlop of Harvard, and David L. Cole, former director of the Federal Mediation and Conciliation Service.

The second significant difference was that the Kaiser panel addressed itself to the development of a pioneering plan for giving the union members a tangible cash stake in greater industrial efficiency. The starting point was a guarantee that no worker would lose his job because of automation, but this was supplemented by an assurance that one third of all the savings resulting from increased productivity would be divided among the work force.

The plan, now in its fourth year, has had some rough spots, especially in periods when the cash bonuses have run low. But both the company and the union have demonstrated ingenuity in adapting the ground rules to changed conditions, and the three public members have served as an invaluable catalyst. Still another help has been a continuing educational drive to let the rank and file know everything there is to know about the plan. Most observers feel that this foundation of membership knowledge and support was even more influential than the financial dividends in protecting the Kaiser plan against the kind of assault that wrecked the Human Relations Committee. Its popularity was demonstrated when 1000 Kaiser fabricating employees clamored for a similar plan—and got it— at a time when the cash return under the original program in basic steel was disappointing workers by dropping to its lowest level. It has since turned upward again.

YEAR–ROUND TALKS

In its monumental report, "Technology and the American Economy," last February, President Johnson's tripartite automation commission called for wider use of the year-round discussion technique to take the countdown element out of collective bargaining. "Basic issues such as adjustment to technological change cannot be resolved by a small team of negotiators working themselves into a state of physical and mental exhaustion for a few months every two or three years," the commission warned. "These issues must be dealt with patiently, carefully and, above all, continuously until satisfactory solutions emerge."

The substance of bargaining also needs review in most industries so that every negotiation does not degenerate into another sterile "battle for the buck" without concern for the larger interests of either workers or society.

Among the most depressing indications of the inertia now general on both sides of the bargaining table is the survival of hourly wages as the basic measure of income for blue-collar workers. Obviously, mechanics have the same need for the dignity and stability of a weekly salary as white-collar employees, engineers, and technicians. A broad variety of income stabilizers has been introduced over the years to mitigate this form of discrimination.

Yet the only large-scale factory enterprise that pays its workers a regular weekly wage is IBM, which has no unions at all. If organized labor is to move ahead again, it will have to reorient its bargaining priorities to get away from the roller-coaster effect of the hourly wage. The progress the New Economists in Washington have made toward ironing out the worst bumps of the business cycle provides strong evidence that many industries could put all their workers on salary without major financial hazard. As technological innovation erases the line between mechanic and technician, the use of collar color to determine the pay system becomes as senseless as it is demeaning.

NO STRIKES AGAINST THE PUBLIC

How much governmental intervention will be required to protect the public interest will depend, of course, on how effectively labor and management discharge their own bargaining responsibilities in fields where strikes or uneconomic contracts inflict their primary damage on the community.

The most apparent deficiencies, as the New York subway tie-up demonstrated, affect relations in the civil service. The number of public employees now exceeds 10 million, and it is expected to rise by 5 million in the next decade, with virtually all the growth in state, county, and municipal agencies. Plainly, what is essential to make the no-strike policy something more than a legal fiction for this vast army of civil servants is a negotiating structure that has some counterpart of arbitration as its terminal point. The subway strike ended when Mayor Lindsay's panel got around to making its peace recommendations; it need never have started if the law had required such recommendations before the old contract ran out.

However, one important caveat goes with the idea of mandatory procedures for an impartial determination of fairness in disputes involving public employees. The citizens must be prepared to pay the price of economic justice for their state and municipal employees and not expect them to subsidize the agencies for which they work by taking less. No city has anything like enough money to do all the things that need doing these days in education, urban renewal, health, and a thousand other fields. But no ban on civil service strikes is going to work for long if fact-finders go below the point of fairness to fit the public purse or if the community reneges on the contract improvements the fact-finders declare just.

In private industry the yardstick for government action must be the extent to which any cutoff in service imperils the national interest. When all the people have to suffer through the willfulness or ineptitude of economic power blocs, it is an affirmation, not a denial, of democracy to provide effective government machinery for breaking deadlocks.

The weakness of the national emergency provisions now in the Taft-Hartley Act is that they delay strikes for eighty days but provide no instrument for putting peace proposals before the economic warriors. The least that is needed, by way of change, is a fact-finding procedure that would assure a third-party judgment on all the issues in dispute. The experience in atomic energy and missile-sites construction disputes, where such settlement machinery has worked well for several years, encourages hope that most controversies would be amicably adjusted on the basis of the fact-finders' recommendations. Compulsory arbitration or government seizure would have to be the instrument of last resort where this hope proved vain.

No formula or law is going to bring an end to all labor-management conflict. Australia has had a system of labor courts dating back to the formation of the Commonwealth in 1901. It still has strikes; but in general, the system has proved beneficial, and it has certainly not put the Australian economy into a totalitarian straitjacket—the bugaboo which foes of compulsory arbitration invariably conjure up.

In some industries the issue of federal intervention has been rendered academic. Automation has already made these industries so strike-proof that all the unionized employees could quit work without any resulting interruption of service. Electric utilities, telephone, and oil refining are cases in point. The list will grow as push buttons replace men in a broader spectrum of industry. The challenge to the nation is to demonstrate that it has enough social imagination to develop equitable and democratic instruments for guarding against strike emergencies without waiting for technology to make all strikes obsolete. That machinery will be equally needed as a safeguard for industrial democracy when labor's economic weapons have lost their potency. Union statesmanship today will be the surest guarantee of union survival in the technocratic tomorrow of industrial disarmament.

2. COLLECTIVE BARGAINING AND THE CHALLENGE OF TECHNOLOGICAL CHANGE

From Arnold R. Weber, "Collective Bargaining and the Challenge of Technological Change," in John H. G. Crispo (ed.), Industrial Relations: Challenges and Responses, University of Toronto Press, Toronto, Canada, 1966, pp. 73–90.

With the exception of the birth of quintuplets and manned space flights, few activities have been the object of such close scrutiny as collective bargaining. Virtually every government official, economist, and newspaper editor has his own fever chart which describes the present condition of the subject. The slightest rise in temperature elicits anxious concern and a variety of remedies ranging from stiff legislative prescriptions to imported patent medicines. . . . Rather than dealing with the broad aspects of collective bargaining, I will focus on the details of a specific set of responses to a particular challenge; that of technological change. . . .

One more disclaimer is in order. That is, for the greater part my comments will apply directly to developments that have taken place in the United States. It's a full-time job keeping up with Mr. Hoffa, let alone Mr. Banks. However, the trends and issues to be identified are also broadly relevant to the Canadian situation. This is not said because of any latent intellectual imperialism. Instead, the similarity of developments in the two countries reflects the fact that, for better or worse, they are linked together by common ties among unions and business enterprises and share many legal and cultural traditions. Indeed, cogent parallels can be made between North American and Western European experiences as well. An appreciation of, and sensitivity to, differences in institutional arrangements should not obscure similarities which arise from economic considerations that cross national boundaries.

THE CHALLENGE TO COLLECTIVE BARGAINING

Observers of the current scene rarely demonstrate sufficient insight to identify periods of momentous change as they occur. However, it seems evident that collective bargaining is presently confronted with the second major challenge of this century. The first challenge arose after the Second World War and reflected the massive gains in trade union membership that had been made in the previous decade. The task of labour-management relations was to develop procedures for the responsible use of power. Major industries were shaken by prolonged strikes which caused considerable concern that the parties lacked the maturity to resolve their differences autonomously. The postwar upheaval proved to be short-lived. Since that time, the incidence of strikes has trended steadily downward, and unions and management alike have demonstrated the ability to develop reasonably constructive relationships. Although the verdict is far from unanimous, there is wide agreement that collective bargaining met the test and has become a permanent feature of the industrial relations systems in the United States and Canada.

The second major challenge to labour-management relations is different in nature. If the first test involved the capacity of organized labour and its corporate counterparts to create a framework for accommodation, this second, contemporary challenge focuses on the ability of the parties to cope with dramatic alterations in the environment within which they interact. This development has taken place against a backdrop of extensive technological change, popularly identified as "automation." Clearly, automation is to industrial engineering as sex was to psychology. That is, it has kindled the public's interest in a heretofore obscure branch of knowledge while giving rise to fears of dire consequences if the practice is carried too far.

Broadly speaking, automation involves the substitution of machines for human effort and judgment in the implementation and control of production. Although automation in the technical sense has been with us for a long time, the tempo and scope of its application have increased substantially in the last fifteen years. Antiquarians may derive some comfort from tracing automation back to Oliver Evans' flour mill in eighteenth century Delaware, but automation in the modern sense owes more to the petroleum refining industry and the now obsolete Ford engine block plant in Cleveland than to these venerable examples of colonial ingenuity. One

index of the pace and extent of the diffusion of technical change is provided by the example of the computer. The first computer to be placed
"on the line" in the United States was used by the Bureau of the Census
in 1951 to aggregate and analyse the results of the 1950 census. At
present, there are over 16,000 known computers in operation in industry
and government and the number seems be growing at an increasing rate.

Automation has had a direct and indirect impact on a wide range of
economic, social, and psychological considerations. The literature is re-
plete with commentaries relating automation to everything from education to the incidence of lower-back injuries. While such analyses may be
useful and significant, they are of limited relevance to industrial relations
developments. When assessing the impact of technological change on
collective bargaining, changes in the level and structure of employment
opportunities will exercise the most profound influence on the policies of
the participants. Although Canadian unions have been more venturesome
in political affairs, they appear to have the same bread-and-butter orientation at the bargaining table as their American counterparts. Thus, as
technological change has impinged on the labour force, trade union
leaders on both sides of the border probably have watched monthly employment reports with the preoccupation of a sea captain eyeing the
barometer as his ship enters heavy seas.

In fact, the effect of recent technological change on employment levels
cannot be easily determined. As the unit of analysis is expanded from
the plant and the individual firm to a particular industry and the economy, it becomes increasingly difficult to isolate the impact of automation
from the host of other variables that determine the level of employment.
The difficulty of making aggregate estimates of the employment effect of
automation becomes more acute when total output and employment are
increasing, as they have been for the past several years.

Any ambiguity about the effect of automation on employment opportunities is removed when examining particular plant or office situations.
Essentially, the consequences of automation for labour-management relations in the United States and Canada are linked to what happens in
the work place. That is, industrial relations in both countries are still
highly decentralized and programs to deal with technical change will
largely reflect the perspectives of the worker rather than the President's
Council of Economic Advisers. Thus it is undeniable that in many specific
instances technical change, i.e., automation, has resulted in a net reduction in employment. This consequence has been observed in particular
plants in the meat packing, oil refining, electronics, coal, steel, and paper
industries. In addition, when the computer enters the office it has shown
the same dispassionate efficiency in sorting out people as it demonstrates
in dealing with punched cards. The magnitude of the reduction varies,

of course, with the extent of the change and other variables. In some cases, however, the decline in employment has exceeded 50 per cent.

Second, automation has been a powerful force contributing to changes in the structure of the labour force. Recent technological advances have dealt the heaviest blows to semi-skilled operatives and industrial labourers—those groups that have long been the exemplification of blue-collar virtue. At the same time, automation has contributed to gains in the number of professional and technical workers, mechanics, repairmen and other occupational groups concerned with the development and maintenance of complex productive equipment. In aggregate, automation has reinforced other trends in the economy which have undermined the dominance of blue-collar workers. Despite the recent "comeback" of the blue-collar worker it is significant to note that the number of semi-skilled operatives has only regained the level attained at the peak of the last boom in 1956, while industrial production increased by 32 percent between 1956 and 1964.

Further evidence of these shifts in the structure of the labour force is provided by the various case studies of the impact of automation. In almost every situation, jobs have been most drastically eliminated at the lower rungs of the occupational ladder. In the typical industrial plant this means the abolition of jobs for materials-handling and machine operatives. In the office, the computer is making the bookkeeper and file clerk as obsolete as the goose quill. One study of the introduction of the computer into an Internal Revenue Service district office revealed that as many as 80 percent of the bookkeepers' jobs were eliminated.

Although the chain of causation becomes more indirect, a third consequence of automation for employment warrants some attention here. When a firm introduces a major technical change it is likely to make other basic economic adjustments, particularly those relating to the geographical location of production facilities. In the meat packing industry, for example, shifts in population and changes in the marketing of livestock have undermined the economic attractions of traditional centres of production such as Chicago and Kansas City. Thus, when advanced technology is introduced it probably will be in a new plant located in an area that meets a broad range of economic requirements. Similar developments have taken place in the automobile, paper, and textile industries. Many of the depressed areas in the United States attest to the effect of this geographical redistribution of employment opportunities.

While the employment effects of current technological change press on the central ganglia of union and management officials, it is important to note that automation also impinges on other major collective-bargaining issues. Under the conditions posed by new technology, adjustments may be required in existing seniority systems. Established methods of wage payment often come under close examination. And work schedules may be modified because of changes in the nature of the production process. Each of these issues merit detailed investigation. However, beyond these specific points of controversy, there is the broader question of the impact of technological change on the character of collective bargaining itself. The discussion on this larger issue will focus on three areas; power relationships and bargaining tactics, bargaining procedures, and the substantive methods for dealing with technological change through collective bargaining. It is probably superfluous but none-the-less necessary to note that collective-bargaining developments in the United States and Canada have consistently confounded the best guesses of generations of experts.

POWER RELATIONSHIPS AND BARGAINING TACTICS

Power, as many observers have noted, is a basic component of collective bargaining. On balance, it appears that current technological change has strengthened management's hand at the bargaining table. First, there is a loose proportional relationship between union membership and union power. To the extent that automation dampens union growth it will limit the economic pressure that can be brought to bear on the employer. In fact, union membership gains have lagged in both countries so that labour organizations command the allegiance of a smaller proportion of the labour force than they did fifteen years ago.

Many factors, of course, lie behind the inability of trade unions to broaden their membership base. These include changes in public policy, worker attitudes toward unionism, and increased management sophistication in dealing with personnel problems. However, these factors have been reinforced by technical changes that are eroding the relative importance of traditional centres of union strength and promoting growth in those sectors which historically have been the most difficult to organize. The successful organizing drives of the 1930's were largely built upon the ability of union leaders to organize the militant discontents of the unskilled and semi-skilled workers in the extractive and mass producing industries. It is precisely these occupational categories which are bearing the brunt of displacement associated with automation. Despite strenuous efforts and the recent "comeback of the blue-collar worker," unions like the Automobile Workers, the Steel Workers, and the Meat Packing Workers have never regained the heights they reached in 1953–4. Similarly, membership in the former behemoth of the labour movement, the United Mine Workers, probably has declined by more than 50 per cent since the end of the Second World War. Sustained by an aging membership which fought the union's battles more than two decades ago, the conventions of the UMW are reminiscent of the commemorative encampments of the Grand Army of the Republic at the turn of the century.

If any major breakthroughs are made by the trade union movement, they will have to come in the expanding white-collar sector. One careful study indicates that in the United States only 2.5 million white-collar workers, or approximately 5 percent of the total white-collar sector of the labour force, are currently union members. As might be expected, union leaders at the highest echelon have been giving concentrated attention to this problem. Thus far, their efforts have been greeted with only limited success and it does not appear that the extension of office automation will create a more propitious climate for white-collar unionism. Although the introduction of the computer and associated hardware into the office invariably will have a disruptive effect on the work force, managers today are forewarned and have been armed with a battery of personnel procedures to avert unionization during the changeover to the new technology. Any inroads that unions make in the office will be hard fought and gained over a long period of time. The Metropolitan Insurance Company is unlikely to capitulate *in toto* as United States Steel did thirty years ago.

Second, union power may be diminished by the nature of the new technology. Automation, by definition, implies greater automaticity in the operation of the production process. Therefore, when a trade union initiates a strike, the effectiveness of this sanction may be reduced by the company's ability to operate using supervisors and other managerial personnel. For example, it is increasingly difficult to mount a successful strike in the telephone, gas and electric utility, chemical, and oil refining industries. In the oil industry, the Oil, Chemical, and Atomic Workers Union has fought several bitter battles with companies in the last five years. In each case, management maintained production at a satisfactory level through the use of management personnel. A dramatic manifestation of management's ability to diminish union power occurred during the strike at the Shell refinery in Houston, Texas. In that case, the Refinery continued to operate at high levels of capacity while the struggle dragged on for a year. Similarly, during a twenty-eight-day strike at the Brooklyn Gas Company there was not a single cold pot of chicken soup in Brooklyn as the firm continued operations. This immunity to the union's economic power has not been attained in industries like steel, autos, construction, and transportation. It is significant, however, that the strike has been neutralized in several important sectors of the economy.

Although automation may, in the long run, reduce trade union's striking power, paradoxically, those strikes that do occur in the next few years are likely to be long and perhaps bitter. On the one hand, many of the issues arising within a context of automation are of extreme importance to both parties: the union seeks to preserve employment opportunities for its members, while management sees the new technology as a broom to sweep clean many of the inefficient practices that have accumulated over the past twenty years. The problem of achieving an accommodation is frequently accentuated by the technical complexity of the controversies. Unlike a strike over wages, the issues are not easily compromised by agreeing on some manifest middle position.

On the other hand, union leaders are doubtless aware that the new technology is blunting the effectiveness of the strike weapon. Therefore, they may be moved to use their power before it is undermined by technical change. In this manner, the union may still be able to command respect at the bargaining table because every time management squirms in indignation at the union's demands it can feel the welts inflicted in previous rounds. Some of this long-run strategy has probably entered into the prolonged tests of power that recently have taken place in the newspaper industry. The industry is presently in a period of revolutionary change and it seems likely that the unions' ability to deal with an adamant employer through direct confrontation of power will be significantly reduced in the future.

In addition to wielding its remaining spears with increased vigour there is also some indication that American unions are consolidating their forces so that they may function more effectively in the new technological and market environment. Union mergers, in contrast to corporate marriages, are usually defensive in nature. Moreover, the tendency toward consolidation is accentuated by the fact that automation is blurring traditional jurisdictional lines. Mergers involving the Chemical and Oil Workers, the Lithographers and Photoengravers, and two paper workers' unions are cases in point. Meanwhile, sporadic negotiations have been carried out among other printing trades groups and the railroad brotherhoods. It is conjectural whether such consolidations will be sufficiently far-reaching to have significant effect on power relationships in collective bargaining. In many instances, internal political factors have presented insuperable barriers to merger. However, the sophisticated union leader is on notice that the Wagner Act and provincial statutes did not exempt them from the Darwinian laws of survival.

CHANGING BARGAINING PROCEDURES

The din of the past and prospective battles should not divert attention from the constructive activities that have taken place at the bargaining table. In an effort to arrive at solutions to the problems associated with technological change, unions and management have developed a major innovation in collective-bargaining procedures—the joint study committee. Such committees have been established in a wide variety of industries which encompass the dominant collective-bargaining relationships in the United States, including steel, automobile, meat packing, newspaper, publishing, longshoring, glass, and agricultural implements. The demand for the formation of these committees was so great at one point that the management of one automobile supply firm with annual sales of $300 million dollars ruefully reported that the UAW had refused its request for a joint study group because the company was too small to justify the use of scarce union staff resources.

In many cases the study committees have not been formed explicitly to deal with the issues arising from automation. It is not coincidental, however, that this innovation has been most widely adopted in those situations in which the scope and pace of change have posed severe threats to the stability of union-management relationships. In addition items dealing with the dislocation stemming from the introduction of new technology frequently have been given top positions on the committee's agendas. The distinguishing characteristic of the joint study committee is the intensive analysis of a limited number of problems by union and management representatives during the term of the collective-bargaining agreement. In some cases, the committee is expanded to include neutral third parties. This apparently innocuous instrument can, and has had, a profound effect upon the bargaining process, especially when vital interests are at stake.

First, the joint study committee often has been a vehicle for informal advance notice of technological change well before the change takes place. In the absence of the committee such notification usually would be limited to the narrow requirements of the contract. Moreover, the highly charged atmosphere during negotiations over the contract terms is hardly the appropriate time for the saber consideration of the company's plans.

Second, the joint study committee has permitted the parties to engage in bilateral fact-finding concerning the probable consequences of technological change and the feasibility of alternative remedial programs. The topics studied have ranged from the protection of future employment in the meat packing industry to possible measures of productivity in long-shoring and the cost of an extended vacation plan for the employees of the basic steel producers. Such bilateral fact-finding does not constitute a shortcut to harmonious relationships, but it does help to provide a neutral framework within which controversies based on conflicting interests may be resolved.

Third, the study committee has helped to free the bargaining process from the political pressures and rigid adversary roles that often characterize contract negotiations. In most cases, the ground rules for the committee deliberations specify that the parties can make statements without fear of retribution or subsequent accusations of inconsistency. In addition, the discussions usually are carried out on a confidential basis so that a free exchange of ideas and information can take place without exciting premature responses from the committee members' constituents. The fact that the study groups carry out their activities long before contract termination periods also helps to maintain a low-key atmosphere and spirit of flexibility.

Fourth, the joint study committee approach has encouraged a certain degree of experimentation in the development of programs to cope with new economic conditions. The Armour Automation Fund Committee introduced important modifications in the operation of an interplant transfer program with the understanding that the changes would not be binding if they did not work to the satisfaction of the parties. A similar escape clause was linked to a formula that was developed by the Human Relations Committee in the steel industry for dealing with subcontracting. In a more dramatic case, the Long Range Sharing Plan devised by the study committee in Kaiser Steel also permits either party to withdraw from the program after the appropriate period of notice. With the knowledge that all mistakes are not irreversible, unions and managements may be expected to demonstrate a greater venturesomeness in collective bargaining.

The achievements of the joint study committees have been notable in several situations. The effort to find a measure for productivity in longshoring operations resulted eventually in the pathbreaking Modernization and Mechanization Agreement on the Pacific Coast. The Armour Automation Fund Committee has carried out a program for the interplant transfer and retraining of workers displaced by the shutdown of obsolete plants. And the Human Relations Committee did much of the spade work for a variety of measures aimed at enhancing the steelworkers' job security.

The joint study committee approach has not been without its shortcomings or failures. In some instances its adoption seemed to represent a vacuous faddism in industrial relations or a tactic to postpone the consideration of hard problems. Thus the committees established in the automobile industry appear to have had little effect on the course of collective bargaining to date. Nor is there any indication that a study committee has melted the freeze in union-management relations in the New York City newspaper industry. In other cases, the confidential aspects of committee deliberations incurred the suspicions of the rank and file and became a political issue within the union. This was an important factor leading to the demise of the Human Relations Committee in the steel industry. To add to this chorus, the leadership of the Packinghouse Workers has attacked the Automation Fund Committee as a "publicity gimmick" but significantly did not force a dissolution of the group at the last contract negotiations.

It is also clear that the study committees will not, or cannot, supplant the essential power aspects of the collective-bargaining process. Instead, they serve the cause of rationality primarily by neutralizing potential controversies over factual questions and by providing some assurance that power will not be exercised over trivial matters. Where the issues are extremely complicated, as in dealing with technological change, these gains may be well worth the price.

PROGRAMS FOR ADJUSTMENT

Despite the signs of impatience and antagonism on both sides, the parties generally have responded with restraint and imagination to the problems posed by automation. Out of a sense of realism or responsibility, few unions have adopted a posture of outright resistance to technological change. Management also has shown a disposition to recognize problems of transition that it studiously ignored in the past. And the use of new procedures has contributed to the variety of measures adopted to deal with the consequences of automation. From this range of experience, three general approaches may be identified; the buy-out, gains-sharing, and manpower management.

The buy-out approach generally involves an attempt to indemnify the worker for economic losses imposed by technical change. The problem of adjustment is then one of arriving at some acceptable formula for estimating the costs to the individual and making restitution as the "property rights" in his job are liquidated. In most cases, these formulae lay no claim to precision. Instead, they are broadly related to previous earnings levels and length of service.

The most widely used form of indemnification for loss of employment is severance pay. Here, a lump sum payment is made to the employee when his job is permanently terminated because of automation or associated economic adjustment. Severance pay provisions are found in many labour-management agreements today and are generally considered a starting point for subsequent attempts to deal with the problems of technological change. In other instances, extended Supplemental Unemployment Benefits augment or replace the concept of severance pay. However, the difference between the two is largely formal in the sense that SUB involves a flow of income over time rather than a single lump-sum payment.

The buy-out has reached its highest refinement in the transportation industries. On the railroads, the Washington Job Protection Agreement, negotiated in 1936 to deal with displacement arising from the merger of two or more carriers, provides the basic framework for the indemnification of employees affected by technological change. Under this approach, workers who are displaced or who are "made worse off" as a consequence of the new conditions are provided with compensatory income payments over a specified period of time, usually five years. This formula has been incorporated in various agreements negotiated between the Brotherhood of Railway Clerks and different carriers to deal with the introduction of electronic data processing systems in offices. It also was a key concept in the arbitration decision that ended the passion play arising from the dispute over the diesel fireman in the United States. As evidence of the continuous flow of ideas and experience across the border, a similar formula, albeit more generous, was an important ingredient in the recommendations of the Kellock Commission which paved the way for the earlier resolution of the fireman issue in Canada in 1959.

The historic agreement between the Pacific Maritime Association and the International Longshoremen and Warehousemen's Union also represents an advanced adaptation of the buy-out formula. In this case, the employers agreed to pay $27.5 million into a special fund over a period of five years. The proceeds of this fund are used to finance wage guarantees and special retirement benefits. Each fully registered longshoreman has a proprietary claim to $7,920 which he may exercise in one form or another.

The buy-out has several advantages to recommend it to both management and unions. As part of the bargain, management is generally given considerable latitude in the introduction of technical change and, once it has translated its "moral responsibility" into financial terms, it can go about the task of increasing efficiency with few restraints. The freedom to modify existing work rules was a major incentive in the West Coast maritime case. The Union, in turn, sees the indemnification payments as a factor retarding the pace at which technical change may be introduced. That is, where management has to make sizable cash payments in the form of earnings, guarantees, or severance pay to its employees, the calculation of costs and returns may temporarily tip the balance in favour of the *status quo*. In addition, once the lump-sum payments are made to the employees they serve as "social shock absorbers" to tide the displaced employee over the period of transition in the labour market at large.

Gain-sharing, the second approach to the problems of automation, also attempts to translate the consequences of technical change into monetary terms. Management is again afforded wide discretion in introducing change while some formula is contrived for distributing the gains from productivity among employees. However, whereas the buy-out generally is directed at those who are displaced, the gain-sharing approach manifests greater solicitude to those who continue to work.

The classic example of the gain-sharing approach to technological change is provided by the bituminous coal industry. In this case, John L. Lewis long ago made a basic policy decision that it would be more desirable to have fewer coal miners working at high wages than to have many coal miners employed at what he considered marginal wages. Accordingly, the UMW adopted an active policy of encouraging the introduction of labour-saving devices into coal mining operations. The consequences of this policy have been drastic indeed. Unionized coal miners, when they work, are among the highest paid manual workers outside of the building trades in the United States today. At the same time, however, employment in the bituminous coal industry has declined from approximately 450,000 in 1946 to roughly the equivalent of 110,000 full-time employees in 1965. The gains from advancing technology have been shared with the UMW, but their distribution has been limited to a relatively small group.

The Long Range Sharing Plan adopted by the Kaiser Steel Company and the United Steel Workers of America, provides another example of the gain-sharing approach. Here, a complicated formula has been established for passing on to the members of the work force the savings attributable to improved method and technology. The implicit acceptance of gain-sharing as a framework for dealing with technological change may also be noted in many sectors of the building construction industry. In the New York City electrical construction industry, for example, the negotiation of a five-hour day-$5.50 per hour bulwark against the employment effects of technological change was accompanied by several concessions to management that would promote the application of new methods.

It is obvious that the gain-sharing approach, by itself, has limited promise in facilitating adjustments to technological change. That is, it tends to distribute income only among a favoured few. For this reason, it is normally used in company and industry situations where management is confronted with intense competition and where total employment opportunities do not decline too sharply. When there are major reductions in the number of jobs available, extreme pressures are likely to develop within the union because of the discrepancy in the economic welfare of the members. This situation has developed in the coal industry where a rash of wildcat strikes has underscored the discontent of the rank and file with the absence of comprehensive provisions for job security.

The manpower planning approach generally rejects the economic maxim that every man has his price. Instead, it emphasizes the need for distributing employment opportunities as widely as possible among union members. In some cases, manpower planning may also involve efforts to promote the occupational mobility of displaced workers in the external labour market once displacement has been carried out. Within the firm, detailed studies are made to determine the level and structure of employment opportunities in the immediate future and to establish criteria for allocating these opportunities among workers with different priorities.

Historically, the manpower planning approach may be traced back to traditional forms of work-sharing. But recent programs have gone beyond this simple formula. First, attrition has been widely used to reduce the level of employment while minimizing actual displacement. Thus, workers are not replaced as they die, resign, or retire. In addition, systematic efforts have been made to induce attrition by the negotiation of generous early retirement plans. Second, collective-bargaining agreements in the auto, steel, meat packing, and glass industries, among others, have established interplant transfer plans so that workers who are displaced by technical change or plant shutdowns in one location may exercise a claim to employment opportunities opening up in other installations. Third, active steps have been taken to retrain workers for new jobs in the firm or labour market at large. Fourth, greater emphasis is being placed on sharing the gains of productivity in the form of compensated leisure rather than increased monetary income. In this respect, there has been both augmentation of conventional vacation plans and a willingness to experiment with new programs. The so-called industrial sabbatical negotiated in the steel industry affords high-seniority workers extended vacations of up to thirteen weeks every five years. A novel variant of this approach developed by the Packinghouse workers and the American Sugar Refining Company limits these extended vacations to workers who are over fifty-five years of age. This modification opens up greater employment opportunities for the younger workers while ostensibly preparing the older employees for the delights of the golden years.

None of the three approaches devised by collective bargaining for handling the problems of automation leads to an economic promised land. The buy-out primarily serves to provide the deceased with a decent burial. There is no guarantee that they will be able to adjust to a new labour market environment without considerable deprivation. Gain-sharing tends to promote the interests of the residual job holders. And manpower planning can largely facilitate distribution of available employment opportunities.

In practice, a combination of approaches has been employed in handling the consequence of technological change in particular collective-bargaining situations, although there are significant differences in emphasis from case to case. Moreover, once some provision is made for indemnification, there is a pronounced tendency for the parties to move toward what has been called manpower management. In many ways, this approach puts the greatest burdens on unions and management in collective bargaining because it continually requires the development of new programs and administrative procedures to fit the specific circumstances of a particular plant or office situation. But it also offers the brightest prospects for minimizing the economic and social costs of a difficult period of transition.

CONCLUSION

In the last year, the public and professional concern over the consequences of technological change has perceptibly subsided. This shift in
attitudes reflects several factors. Undoubtedly, the initial fears regarding automation were exaggerated. In addition, fiscal policies have blunted
the cutting edge of unemployment. Beyond these factors it is clear, however, that collective bargaining has made a major contribution to the
process of adjustment. It has helped to create a greater awareness of the
specific dimensions of the problem where casual indifference or empty
generalizations might have prevailed. It has substituted orderly procedures for improvisation. It has sought some acceptable basis for distributing the costs and benefits of the new technology among those who are
directly affected. And it generally has carried out these functions without
the promiscuous exercise of power.

As part of a decentralized system of decision-making, the contributions
made by collective bargaining inevitably are limited by the scope of the
units under the parties' control. Within this constraint, however, collective bargaining has responded to the challenge of technological change
with more vitality than resignation. Despite the forebodings of its friends
and the hopes of its enemies, collective bargaining will continue to play
an important role in mediating the claims of competing economic groups.

3.   UNIONS AND THE MANAGERIAL PROCESS

*From Neil W. Chamberlain, "Unions and the Managerial Process," first
published as* "Gewerkschaften und Unternehmensführung" *in* Automation-Risiko
und Chance, *Günter Friedrichs* (ed.), *Frankfurt am Main, 1965, Band 2,
Seite 795–816.*

Ever since unions came into existence, management has regarded them
as a threat to unified control over corporate affairs. They have frequently
been looked on as revolutionary instruments whose objective is in fact
the overthrow of traditional systems and methods of business management. Whether what they would put in its place is "socialism," or "industry councils," or "codetermination" is not especially consequential
to management. The essential consideration is that the unions would
fragment control and confuse corporate objectives.

Some union leaders in certain countries of Western Europe may indeed
have such an intent or objective. There may be an important element of
doctrinal motivation which leads some British labor officials, for example,

to make nationalization of specified industries an avowed goal. But these tend to be the exceptions. Looking over the West as a whole, and certainly speaking from the viewpoint of unionists in the United States, there is no programmatic intent to engage in drastic surgery on the corporate organization. On the whole, Western business management has been a good thing for Western workers. It has failed in some particulars, however, and it is these particulars which unionists would like to correct. They seek not control over the corporation but correction of its conduct and modification of its mores.

I.   MANAGEMENT PREROGATIVES AND UNION PURPOSE

By and large, most union officials with whom I have come in contact would echo the words of one American leader: "We have no plan. Unions work from particulars to generals. We are empiricists without knowing it. It is simply a matter of meeting problems as they arise." In such a position there is little dogma or doctrine.

But to emphasize this pragmatic approach exclusively would obscure the persisting underlying drive of the labor unions and would convert them into a collection of economic opportunists. To dwell upon their tactics of expediency would divert us from examining their goal-oriented strategy. We can scarcely avoid asking such questions as the following: By what longer-run standards do labor unions assess their needs of the moment? What is the nature of the particular problems from which unions work to general solutions? In what situations do unions feel a compulsion to challenge the existing structure of management "prerogatives"? What objectives do they seek to achieve and what responsibilities do they recognize—to their memberships—as they attempt to build on strength or remedy weakness and spread their influence further within the corporation?

There is probably nothing more treacherous than trying to identify basic motivation. It is hard enough to understand ourselves, let alone others. But we cannot avoid the attempt, since we can analyze problems of power relations only if we have at least a rudimentary appreciation of the springs of action. In the case of the unions and their members, the basic drive, it seems to me, is for security. But security is not a single-dimensional quality. There are three interrelated kinds of security involved in the worker's age-old struggle with those who control his fate—security of income, function, and status. These are so closely intertwined that it is sometimes difficult to disentangle them, but they constitute three sufficiently distinguishable objectives that failure to recognize the special quality of each is likely to lead to difficulty.

It is probably unnecessary to dwell on the specifics of these basic drives, but I do want to discuss them briefly if only to remind ourselves how sharply these objectives may at times challenge traditional ways of doing business, thus appearing to challenge the system of private enterprise itself. This latter fear is, I think, the result of fallaciously identifying the *temporary* forms of management control with the *persisting* philosophic motif which underlies our Western civilization.

By private enterprise we principally mean, I think, the decentralization of our economy into numbers of nongovernmental units, a philosophic design for the fragmentation of the power of some over others. At any moment of time the trustees of those private units enjoy (and *must* possess, for organizational effectiveness) certain autonomous privileges— call them managerial prerogatives, if you will. But the shape of those privileges is constantly undergoing change. This is due to the changing technological nature of our economic institutions, our expanding knowledge of the social effects of private economic actions or inactions, and our slowly growing experience with how private activity can be influenced and coordinated without destroying autonomy. So the forms of management control and the degree of management discretion change, but we retain our strong desire to prevent the centralization of power.

But let me return to the unions' drive for security of income, function, and status on behalf of its members—a drive which is partly responsible for the more or less constant pressure on management to accept changes in the structure of its authority.

II. THE DRIVE FOR INCOME SECURITY

The union starts with the fundamental premise that workers' welfare in a pecuniary society depends on steady employment providing an adequate income. Its conception of what is adequate is subject to upward adjustment in the light of a country's economic advancement. Security is not defined as Malthusian subsistence. It calls for "fair shares" in a socially established standard of living.

Income security depends on continuity of employment and an employer's ability to pay an "appropriate" level of wages. If the management of a company cannot provide these, workers want to know why, and marshal such pressure as they can, both economic and political, to try to do something about it.

The resulting implicit challenge to managerial autonomy is perhaps made most explicit in the demand for an annual wage. Who can deny that there is something oppressively archaic in the notion that a man's income can be paid to him an hour's worth at a time? Under the guise of market necessity, it forces workers to accommodate themselves to the convenience of management. It constitutes a device by which managements can too easily escape from what should be a social obligation to plan their operations to provide some measure of employment continuity.

Bit by bit unions have moved us in the direction of considering the hourly rate purely as a unit of measure and not as a price for the purchase of a discrete unit of a commodity. By negotiated provisions for income guarantees of varying duration, by requirement for advance notice before layoff, by legislated unemployment insurance, and by collectively bargained supplementary unemployment benefits we have moved rather far in the direction of recognizing a continuing obligation to maintain the income flow of a worker's household.

This still-to-be completed struggle to assure a family's pecuniary lifeline has its implications with respect to managerial discretion. Freedom to lay off workers when they are not needed—that is, to terminate them as a cost of production—has been hedged about. The obligation to provide job continuity is not, of course, an indefinite one. Nevertheless, an employer no longer can treat manual labor as primarily a direct cost of production, varying up and down directly with output. Much of labor has taken on the character of a semi-fixed or semi-variable cost, to which the employer is committed for a period of time regardless of fluctuations in production. The conversion has not yet fully been made, but we are in the process of making it. Steadily and inexorably we are recognizing that income maintenance of all households is a social obligation, and that it can be satisfactorily met only by devolving a large share of that responsibility on the business firms which have members of households on their payrolls as factors of production.

III. THE DRIVE FOR FUNCTIONAL SECURITY

The workers' drive for a secure income is thus a principal reason why unions have sought to limit the scope of managerial authority and to enlarge its responsibility. But income security is not enough to satisfy the worker. He asks functional security—job security—as well. Most people experience a need—Professor Frank Tannenbaum calls it a "moral" need [1]—to be useful, to be engaged in activity which has meaning and purpose. To have money flowing in without having to work for it is often pictured as a kind of materialistic paradise, but few of us would choose to inhabit it except in our dreams. However much we complain about our jobs, most of us would not want to do without them. They fill our time with purposeful activity, in the absence of which we would have to engage in the dreary and deadly business of "killing" time.

The controversy over "make-work rules" is based in large measure on this effort to protect not just an income but a job. To be sure, there are enough instances of the use of union power to secure payment for not working to make it abundantly clear that the motive for some work rules

[1] Frank Tannenbaum, A *Philosophy of Labor,* Alfred A. Knopf, Inc., New York, 1951, p. 106.

—"featherbedding"—may be nothing more than an exaction to pad out someone's income. Should that surprise us? But to believe that "make-work rules" are always a form of exacted tribute would be to miss the basic drive by workers to protect their function. If they try to insist on performance of jobs in traditional and uneconomic ways, they are often seeking, above all else, to insure that their services are made functionally necessary.

Probably few threats to a worker's position loom more ominously than his possible obsolescence through a technological change. The spreading applications of the computer are now making that fear more understandable to members of the managerial hierarchy. Automation is a term of foreboding in work society, perhaps less because it threatens to deprive people of a stream of income—that is bad enough, but it may sometimes be replaced from other sources than a job, at least for a period of time; it is a term of despair because it threatens to leave people functionless, things to be kept alive but of no use to anyone.

Hence the effort to control technological change—if not to stop it to slow it, if not to quash its economic value, then to reduce that value with barnacle-like work rules which have the double effect of saving a few jobs and retarding the rate of technological innovation.

Here again there is a direct conflict between the drives of workers, with their union agents, and the traditional incentive of managements to economize, often under competitive pressures, by seizing on technological advantage whenever it presents itself.

IV.   THE DRIVE FOR STATUS

The last of the basic security drives of workers is for protection of status. To be sure, status derives in large part from income and job function so that it may appear repetitive to list it separately. Thus the demand for an annual wage, which we earlier interpreted as an effort to assure income continuity, is also part of a status impulse. Even if the money earnings add up to the same amount at the end of the year, there is something demeaning that it comes calculated in hourly droplets rather than in the salaried form accorded professional and supervisory personnel. It suggests a more tenuous tie and less significant service to the firm and society both, and as such constitutes a status symbol which with each passing year is harder to justify. But the drive for security and equality of social status has a nonpecuniary as well as a pecuniary basis, and extends to personal as well as functional relations. A worker may be left with his income and functions, and still his status might suffer. It could suffer through the arbitrary exercise of power over him by members of the management cadre—discipline meted out, orders given, respect withheld. The struggle to maintain and secure status in Western society is basically a struggle towards egalitarian relationships, where power by some over others is curbed by rational and institutionalized restraints. Some analysts have pictured workers' drives as including a desire to participate in decisions, to express one's self creatively on his job. I am sure such a drive exists for a number of workers, and perhaps even more for their union representatives. I am not convinced, however, that it is a generalized objective for most workers, who often would prefer to leave decision to others, such as management. It is not a drive to participate in the exercise of authority which characterizes workers as much as a desire to protect themselves from its exercise, to safeguard their social relationship to others. They can do this by appropriate restraints on authority and by sensitizing those in authority to the obligation to justify the use of their power.

These, then, are the chief drives which as I see it characterize most workers and instruct their union agents in dealing with management—the security of income, the security of function, and the security of status. Would any of us—management included—ask for less?

V. TRADITIONAL APPROACHES TO SATISFYING THE DRIVES

If these drives are in some loose sense "elemental," then the conflict between unions and managements comes not only over a division of spoils. That of course is always present. Wherever scarcity intrudes, more for some means less for others, and a contest is inevitable. In addition, however, conflict comes over method—the approaches which the parties (and here I shall speak principally of the unions) have adopted in trying to secure their objectives.

The method which unions have traditionally employed in pursuing the security objectives of their members has been to confine management authority within a framework of rules. The coverage of such rules varies from one agreement to the next, but they may relate to such matters as the filling of vacancies from within rather than through outside hiring; application of the seniority principle (that is, preference based on length of service) to layoffs, promotions, transfers among jobs or plants, work assignments, and shift preferences; provisions for an equal sharing of work rather than the total layoff of some workers, under specified circumstances; limitations on the freedom of management to subcontract particular operations; requirements as to the size of a work crew, the permissible pace of operations, the way in which certain tasks are to be performed; circumstances under which wage rates once established may be reviewed, or new wage rates may be challenged; a body of rules—usually developed through custom or precedent rather than by written agreement—as to disciplinary penalties—their cause, penalty, and review.

So extensive have such bodies of working rules become that they have been referred to as an "industrial jurisprudence."[2] They constitute an effort on the part of workers, through their unions, to envelop managerial discretion in a "web of rules" which provide economic security through a measure of certainty and control introduced into the industrial environment. They create a rule of law which in effect says that managerial discretion in specific types of situations must be limited in certain ways.

Perhaps the classic rationalization of this approach has been made by Professor Selig Perlman in his *Theory of the Labor Movement*.[3] In capsule form his argument runs about as follows.

In contrast to the businessman, the worker's outlook is typically one of a consciousness of scarcity. Good opportunities are few and competitors for them many. This situation of scarcity is one that the worker seeks not so much to change as to adjust to. Adjustment takes the form of rules such as have been noted above, within a shop or company or trade, for parcelling out the limited number of job opportunities, and apportioning the better jobs among the claimants. His objective and that of his fellow is some measure of control over the whole relevant collection of job opportunity so that they may administer it themselves, in ways that give a greater sense of security to themselves. This can be done through a union.

In effect, the manualists seek to assert a kind of proprietary control over the production process. In essence, they attempt to strike a bargain with their employer in terms which say, You pay us, as a group, an agreed-upon amount of money for an agreed-upon amount of work, and leave to us to decide who does what, how he does it, what his obligations are to the rest of the group, and how he should be disciplined for failing to live up to those obligations.

This scarcity-consciousness which expresses itself through attempted job control eschews any notion of overthrowing the economic or social system and substituting something else for it. For one thing, the manualist worker has no clear idea of any "system" which he might substitute for the one he knows and works under. He seeks only a sufficient degree of control—through organization—over the existing system to permit him to manage scarcity in ways which give him a sense of security.

A more recent student of trade union sociology and philosophy carries Perlman's argument a stage further. Whereas Perlman envisaged Western unions as compatible with Western capitalism, hence non-revolutionary in their orientation, Professor Frank Tannenbaum sees modern unions

---

[2] Sumner H. Slichter, *Union Policies and Industrial Management,* The Brookings Institution, Washington, D.C., 1941, p. 1.

[3] Selig Perlman, *A Theory of the Labor Movement,* new ed., Augustus M. Kelley, New York, 1949.

as having an impact on Western society which profoundly changes its character. He agrees as to the springs of worker motivation, but believes that the outcome of the worker's basic drives will be a reversion to the society of status which Sir Henry Maine once told us we had left behind in exchange for a society based on contract.[4] In Tannenbaum's words, "The search is always for greater security, the method is always increased power for setting up standards of economic life that will stabilize the job and, by implication, the economy. The effects have always been increasing limitation of freedom of action, and an increasing trend toward equality of income."

One of the long-run and unforeseen byproducts of the individual worker's attempt to achieve "economic security" is the gradual remolding of industrial society on the older order of "estates." The Industrial Revolution destroyed a social system in which each man had his place in a "society" and in which he could fulfill his role as a human being. . . . The industrialism that destroyed a society of status has now re-created it. The last one hundred and fifty years are a strange interlude in the history of man in the Western World, a period in which man was "freed" from one age-old association and, after a lapse, gradually reidentified with another one.[5]

In Tannenbaum's view, the belief that workers would subject themselves to the vagaries and uncertainties of a market economy was a delusion. The insecurity of such a system is intolerable. He sees two alternatives, and it remains a question as to which will win out. On the one hand, the state may move in to provide the security which the free market destroyed. If or when this happens, Tannenbaum envisages that it will lead to a destruction of all lesser authority and establish an authoritarian directorship for economy and society alike.

The alternative is the development and improvement of the trade-union approach. "If the workers do not succeed in making the industry and the union the vehicle for the provision of essential security, then the state will perform the task. . . . If the trade-union succeeds in doing it, it will re-create a society of status, where the rule of the larger community law may survive as a means of protecting the individual against paying too heavy a price for the security he is given by the union."[6]

I do not intend to suggest that Perlman's and Tannenbaum's views constitute the total spectrum of theories concerning the nature and effects of union efforts to assure their members economic and social security. I have alluded to these two in part because they are so widely

[4] Sir Henry Maine, *Ancient Law* (London, 1861; new edition with introduction by F. Pollock, London, 1930).
[5] Tannenbaum, *op. cit.*, pp. 142–143.
[6] *Ibid.*, pp. 150–151.

quoted in the literature, in part because the emphasis of the role of "rules" which runs through both their conceptions is also to be encountered not only in other interpretations of the labor movement but also in union tactics and strategy, and in part because they represent a point of view which I propose to challenge as obsolete.

The basic argument which I would like to put before you today is that dependence on a "web of rules" or a system of status to satisfy the security drives of workers in the contemporary world is a delusion. Both are inherently static concepts. They are premised on a world of slow and controlled change. They confuse security with stability, at a time when the latter is becoming more and more remote.

I do not want to carry my argument too far. Obviously at any time there must be some rules and some relationships of status, or there would be no basis for expecting particular responses and reactions from others. Some ability to predict how others will react to given situations and stimuli is essential in any society. When we speak of a society of laws in contrast to a society of arbitrary authority we posit our preference for some dependability of rules and status relationships. I have no dispute with this elemental dependence of men on rules of relationship. But I take it that those who argue that worker security is served by a system of regulations in the workplace and by a system of status relationships such as those based on seniority have something more in mind. They are looking to a more comprehensive economic code which spells out the rights and perquisites which workers are to enjoy in a system of advanced industrialization. And it is that which I will contend is not only unworkable but undesirable, not only false but foolish.

VI.   THE OMNIPRESENCE OF CHANGE

The managements of our large corporations, and other segments of our societies as well, have become geared to an *expectation* of change— change based on numerous factors such as shifting international power relations, rates of increase and composition of populations, resource availability and market locations, but above all else change based on technological advances, and beyond that on the increase of knowledge. The ingredients for rapid industrial change are built into the very fabric of our society by our increasing emphasis on education, and by the increasing number of highly trained individuals and specialized institutions whose sole preoccupation is with the creation of new knowledge. Knowledge, once loose, gets put to use. Sooner or later its byproduct is economic and industrial change, and along with change, job insecurity.

The more people we educate, the better their training, the more knowledge we create—this combination of *objectives* to which our Western societies are dedicated—the more certain and rapid will be the changes in our economies and industries, and the more frequent and sweeping their impact on job skills and professional expertise. If security in the sense of stability is what we are seeking, then we have made an enormous blunder. For the kind of society we have all been striving for—one which stresses education and research and advancement of knowledge—that kind of society is *inherently* the foe of stability.

The workers' search for security through the static approaches of an economic code, a system of rules and status, runs counter to management's imperative need to be able to cope with change. For a company to remain viable, it must be prepared to meet and deal with the new and the uncertain. It seeks to do this in a variety of ways. One is by increasing attention to research and its applications. To cope with changes initiated elsewhere in the economy, it must itself initiate change. This is the process which Schumpeter labelled "creative destruction" [7]—the effort by corporate managements to make obsolete their own products and processes by creating new and better ones—before a competitor succeeds in doing so and thereby lowers the value of corporate assets frozen into outdated forms.

Companies also seek to deal with change by improving their own planning and budgeting processes. The budget becomes the mold within which plans are set, assuring that resources are available for commitment when needed and in forms which have been adequately explored for future value. Projecting the company's activities as much as five or ten years into the future, the corporate planners do not then sit back and rely on hope or soundness of some prophetic vision to do the rest. As time passes, a data-and-analysis network feeds in information indicating where changes in plans may be needed, revealing where expectations are not materializing, suggesting where new measures may need to be taken to increase the likelihood of a favorable outcome. The continuity and flexibility of the modern corporate planning process distinguish it from the older, more time-segmented and phlegmatic programs which used to pass as business planning.

This new corporate emphasis on maneuverability is fundamentally incompatible with the union's emphasis on maintaining work practices, customs, and job rights. Moreover, the latter's static approach to security has at least two weaknesses, even from the point of view of the workers whom it represents. First, by conflicting with the company's ability to adapt promptly and effectively to change, it jeopardizes the profitability and even survival of the very institution on which the employees must rely for job and income security. Second, it is in part illusory. A union may be powerful enough to retain customary jobs and practices in the

[7] Joseph A. Schumpeter, *Capitalism, Socialism and Democracy,* Harper & Brothers, New York, 1942, Chap. 7.

present, but it is not powerful enough to retain them in the future, for there is nothing to prevent a company from closing down a whole plant or process, or suspending production of a product, as it shifts into new products, new markets, new processes in its continuing preoccupation with metamorphosizing its assets, in order to retain their value, transforming their shape and function and location with the passage of time.

There is here, then, an intensifying clash between labor's traditional approach to the security goals of its members, with the stress on security through protective rules and protected roles, and the developing corporate planning and budgeting processes, which attempt to achieve greater fluidity and flexibility in business operations by anticipating change and adapting as necessary. The collective bargaining process as now practiced is simply not as flexible as effective business planning requires. It is no accident that in recent years—in the United States, at least—management's major complaint against the union has been with respect to "work rules," while workers' major protest has been in the area of job insecurity. The objectives of each party collide with a process important to the other—flexibility confronting status and rules, and job security clashing with continuous planning.

VII.   NEW APPROACHES TO THE OLD GOALS

If traditional collective bargaining methods are inadequate in the modern economy, then we need new devices which satisfy business requirements, on the one hand, and the aspirations of workers, the households whom they represent, and the unions which represent them, on the other hand.

The principal specifications for such new procedures are apparent. If management wants flexibility in adapting to changes in its plans and variances in its budgets, it must give the union a chance to be heard on all the decisions affecting the interests of workers *on a continuing basis*. If management wishes to avoid the rigidities of "past practices" and custom, it has to accept a bargaining process which is as continuous as its own planning process. At the same time the union must recognize that a right of initiative must lie with management, or else the whole purpose of flexible planning is lost. If continuous bargaining means that management is prevented from acting until agreement has been reached with the union, then it stands in the way of that *prompt* adaptation to changed circumstances which is the objective of continuous planning.

Despite the equity of the logic, it is problematical whether many managements will accept continuous negotiation with their unions as a price they are willing to pay to earn the flexibility of action which they insist they need. Old forms of authority die hard. They are likely to look on such an approach as a further invasion of historical prerogatives rather than an adjustment in the structure of authority brought on by the processes of change which they seek to master.

The adaptation which would be required of unions might be no less difficult for them. In order to do something more than merely react to management's initiative, they would themselves have to develop some sense of new ways in which economic change can be *managed* to satisfy the security drives of their members. If they are to move *from* efforts to assure security through a body of rules or a code of rights, they must move *to* alternatives which make change work on behalf of their members, just as it now can be made to work on behalf of an alert management.

The most promising alternative would appear to lie in *anticipating* the effect of change on the skills and training of their members, and offering the latter, as an integral part of their employment, opportunities for a continuous upgrading of their abilities. The kind of educational programs which are needed are not those directed to specific jobs but to general skills. If modern industry values mathematical competence more highly than in the past, or an understanding of physical, electronic, or chemical relationships, or verbal facility, or competence in computer applications, or any of a number of other fields of skill and knowledge, then workers— if they are to assure their income, function, and status in *that kind* of a world—should be given opportunities to pursue such fields of study. And since learning, for most of us, is not play but work, the time for such activity should be considered part of the regular work day or work week and paid for at regular rates.

This approach to the relationship of the worker to his company and career has remarkable parallels to the planning and budgeting procedures which so many managements have adopted to assure their firm's future. Just as management is viewed as managing a bundle of assets, so too may the worker be viewed as managing a bundle of assets—not just figuratively but literally, assets which have a financial value to him. The worker's assets are his abilities and skills. Like a company's assets they must be metamorphosized into a new bundle of assets if their value is to be preserved and enhanced. This transformation and upgrading of the worker's assets must too take place continuingly, and *before* the value of current assets has been lost to the degree that they provide no basis on which future values can be rested.

As with corporate planning and budgeting, this requires programs which are specific as to the educational investment which is needed and the time when it should be made. Like management's approach to corporate survival, this approach to job security stresses future development rather than present position. The latter is viewed as temporary and subject to erosion by the forces of change. Only through continued effective upgrading of assets, both corporate and personal, can security be achieved.

Such an approach to the management of human assets by unions still awaits the kind of expression and refinement which managements have brought to the management of corporate assets in the last few decades. Not until unions catch up with the idea that change not only creates its problems but also offers its opportunities, which can be realized only by their proper management of the assets which are under their supervision, will they—and their members—be able to face the future with some assurance. The skill of their members is not only something which can lose its value, it is something whose value can be increased—with proper management. The rate of return on the assets of their members (that is to say, the qualifications which they bring to their jobs) can be improved more by upgrading the quality of those assets than by trying to extract a few pennies more an hour for unchanged assets which technological change is obsolescing ever more rapidly.[8]

It takes programs and planning to move in that direction. It takes a radical reorientation in the thinking of leadership and membership alike. Undeniably it is easier to proceed along familiar patterns, shutting one's eyes to the inevitable outcome or placing the blame on others. But until genuine career planning—for the future—substitutes for makeshift efforts to hang on to present job opportunities, the unions will continue resolutely to face the past. Their time stream will continue to flow in the wrong direction.

VIII.   CONCLUSION: A CHANGING UNION–MANAGEMENT RELATIONSHIP

This kind of forward planning cannot be realized by the unions alone. Even with a panoply of educational advisers it would be impossible for them to outguess management as to the future direction and needs of industry and commerce. And here is where the jointness of the problem returns, the need for a new configuration to the union-management relationship: Instead of a term contract, continuing joint consultation and planning in the field of manpower. Instead of a power struggle over rules and status, negotiation over the way in which anticipated changes can be made to open up new career opportunities. Instead of abbreviated training programs to adapt workers to other tasks after their old job has been lost, the continuing development of new skills along lines which give men more mastery over their environment.

To rebuild the union-management relationship along these lines will not be a simple matter. It will require a new sense of the time dimension of bargains, new conceptions of the way in which the security drives can

---

[8] I have developed these ideas further in "What's Ahead for Labor?" *The Atlantic Monthly,* July, 1964.

best be satisfied, fresh imagination in exploring training and educational programs, indeed, even a new image of our present culture.

If this last requirement sounds too sweeping, too academic, on first encounter, on continued reflection it may seem less apocalyptic. If the roots of our insecurity do indeed lie in the rapidity of change, and if change has its origin in new knowledge, then it is only by involving ourselves directly in the processes of change that we can keep in tune with our times.

It is this—keeping up with our times—and not the building of higher fences around existing rights and roles—which brings security in contemporary society. And for the average man—for the millions who are members of unions—there is only one place that can provide them the opportunity to stay abreast of changing times. That place is the workplace. As I have argued elsewhere,[9] it is time that we gave industry a new role, a role as educator. The corporation must become a college, making use of its own professional and technical personnel to provide continuing instruction to its workforce, so that they move with the times.

To be sure, few business firms may be able to muster a large enough staff of competent professional people so that (on a released time basis of perhaps half a day a week) they could meet the educational needs of all those in the workforce who chose to take advantage of the opportunity. But within the urbanized centers where the largest part of the labor force is located, business firms, as a group, could put together a very respectable curriculum of courses ranging from some dealing with simple arithmetic and verbal composition on up to advanced work in the physical sciences comparing favorably with what is taught in the universities.

Whether business managements would relish the notion of sponsoring courses open to employees of other firms, or whether they might fear that their own employees might become overtrained for their present jobs and be induced to look for superior employment elsewhere, are considerations that would have little practical significance. If they are unresponsive to the valid argument that the distribution of benefits between themselves and other employers is likely to be reciprocal, then it is up to the workers to "persuade" them to cooperate by the use of sanctions, including the strike. Bargaining power has been the traditional means of convincing managements that certain concessions are in order.

This is not to say that business firms may be financially able to bear the cost of such an educational program on their own. Some state subsidy may be needed—as it always has been needed for mass education programs. Obviously such a program is one which would call for effective cooperation among labor, management, and government, but the objective of that cooperation is one which is instinctively appealing to us all.

[9] In "The Corporation as a College," The Atlantic Monthly, June, 1965.

We have all been conditioned to the value of education—social value as well as private value, value to the employer as well as to the worker.

Or is that perhaps an excessively optimistic estimate of the situation? It is quite possible that many workers would face such a prospect with suspicion and even dread, especially those who have been away from the learning process for some time. But the transformation need not come overnight. We can still rely on protective rules to give some security to older employees, while emphasizing to younger workers the importance and promise of a lifetime of learning.

In a realistic sense a response to new educational opportunities requires decision and choice only on the part of *individuals*. The *social* decision has already been made. The evolution of our society is clearly in the direction of choosing for preferred positions and security of income, function, and status those who accept the heavier educational demands. Individuals who choose otherwise for themselves will simply drop behind in the evolutionary process.

For union leaders the challenge to conceive a new relationship with management and industry is of truly heroic proportions. It calls for the devising of practical programs which will simultaneously meet the needs of their own members and of business. It requires the strategic use of power to induce managerial acceptance of long-range manpower planning programs in which unions play a part. And—perhaps most importantly—it requires convincing their memberships of the desirability of embracing a course of action which promises future benefit rather than present gain.

the new technologies
and government

INTRODUCTION

HE massive transformations in modern society due to the new partnership of science, technology, and government are discussed here. The first selection is by Don K. Price, Harvard political scientist, with a wealth of practical experience as an adviser to Presidents Eisenhower, Kennedy, and Johnson. Professor Price argues that scientists are as indispensable to a modern government as the government is to them.

The second selection, written by Barbara Ward, the British economist, outlines in broad strokes the interrelationship of both economics and politics with new scientific and technological breakthroughs in the modern world. Just as Price argues that our scientific communities can no longer live in isolation from politics, so Miss Ward narrates the story of how industry and government have become partners, not only in the space industry and weapons manufacturing, but in many other important areas. By using the phrase "Spaceship Earth" as the title of the lecture series from which this selection is taken, she underscores the global character of every man's destiny in the modern world.

BIBLIOGRAPHY

Born, Max: *Physics and Politics*, Basic Books, Inc., Publishers, New York, 1962.

Committee on Science and Public Policy, *Federal Support of Basic Research in Institutions of Higher Learning*, National Academy of Sciences, 1964.

Hitch, Charles J., and Roland N. McKean: *The Economics of Defense in the Nuclear Age*, Harvard University Press, Cambridge, Mass., 1960.

Killian, James R., Jr.: "Research and Development in a Dynamic Economy," in *Proceedings of a Conference on Research and Development and Its Impact on the Economy*, National Science Foundation, Washington, 1958.

Myrdal, Gunnar: *Beyond the Welfare State*, Yale University Press, New Haven, Conn., 1960. (See Part II, especially chap. 13, "Towards a New World Strategy.")

Neustadt, Richard E.: *Presidential Power*, John Wiley & Sons, Inc., New York, 1960.

Nieburg, Harold L.: *In the Name of Science*, Quadrangle, Chicago, Ill., 1966.

Orlans, Harold: *Contracting for Atoms*, The Brookings Institution, Washington, D.C., 1967.

Peck, Merton J., and Frederick M. Scherer: *The Weapons Acquisition Process: An Economic Analysis*, Harvard Business School, Boston, 1962.

President's Science Advisory Committee: *Scientific Progress, the Universities and the Federal Government*, Washington, 1960.

Rabinowitch, Eugene: "The Scientific Revolution," *Bulletin of the Atomic Scientists*, October–December, 1963.

Report by Science Policy Research Division of Library of Congress (Edward Wenk, Jr., division chief) for the Military Operations Subcommittee (Chet Holifield, chairman), House of Representatives, Washington, D.C., 1967.

Science, published by the American Association for the Advancement of Science, frequently has editorials and comments on the relation of government to scientific research and the universities.

Simon, Herbert A.: *The New Science of Management Decision*, Harper & Row, Publishers, Incorporated, 1960.

Solo, Robert A.: "Gearing Military R & D to Economic Growth," *Harvard Business Review*, November–December, 1962.

Wiesner, Jerome B.: "Statement of Dr. Jerome B. Wiesner, Director, Office of Science and Technology, before the subcommittee on Science, Research and Development; House Committee on Science and Astronautics," Washington, D.C., October 16, 1963.

1. SCIENCE, THE NEW TECHNOLOGIES, AND GOVERNMENT

From Don K. Price, The Scientific Estate, The Belknap Press, Harvard University Press, Cambridge, Mass., 1965, pp. 15–20, 35–39, 274–278.

The scientific revolution in nuclear physics and in such fields as genetics . . . seems certain to have a more radical effect on our political institutions than did the industrial revolution, for a good many reasons. Let us note three of them.

1. *The scientific revolution is moving the public and private sectors closer together.*

During the industrial revolution, the most dynamic economic interests were more or less independent of the political system. They might depend on it, as many American corporations did by relying on tariff protection, and they might try with some success to control it, but they were not incorporated into its administrative system, they did not receive support from taxation, and the main directions of their new enterprise were controlled by their owners and managers. Today, our national policy assumes that a great deal of our new enterprise is likely to follow from technological developments financed by the government and directed in response to government policy; and many of our most dynamic industries are largely or entirely dependent on doing business with the government through a subordinate relationship that has little resemblance to the traditional market economy.

2. *The scientific revolution is bringing a new order of complexity into the administration of public affairs.*

The industrial revolution brought its complexities, and relied heavily on new forms of expertise, but it did not challenge the assumption that the owner or manager, even without scientific knowledge, was able to control the policies of a business. And the same general belief was fundamental to our governmental system: the key ideas, if not the lesser details, could be understood by the legislature and debated before the public, and thus controlled by a chain of public responsibility. In one sense this was never true; in another and more fundamental sense, I think it is still true. But it is much less apparently true today than it was, and a great many more people doubt it. The great issues of life and death, many people fear, are now so technically abstruse that they must be decided in secret by the few who have the ability to understand their scientific complexities. We were already worrying about the alleged predominance of the executive over the legislature; now we worry lest even our elected executives cannot really understand what they are doing, lest they are only a façade that conceals the power of the scientists—many of whom are not even full-time officials, but have a primary loyalty to some university or corporation—who really control the decisions. If (as I believe) this is not really true, it is nevertheless true that the scientific revolution has upset our popular ideas about the way in which policies are initiated and adopted, and in which politicians can control them and be held responsible for them. We have to reconsider our basic ideas about the processes of political responsibility.

3. *The scientific revolution is upsetting our system of checks and balances.*

From a moral or ethical point of view, the industrial revolution raised

problems that were relatively simple. Everyone admitted that it was possible for economic interests to control politics, but the remedy seemed to
be clear: regulate business to prevent abuses, and keep selfish business
interests out of the political process. This seemed clearly the basic formula for dealing with the obvious conflict of the public interest with the
special interests of business. And the formula of separation of business
and government was analogous in a comforting way to the formula for the
separation of church and state. A church that was not dependent on
government support was able to provide an independent source of moral
judgment which could help to control the ethical standards of our politics
and our business. As the problems began to seem a bit complex for
unaided theological opinion, the universities began to provide an additional source of more scientific, but equally independent, advice to the
public on the basic value judgments that should govern our policies. This
was the fundamental system of checks and balances within our society:
the check on practical political affairs imposed by sources of utterly independent criticism, based on a system of values that was not corrupted
by the political competition for wealth or power.

But the scientific revolution seems to threaten to destroy this safeguard in two ways: First, it has gradually weakened the moral authority
of religious institutions by the critical skepticism that it has made predominant in Western intellectual life, most notably in the universities.
Second, it has made the universities themselves financially dependent on
government, and involved them deeply in the political process. Thus,
after helping to disestablish churches and free most universities from
ecclesiastical control, science has now made those universities dependent on a new form of establishment, in the guise of government grants,
and allied them more closely with a military power that is capable of
unlimited destruction.

These three developments make some of our traditional reactions—
our automatic political reflexes—unreliable in dealing with our present
problems. We are automatically against socialism, but we do not know
how to deal with an extension of governmental power over the economy
that technically leaves ownership in private hands. It is almost an instinct
with us to distrust the political bosses who, by controlling the votes of
the ignorant masses, seek personal profit or power without accepting
official responsibility. But we do not know how to deal with irresponsible
influence that comes from status in the highest sanhedrin of science,
untainted by any desire for personal profit. And we are fanatically against
the public support of any institutions that might impose religious values
on public policy, but when the institutions of organized skepticism tell
us what science believes or how much money science needs, we have no

reliable procedure for questioning their infallibility, or even for criticizing their budgets.

Science has thus given our political evolution a reverse twist. It has brought us back to a set of political problems that we thought we had disposed of forever by simple Constitutional principles. These are the problems of dealing not only with territorial subdivisions of government, and not only with economic interests and classes, but also with various groups of citizens which are separated from each other by very different types of education and ways of thinking and sets of ideals. This was the problem of the medieval estates.

The three estates of the realm, whose customary privileges grew into constitutional functions, were the clergy, the nobility, and the burgesses —those who taught, those who fought, and those who bought and sold. In our impatience with privilege at the time of the American Revolution, we abolished the estates in our political system so thoroughly that we have almost forgotten what the word meant. To abolish the first estate, we disestablished the church and provided secular education through local governments. To abolish the second, we forbade titles of nobility, made the military subordinate to civil authority, and relied on a popular militia rather than a standing army. To abolish the third, we did away with property qualifications on voting and exalted freedom of contract and competition above legislative interference.

But now the results of scientific advance have been to require federal support of education and the appropriation of a tithe of the federal budget for research and development, to set up the most powerful and professional military force in history, and to make free competition a minor factor in the relationship to government of some of the major segments of the economy.

Thus we are left to face the second half of the problem which we were afraid to face during the depression, and tried to escape at the end of the Second World War: the necessity for discovering a new basis for relating our science to our political purposes. We learned half of our lesson from the scientists: the lesson that we could not have a first-rate scientific establishment if we did not understand that first-rate science depended on fundamental theoretical work and required the support of basic research for its own sake, and not merely as a by-product of applied science. Now the outlines of the second, or political, half of our problem are becoming more clear. Basic science as such became steadily more powerful as it freed itself from the constraints of values and purposes. As an institution in society, it had to free itself in an analogous way from subordination to the applied purposes of the industrial corporation or the government bureau or the military service. And in the unpredictability of its progress it challenges the old notion that in matters of public policy the scientist must be controlled completely by purposes defined by politicians. So we must face the possibility that science will no longer serve as a docile instrument toward purposes that are implicit in a system of automatic economic progress, or even toward purposes that are defined for scientists by business and political leaders. In short, we can no longer take it for granted that scientists will be "on tap but not on top."

Accordingly, we need to consider not only the practical relation of scientific institutions to the economy and the government, but also the theoretical relation of science to political values, and to the principles that are the foundation of the constitutional system. Only with the help of scientists can we deal with the great issues of war and peace, of the population explosion and its effects in the underdeveloped countries, or of the dangers to our environment from our technological advances not only in weaponry but also in civilian industry and agriculture. But before we are likely, as a nation, to let science help us solve such problems, we are sure to want to know the full terms of the bargain. For although some of the political reflexes that we have acquired by several centuries of constitutional experience may be out of date, one of the most automatic is still useful: we want to know not only whether some political pronouncement is true, but why the speaker said it, having a healthy suspicion that we need to know whose interests it would further, and what its effect would be on our capacity to govern ourselves, or at least to hold our governors responsible.

The scientific community in the United States is not an organized institution, or a group with definite boundaries. It is not a hierarchical establishment. But its existence as a loosely defined estate with a special function in our constitutional system is becoming apparent, and we would do well to assess its political significance.[1] If we do, we may find that a deeper understanding of the basic relation of science to government will help us to give it the kind of support it needs for its own purposes, as well as use it more effectively for the practical ends of public policy. And if we are willing to renounce the utopian hope that science will solve our problems for us, we may find that science by its very nature is more congenial to the development of free political institutions than our anti-utopian prophets would have us believe.

THE FUSION OF ECONOMIC AND POLITICAL POWER

And here, of course, is where government comes in. The federal government, by 1963, was paying for nearly three fifths of the more than twelve billion dollars spent annually for industry for research and development. The amount spent by industry for research and development out of its own funds doubled between 1953 and 1960, but the amount of research and development it actually conducted nearly tripled, for during these eight years industry's use of federal funds for these purposes went up more than fourfold. Industry, in short, was during the Eisenhower administration accelerating its reliance on federal research funds, and the process slowed down only a little during the Kennedy administration.[2]

Some impression of the magnitude of the expense involved may be given by the testimony in 1962 of the Defense Department comptroller, Charles J. Hitch, who told the House Committee on Government Operations that there were then under development seventeen weapons systems big enough to cost over a billion dollars.[3] All this would have very little effect on the internal structure and operations of business if these government funds were purchasing items that could be specified in advance, like shoes or rifles. But the key point here is uncertainty, requiring continual collaboration between the government officials and the corporate executives.

Very few complex systems are ultimately developed along the lines laid down at the beginning; for example, more than half the aircraft developed since the Second World War were finally built with engines quite different from those originally planned for them.[4] Some idea of the extent of uncertainty was suggested in the same testimony by Mr. Hitch, who remarked that "about 40 percent of our total development appropriations are going into the funding of cost overruns," [5] that is, into expenditures beyond the amount originally planned. About 60 percent of the contracts, in any case, are not fixed-price contracts, since neither the government nor the corporation can even pretend in legal form that it knows just what is to be done and what it should cost, and formally advertised competitive bidding has become the exception rather than the rule.[6] The very uncertainty of the research and development process requires the government and business to work out a joint arrangement for the planning and conduct of their programs; the relationship is more like the administrative relationship between an industrial corporation and its subsidiary than the traditional relationship of buyer and seller in a free market.

Although this system is a part of a much older stream of political and constitutional development . . . , its immediate origins were in the weapons research programs of the Second World War. In the Office of Scientific Research and Development, and in the atomic energy program that grew out of that office and was carried through by the Manhattan District of the Army Engineers, the basic operating system was one of enlisting industrial corporations and universities in the war effort under contractual arrangements, rather than setting up a centralized system of military laboratories.

The outlines of the postwar development, which in the main continued the wartime pattern, are well known. Through a continuation of this system of administering research and development programs by grant or contract, the Atomic Energy Commission, which was hailed by the draftsmen of the Atomic Energy Act as a triumph of socialism,[7] supports a program in which some nine tenths of the employees work for private corporations. The adamant arguments of many scientific leaders of the 1930's against federal support of science now seem as ancient and irrelevant as debates over infralapsarianism or supralapsarianism; no major university today could carry on its research program without federal money.[8] The Massachusetts Institute of Technology, California Institute of Technology, Chicago, and Johns Hopkins, of course, all administer special military or atomic energy programs and consequently draw from three fifths to five sixths of their budgets from government. Harvard, Yale, and Princeton now get a larger proportion of their operating revenues from federal funds than do land-grant colleges like Illinois, Iowa State, and North Carolina.[9]

In dollar volume, the biggest contracts are between the military services and industrial corporations. Though most of this money goes for procurement, much of it goes for research and development, and for the systems analysis and the direction and supervision of subcontractors that in a simpler age would have been done by the technical services of the Army and Navy. And even in the business of procurement, the contractual relation is not the traditional market affair: the contract is not let on competitive bids, the product cannot be specified, the price is not fixed, the government supplies much of the plant and capital, and the government may determine or approve the letting of subcontracts, the salaries of key executives, and a host of other managerial matters. A sizable proportion of the government's (and nation's) business is done this way; each of five industrial corporations spends more than a billion dollars a year from federal taxes—which is more than any one of five of the executive departments.[10]

In the industries in which this process has gone furthest, such as aircraft and electronics, the result is a striking change in the internal composition of their production systems. As the Bureau of the Budget pointed out in "Government Contracting for Research and Development," a study made for the President in 1962, the older industries were organized on mass production principles and used large numbers of production workers, but "the newer ones show roughly a one-to-one ratio between production workers and scientist-engineers." Between 1954 and 1959, the number of scientists and engineers in the aircraft industry went up by 96 percent while the number of production workers went down by 17 percent. This is the industry in which the corporation least dependent on government business had less than a third of its sales to nonmilitary buyers, and the Martin Company had less than one percent.[11]

These developments led the Bureau of the Budget to ask in the same report, "In what sense is a business corporation doing nearly 100 percent of its business with the Government engaged in 'free enterprise'?" and to note that "the developments of recent years have inevitably blurred the traditional dividing lines between the public and private sectors of our Nation." The House Committee on Government Operations, after a general review of the relation of the federal government with its contractors, had decided a year before that "if we look at the nature of the function, there are no clearcut criteria for determining what should be done by Government personnel and what by outsiders under contract." [12] The study by the Budget Bureau in effect replied by recommending useful general criteria, but they were certainly not the clear-cut rules that we once would have expected to distinguish the public from the private sector of the economy.

This rapid mixture of government and business interests depended, of course, on the realization of what had happened as a result of the advances in the sciences, their marriage with engineering, and the consequent acceleration of technological change. At the same time its immediate political motivation was obviously a military one. One of the basic reasons for the blurring of the boundaries between business and government was the earlier blurring of the boundaries among the sciences, and between the sciences and engineering; but the more urgent reason was the need to advance weapons technology in the interest of national defense.

But this reason, too, was a result of the changes in the sciences. For science, by making possible hydrogen weapons and intercontinental missiles, had made obsolete the old habit of relying for defense on an industrial mobilization after the outbreak of a war. Another boundary was blurred: the boundary between war and peace. So we had to turn not merely to a state of constant armament and psychological warfare, but to a process of looking a decade ahead with respect to the production of the scientists who were to carry on the basic research that would serve as the technological basis for future weapons systems. Industry was no longer to be mobilized by government only in time of a hot war and then demobilized as quickly as possible. The mobilization had to be a permanent arrangement. It had to be organized and professionally staffed. It required the continuous managerial supervision by government of a large segment of private industry and the continuous subsidy by government of the higher education of scientists and others. . . .

SCIENCE AND FREEDOM

Politically, science has a profound influence on the way we all think about ends and values, and the political system has to accommodate itself to that fact. This has nothing to do with the abstract question whether science can provide any knowledge of ultimate purpose or of ideal values. Some would say that only theology and philosophy and the arts afford such knowledge, and that science never can. Others would say that ultimate purpose and ideal values are concepts without real (that is, scientific) meaning, being at worst mere rationalizations of irrational preferences, and at best mere verbal statements of propositions which for the time being science has not yet reduced to systematic knowledge. But this dispute can be ignored in dealing with the political problem; in politics, ends and values are those purposes and policy judgments on the basis of which politicians in a free system have to be responsible to the electorate. And obviously science has a profound effect on the ways in which a political system makes its most important choices.

Science supplies much of the great body of factual knowledge that men must agree on (at least they must agree on most of it) if their arguments about the choices that are open to them are to be conducted on some rational and orderly basis. It sweeps away superstitions that paralyze political responsibility. It opens up new opportunities and new possibilities for cooperation, and thus makes the concept of a public interest more meaningful, though at the same time more complicated and difficult to define. Accordingly, it is impossible to expect either science or scientists not to be deeply involved in the major issues that confront a modern government.

So science cannot either solve our policy problems for us or stand aside from them. And that is why the scientific community and the politicians need to develop the clearest possible idea of the working rules that govern their relationship. But it is not easy to define the ways in which scientists should be given support by government and permitted to exercise their initiative or influence in policy issues of interest to government.

Disestablishment is obviously no longer an acceptable formula. In other times the government of the United States left the support of education and research, except in fields related directly to governmental programs, to state and local governments and private philanthropy. But it now considers the direct support of fundamental science a primary national purpose. And the change is a profound one in ways that are more important than the appropriation of funds; politicians now recognize that their decisions depend on scientific considerations, and that their established policies may be upset by new scientific discoveries. They stand in some awe of the scientists. It seems we have come a long way from the Jacksonian belief that the duties of government are so simple that they can be discharged by any ordinary citizen.

Yet in a way we remain as overconfident as ever of the competence of our fellow citizens. If science is involved in policy, then we expect science to solve our problems for us. And so we look to elected politicians to base their decisions directly on the advice of pure scientists, or even less plausibly we think that scientists as such should be given positions of political authority.

It is very hard for Americans to admit that practically all policies are based on a mixture of ideas that only scientists can understand with other ideas that most of them do not bother to—such as considerations of cost, administrative effectiveness, political feasibility, and competition with other policies. As a result, policy questions cannot either be solved like an equation or disposed of by a statute. On the contrary, political authorities can deal with them only within the context of a politically responsible organization. They do so partly by coming to understand the facts themselves, but mainly by granting their support and confidence to an appropriate balance of scientific, professional, and administrative talents within the public service. The United States finds it hard to adjust itself to the idea that it must now seek to maintain effective control over the experts not by the tactics of pure individualism, and not by breaking up the power of established institutions and professional corps within the government, but by maintaining a proper balance among competing estates.

It should be possible for political leaders to encourage the initiative of scientists in matters of policy, and at the same time to distinguish between their precise scientific knowledge and their political prejudices. (And if the politicians cannot tell the difference themselves, the scientists' colleagues and rivals will help them do so.) Nevertheless, politicians are obliged to be on their guard in such matters. For whether or not most scientists wish it, laymen are likely to push scientists into the position of prophets. A sophisticated generation that has given up much of its faith in traditional religion may be beginning to worship science mainly for the magical benefits that it can provide through technology. As a result, the established institutions of science are now under as much temptation to resort to casuistry as any ecclesiastic: to what extent are they to advocate the appropriation of billions to support particular programs of technological magic in order to dazzle the vulgar voter into letting them have millions for the advancement of scientific truth?

As a practical matter of institutional politics, science is no longer seriously threatened by the rivalry of the magic of religion; its own technological magic is what it has to worry about. The advancement of basic science will doubtless get still larger appropriations as a result of the emphasis on the purposes of military or nuclear or space technology or the demand for new wonder drugs. But it may also suffer considerable distortions in the directions of its development and in the distribution of its best talents, and its leaders are fearful of threats to the autonomy of its institutions. For this reason, the selection of men concerned with basic research as advisers to the President is an appropriate one. It is not at the level of the Presidency that a combination of secret bureaucracy and technology is likely to dominate the policies of the United States in irresponsible and inhumane directions. The Presidency is too open to public scrutiny, and too effectively checked by a variety of bureaucratic interests and Congressional committees, and too sensitive to its quadrennial accountability to the nation as a whole, to become committed to highly specialized technical purposes. The threat of technocracy is more likely to come through an alliance between particular Congressional committees and the professional interests within a particular agency or department. For though the committees of Congress have been multiplying the procedures by which they can hold the executive branch accountable, no one has yet found ways by which the committees themselves can be regularly called to account by the Congress.

Five successive Presidents, from Roosevelt to Johnson, brought to their Executive Office science advisers drawn mainly from basic research and academic institutions. The main reason why the President has turned to the scientific rather than the professional estate for his advisers is probably that the basic scientists, on issues that do not affect their own types of establishment, are relatively able to give objective advice. On the issues of political action, entailing the largest expenditures, they tend to be somewhat less committed to particular ways of thinking, and particular projects and policies, than are the industrial engineers and the physicians in private practice—less committed, and less subject to charges of conflict of interest. With their help, and with an understanding of the limitations on the contribution that they can make to issues of policy, a political leader has a better chance to maintain responsible control over the technological programs of government and to prevent his subordinates from presenting him with recommendations to which he can find no practicable alternative.

The establishment of science (and other forms of learning) in free universities and professional societies, governed on principles quite different from those of politics, has provided an essential counterbalance in the American constitutional system to the democratic competition for political power. It has provided the answer to those who feared, after the abolition of aristocracy and an established church, that democracy could never foster the arts or the theoretical sciences, and would steadily decline in intellectual energy and in the freedom and initiative of its independent institutions. At the same time, science has turned loose technological forces in society which we have not yet learned to control in a responsible manner, and it shows little promise of discovering a new system of absolute values by which to judge them.

In view of the way in which science seems to condemn us to live in a world of rapid social change, we may have to get used to a constitutional system that does not operate according to absolute rules or fixed procedures, but one that adjusts itself to meet new conditions in a world that we do not expect to become perfect in the predictable future. Perhaps indeed a nation can be free only if it is not in too great a hurry to become perfect. It can then defend its freedom by keeping the institutions established for the discovery of truth and those for the exercise of political power independent of each other. But independence should not mean isolation. Only if a nation can induce scientists to play an active role in government, and politicians to take a sympathetic interest in science (or at least in scientific institutions) can it enlarge its range of positive freedom, and renew its confidence that science can contribute progressively to the welfare of mankind.

NOTES

1. Jacques Maritain, Miguel de Unamuno, and Jose Ortega y Gasset represent the conservative critics of the Enlightenment; J. D. Bernal may be taken as a sample on the socialist side. Judith N. Shklar, whose *After Utopia: The Decline of Political Faith* (Princeton, N.J.: Princeton University Press, 1957) begins with the observation that "nothing is quite so dead today as the spirit of optimism that the very word Enlightenment evokes," goes on (p. 3) to admit that "the less reflective public, certainly until 1914, remained cheerfully indifferent to the intellectual currents of despair." In this optimistic category I would include many American scientists, and bring the date up to the present.

2. "Government Contracting for Research and Development," a report to the President by the director, Bureau of the Budget, April 30, 1962, Annex 4 (mimeo.), reprinted in *Systems Development and Management,* Hearings before a Subcommittee of the Committee on Government Operations, House of Representatives, 87th Cong., 2d Sess., 1962, Part 1, Appendix I. See also National Science Foundation, *Reviews of Data on Science Resources,* December 1964, p. 5.

3. Charles J. Hitch in *Systems Development and Management,* just cited, Part 2, pp. 539–540. These were "items, in some phase of development" which might involve "development and investment costs in excess of $1 billion."

4. A. W. Marshall and W. H. Meckling, *Predictability of the Costs, Time and Success of Development,* RAND Corporation, Santa Monica, Calif., 1959.

5. Hitch, p. 543.

6. Committee on Appropriations, U.S. House of Representatives, Department of Defense Appropriations Bill, 1962, Report No. 574, 87th Cong., 1st Sess., pp. 40–41.

7. "The field of atomic energy is made an island of socialism in the midst of a free enterprise economy." James R. Newman and Byron S. Miller, *The Control of Atomic Energy* (New York: Whittlesey House, 1948), p. 4. Mr. Newman, writing a preface to this book a year after the text was completed, noted that "only one major policy formulation, the decision by the Atomic Energy Commission not to conduct research in its own laboratories, departs sharply from the interpretations of the Act set forth in these pages" (p. xi).

8. The universities do almost half of the basic research in the United States, and their influence within the scientific estate is much larger than that figure

suggests. Of the $695,000,000 that they spent in 1961–62 on basic research, $442,000,000 came from Congressional appropriations; $73,000,000 came from industry and foundations, mostly in short-term gifts; and a substantial proportion of the remainder was spent by state universities from state appropriations. Price, p. 178.

9. The comparison is made on the basis of financial reports for the 1960–61 academic year.

10. By tax dollars, this statement refers to the so-called "administrative budget funds," which do not include trust funds and certain revolving funds. For a general discussion of this problem from the legal point of view, see Arthur S. Miller, "Administration by Contract: A new Concern for the Administrative Lawyer," *New York University Law Review*, vol. 36 (1961), pp. 957–990. The economic aspects are discussed in a study by Carl Kaysen, "Improving the Efficiency of Military Research and Development," *Public Policy XII*, the 1963 yearbook of the Graduate School of Public Administration, Harvard University. The general problems of weapons development and procurement programs are discussed in a study published by the Harvard Business School: Merton J. Peck and Frederic M. Scherer, *The Weapons Acquisition Process: An Economic Analysis*, 1962.

11. "Government Contracting for Research and Development" (note 2, above). In *Systems Development and Management*, see Appendix I, pp. 204–209.

12. U.S. House of Representatives, Third Report by the Committee on Government Operations, "Air Force Ballistic Missile Management," House Report No. 324, 87th Cong., 1st Sess., May 1, 1961, p. 50.

2. POLITICS, ECONOMICS, AND THE NEW TECHNOLOGIES

From Barbara Ward, Spaceship Earth, *Columbia University Press, New York, 1966, pp. 1–15.*

In our world today, all the irresistible forces of technological and scientific change are creating a single, vulnerable, human community. Yet three great disproportions—of power, of wealth, of ideology—stand in our way when we try to devise functioning worldwide institutions to civilize the vast energies of change. Until we overcome these obstacles, we are likely to be left with the energies in their raw, irrational state. And this spells disaster.

In a world that is being driven onward at apocalyptic speed by science and technology, we cannot, we must not, give up the idea that human beings can control their political and economic policies. They must have some sense of where they are trying to go, of what they are trying to do, of what the world may look like twenty years from now. It is surely inconceivable that we should turn the whole human experiment over to forces of change which we can neither master nor even fully understand. If one thing is true about the world we live in, it is that these forces are now in such spate that the physical background of our world twenty years hence will be almost completely different from what we see today. Unless, as a human society, we have some sense of direction, blind chance will take over while we shall be reduced to mounting not on our horses but on our rockets and blowing off in every direction. Such submission to chance or fate or accident neither guarantees us the best of our extraordinary and growing resources nor offers us the faintest hope of future stability. A man can go safely to sleep fishing in the middle of a quiet lake. But if he is out in the rapids, he had better reach for a paddle. If we have no sense of direction, then we shall have no sense of mastery, and if we have no sense of mastery, I doubt very much whether we shall be able to survive the enormous forces of change that sweep down upon us.

There is no need to describe in any great detail what these forces are or the degree to which the process of change is accelerating. Technology and science have become the common mode of human living and are invading every human institution and activity. The total effect is to submit the human race to a transformation more startling and complete than anything that has ever happened to it before. For any process comparable in scope and scale, we would have to go back nine or ten millennia to the invention of settled agriculture. When people stopped collecting berries and hunting for fish and meat and skins and moved on to the settled and sedentary organization of farming—tilling, sowing, weeding, and harvesting—they changed much more than their methods of work. They had to study the cycle of the seasons and begin to grasp the interactions of nature and man's activities. Care, knowledge, control, understanding lessened chance and laid the first foundations of civilization. The process lasted thousands of years and it took millennia more to work out all the potentialities of such splendid, archaic civilizations as those of Babylon or Egypt, of the Indus or the Yellow River. Change in those days was rather like the slow, steady, rising inundations of the Nile—in Andrew Marvell's words: "Vaster than empires, and more slow."

But today, suddenly, the experience of the human race is much more like that of being put in a barrel and sent over Niagara Falls. It is not simply that change is infinitely more drastic and affects everything we do. It is also occurring at a speed which is geared to none of the old speeds —of years, seasons, lifetimes, generations. Now it is hardly even geared to the flash of human intelligence. It is computer speed, accomplishing the 500-year work of 500 scientists in five minutes.

This accelerating process will, I believe, be checked by no traditional attitudes or institutions since its methods, quite apart from its aims, are essentially revolutionary. We cannot study, analyze, check, and compare without modifying the object of our studies.

Take the most primitive people we can choose—say, the bushmen of the Kalahari Desert. In one sense they are not primitive—if primitive means ignorant. By becoming the most extraordinary observers of natural things, they know more about the behavior of plant and animal than, perhaps, the most trained modern zoologist. But if we go to the bushmen

these days, what do we find? We find anthropologists and zoolgists studying them. So, inevitably, their way of life is on the way out. Even if a tribe
is primitive now, it is probably being studied to a pitch that stops it being
primitive in short order. The older people become self-conscious; the
younger ones want to train as anthropologists. There is thus a unique
pervasiveness about our new habits of scientific and technological
thought and practice which no one can evade. Cultures and societies,
like watches, are rarely the same when they have been taken to pieces.
This, essentially, is what our new methods of analysis and comparison
entail. Quite apart from common tools and methods, we also have mental
attitudes that do not vary from culture to culture and are common to a
single world civilization.

This is only one example among many of our underlying trend towards
unity. I need not underline the conquest of space. Whatever the delays,
we shall have supersonic planes and I—alas—will probably fly in one,
reaching London from New York before breakfast, having left after breakfast. Total, worldwide, communication is also nearly a fact. With Early
Bird we are almost a world society of village gossips. In 1963—if I may
be allowed a brief illustration—my husband was on one of his journeys
for the United Nations Special Fund. He went, as I recall it, to India,
Malaysia, Ethiopia, Liberia, and Ghana. When he reached home, I said:
"Lovely to see you, dear. Tell me about it. How is development getting
along? What are they talking about?" His reply was: "Christine Keeler."
There you have the village gossip.

But the issue is much more serious. This extension of all our senses
by electronic means of communication creates a world awareness of what
is going on in our planetary society, and this is bound to become a new
factor in the pressures at work in world politics. I very much doubt
whether, even five years ago, the scale of the world's grief at the death of
Pope John and the world's shocked horror at the death of President
Kennedy would have been even conceivable. The new means of instant
communication did, in a strange way, give people the feeling that they
were taking personal part in a tragic, worldwide wake.

I was in Northern Rhodesia when the news of the appalling tragedy in
Dallas came through, and there Kenneth Kaunda, who is now president of
this new country, was about to address a large political meeting. When
the news reached him, he broke off the proceedings to lead his large
African audience in a prayer and a hymn. Within hours, it was possible
for remote cities—Accra, Lagos, Monrovia—to watch the raw grief and
stunned shock of the American people. Within days, millions followed
"the captains and the kings" along the funeral route. We do not yet know
the full consequences of this instantaneous transmission of human emo-
tions, reactions, and needs across all the physical barriers of our planet.

But we know enough to guess that it will enormously strengthen the sense of nearness and human proximity—not always for good, for who loves all his neighbors?—but always for awareness, and always for attention, for influence, and concern.

Now let me take another factor of unity—the underlying resemblances of the modern economic system. I am not talking about the interconnections of markets and trade and investment on a worldwide scale. We will turn to them later. Here I would like to pick up something more profound—the degree to which certain necessities in the whole process of modernization tend to produce similar structures and policies all round the world—and to do so without any regard to differing political and social philosophies.

The transformation of man's productive system by capital and technology began in the West at the end of the eighteenth century within the framework of private property and the competitive market. But after a hundred years or so, the private element has been supplemented by a whole range of governmental powers. No one planned this development. As we shall see, it has been almost a byproduct of a single, overwhelming, human activity—war. But the fact that it has been the consequence of practice, not of dogma, shows the degree to which it is a reflection not so much of human foresight as of technological necessity.

At the outset of the modern economy—in Britain—a number of separate entrepreneurs worked for profit and, by reinvesting the profit, created the capital they needed for further advance. But most early economists were not too optimistic about the continued development and expansion of this new system. They feared that as resources were used up and became scarcer and as the available labor supply was absorbed, thus pushing up wages, the entrepreneur's essential profits would be squeezed out and he would therefore cease to invest. If he did so, the whole dynamic expansion of the system would come to an end since the only people capable of making expansive decisions would have ceased to make them. Nor did there seem to be alternative centers of decision-making. Economists either did not believe in the competence of government to pursue effective policies after the incompetence and corruption of state-run mercantilism, or—with Marx—they thought the state simply reflected business interests and would not intervene on ideological grounds. This underlying pessimism is one reason why, in the early nineteenth century, economics was named "the dismal science."

Yet in spite of temporary, though regular, crises of stagnation—the down-turns of the trade cycle—and in spite of a depression of catastrophic proportions in the 1930s, the prophets of doom have been disproved by the behavior of the market economy. They reckoned without the impact of man's oldest and least reputable occupation—war. War did two things. It accelerated tremendously the speed and range of inventions and hence the productivity of the new technology. Think of the impact of naval warfare on the elaboration of the lighter metals needed to make weapons that ships could carry without sinking. Think of the expansion of grain production with a reduced labor force in two world wars. Think of tanks into tractors. Think of the forced-draft development of the car, the aircraft, the rocket, under the insistent demands of war. Think, above all, of nuclear energy. All these tremendous breakthroughs were speeded up a thousand times by the frantic search for victory.

The second modification introduced by war was the realization that private consumption and production to satisfy it are not the only sources of effective demand. Government also has a part to play. Government orders and government expenditure did, of course, play some part in the traditional Western economy. But the assumption, broadly speaking, was that government would secure its own purchasing power—through taxation—out of the wealth already created by the private economy. There was little belief that the government might, by its own direct intervention, take decisions which expanded the whole base of the economy and thus added to the total sum of wealth available to the community. The pioneering British had little confidence in government. Their economy had emerged from a period of clumsy governmental interventions and inefficient governmental monopolies, and early economists wanted only to free the market from the dead hand of Whitehall and the "Circumlocution Office."

Yet throughout the nineteenth century, as the scale and mechanization of war increased, government orders in time of war hastened the expansion of heavy industry. In World War I, such developments as the setting up of the Ministry of Munitions in Britain was a revelation of how to speed up heavy industrial growth. In World War II, the United States doubled its industrial capacity between 1940 and 1944, adding in four short years the equivalent growth of over a century. Such massive interventions, creating wholly new levels of capacity and output, were not financed only by withdrawing wealth, via taxation, from the existing private economy. In most ways, they were simply additions. They built, at the cost, admittedly, of some inflation, almost a completely new wealth-producing apparatus on top of the old. Civilian demand, held back by shortages and forced saving during the war, surged forward afterwards to take advantage of the new facilities and, as a result, the war which was the ruin of some countries led, in others, to undreamed-of levels of new wealth.

These two war-based experiences—of a vast acceleration of technical sophistication and of the effectiveness of government decisions to expand the economy—effectively broke the gloomy trap of the earlier economists. Rising productivity springing from new energy, new materials, new techniques rose sharply and steadily enough for profits and wages to rise together—the wages helping to provide the mass market in which profits —à la Henry Ford—could be earned by a small return on a vast turnover.

And the effectiveness of government intervention to increase capacity in time of war led inescapably to the conclusion that government could also intervene effectively to ensure that the economy did not fall away into depression in peace time but would maintain, on the contrary, a steady rate of expansion. At first, this new responsibility of government took such forms as the Congressional Act of 1946, bidding the government to prevent unemployment. But in the last two decades, the responsibility has been more clearly defined as the government's duty to see that total demand in the economy is such as to employ all its resources and to maintain their upward expansion. Not wild radical thinkers but such formidably respectable economists as the official consultants of the Organization for Economic Cooperation and Development (the OECD) now state without hesitation that the secret of economic stability and growth lies in the steady maintenance of demand, and it is one of the government's responsibilities to see that the balance is kept.

Thus, not by theory or dogma but largely by war-induced experience, the Western market economies have come to accept the effectiveness and usefulness of a partnership between public and private activity. The government has its essential part to play in keeping demand stable and ensuring an upward movement in the whole economy. Sometimes the stimulus to sufficient demand will come from an unbalanced budget or higher public spending on public needs, sometimes from a tax cut which increases private purchasing power. But there is now no question of exclusive reliance on any one instrument or any one method. The pragmatic market economies have worked out their own evolving combinations of public and private responsibility and the result is the dynamic but surprisingly stable mixed economy of the Western world.

Meanwhile changes which may ultimately prove as far-reaching are taking place on the Soviet side. In some ways, of course, change is more difficult for the Communists. On the whole, Western nations are not too much given to dogma. We have a few enthusiasts who refuse to pay federal taxes because of the encroachment of "big government." America employs perhaps rather more jargon than Europe on the issue of "creeping socialism" and Communist plots to induce inflation and national bankruptcy. But, on the whole, in economics the Western world can move from position to position with little sense of contradiction and incompatibility. We had no very fixed views before so we do not have to bother too much about what we believe now. It is a considerable source of strength.

The unfortunate Russians, on the contrary, set out to build a modern economy on the basis of strict doctrine. This doctrine demanded that all economic decisions be made by the State. They were not pushed into this by the chance effectiveness of war. In a queer way, they were not even pushed into it by Marx, who believed that in a classless society, the State would "wither away." But if a doctrine demands the abolition of all private entrepreneurs—the prime movers and decision-makers in the Western experiment—you are really only left with public entrepreneurs, in other words, the government and its civil servants.

Now, the early decisions in Soviet Russia may not have been too difficult for public authorities to take. They mainly covered the kind of decisions Western governments make in war—a massive increase in all the capital components of heavy industry and all the services needed to support industrialization. (The Soviet planners also made brilliantly successful decisions in another area in which, in the West too, the role of the State is paramount—the field of education.) The first Five Year Plans for industry underlined the effectiveness of what one might call "war planning." Indeed, they enabled the Russians to resist one of the most overwhelming armed attacks in history. In those first decades, only in agriculture were the hints beginning that a command system, based on rigid planning from the center, might contain its own "internal contradictions" and require reforms of structure as drastic as anything the Communists postulate for private enterprise.

Today, the retreat from total central state decision has become a dominant fact in Soviet and Eastern European economics. The reasons behind it stem from the inability of planned quotas of resources, planned wages, planned prices, and planned returns to produce the variety and quality of goods the consumer in Communist countries is beginning to demand. In central planning and accounting, a badly made television set fulfills the factory's quota just as well as a well-made one. Dresses which fit dwarfs, or shoes for two left feet still satisfy norms fixed by weight or number. So, in order to produce goods which consumers really want, the Soviet world is beginning a variety of experiments all of which tend towards the procedures of the decentralized market economy.

Spurred on by Professor Liberman's advocacy of profits as a guide to efficiency, the Russians have allowed a wide range of factories producing consumer goods to make their own arrangements with retailers, fix their own prices and profit margins, and share their own bonuses. The Czechs are experimenting with prices that rise or fall according to demand. The Poles are handing down some planning and price-fixing functions to groups of manufacturers. The Yugoslavs have gone further than anybody, not only leaving factories to fix their own prices and earn their own profits but bringing in Western goods to compete with local products and thus establish external standards of efficiency and competence.

So the outcome of years of experiment in the processes of industrialization has been to lead the market economies towards planning and the planned economies toward the market. Of the two, the restoration of the market in the Soviet sphere is perhaps the most remarkable since, as I have already pointed out, a freight of doctrine has had to be shed in the process. Ultimately one can perhaps hope that the new attention to the consumer in market terms may have some effect on the "consumer" or voter in terms of politics. But for the present it is surprising enough, in view of Marxist dogma, to see commissars getting down to the problem of interest rates and possibly even saying: "Comrade Ivanovitch, your rate of profit has been very low these last six months. Go to Siberia!"

I have dwelt at some length on this remarkable reversal of traditional attitudes—in both West and East—not simply because it is a fascinating commentary on the supposed immutability of doctrine and the actual influence of need and fact. It is more than fascinating. It is highly significant. It suggests that whatever the starting point a nation may adopt in the application of science and technology, through savings, the processes of production, it is likely at some point to produce a version of mixed economy. It therefore suggests—as do our experiences in transport or communication—that in this new world order of technological and scientific change, the forces leading towards a certain unity of human experience are stronger than the forces leading to increasing difference and division.

Now I do not mean by this example to suggest that ideas and beliefs are not important. We shall be looking at them later. But the economic example I have chosen illustrates the likelihood that a certain inner logic in the deployment of our new technological tools leads to remarkable resemblances of organization and practice even in societies which think of themselves as widely or totally divergent.

One can think of other examples. The pattern of the birth rate is one. As nations begin to modernize, one of the early consequences—in democratic India as in Communist China—is a spurt in the growth of population. Even more striking is the worldwide acceleration in urban growth. All round the world, in developed or developing societies, in planned or market economies, the same irresistible movement to the cities goes on. If world population on the average is growing by 2 percent a year, cities grow by 4 percent, the great megalopolitan areas by 8 percent. Moscow grows as quickly as Paris, Rio de Janeiro as Chicago. It is a gloomy footnote to this common experience that virtually all the urban patterns that result are equally inhospitable to the human race—but this, again, only underlines the degree to which the impact of modernizing science and technology is creating a common experience, common dilemmas, common mistakes, and, more hopefully, common opportunities for the entire human race.

The last of these overriding resemblances is both the most obvious and the most fateful. For the first time in human history, a nation can lob a little device over a neighbor's backyard and blow him up and everything else with it. If this fact does not create a "community," I do not know what can. If we can all be destroyed, together, in two or three acts of grandiloquent incineration, then we are neighbors.

In short, we have become a single human community. Most of the energies of our society tend towards unity—the energy of science and technological change, the energy of curiosity and research, of self-interest and economics, the energy—in many ways the most violent of them all—the energy of potential aggression and destruction. We have become neighbors in terms of inescapable physical proximity and instant communication. We are neighbors in economic interest and technological direction. We are neighbors in facets of our industrialization and in the pattern of our urbanization. Above all, we are neighbors in the risk of total destruction. The atomic bomb would rain down on the just and unjust, on the Communist and the non-Communist, on the slave and the free, and could leave us all with our last appalling unity—the unity of annihilation.

The society of man has never before been in this position. Individual societies have succumbed. I suppose one could argue that our remoter human ancestors before the second Ice Age would have faced the same risk of annihilation if they had not taken shelter in the caves in which they drew their remakable pictures of animals—how strange it is, after perhaps a hundred millennia, to come back to the possibility that we may need to retreat once more into caves in order to survive. But I can think of no other analogy. In the past, whatever the horrors of war, other societies in other regions would be sure to carry on. Now, it seems, we have reached a planetary point of no return.

In fact, I can think of only one way of expressing the degree to which interdependence and communnity have become the destiny of modern man. I borrow the comparison from Professor Buckminster Fuller, who, more clearly than most scientists and innovators, has grasped the implications of our revolutionary technology. The most rational way of considering the whole human race today is to see it as the ship's crew of a single spaceship on which all of us, with a remarkable combination of security and vulnerability, are making our pilgrimage through infinity. Our planet is not much more than the capsule within which we have to live as human beings if we are to survive the vast space voyage upon which we have been engaged for hundreds of millennia—but without yet noticing our condition. This space voyage is totally precarious. We depend upon a little envelope of soil and a rather larger envelope of atmosphere for life itself. And both can be contaminated and destroyed. Think what could happen if somebody were to get mad or drunk in a submarine and run for the controls. If some member of the human race gets dead drunk on board our spaceship, we are all in trouble. This is how we have to think of ourselves. We are a ship's company on a small ship. Rational behavior is the condition of survival.

the knowledge revolution and industry

INTRODUCTION

tHOMAS J. Watson, Jr., president of IBM, remarked in 1965: [1] "In the next few years, technology itself will need a new speedometer for its ever quickening pace, spurred by more and more *knowledge networks*." (Italics added.) He then cited as a modest example of such a network the central computer complex at M.I.T., which was serving scholars at fifty-odd universities scattered throughout New England. "From an industrial economy," he continued, "in which most people work producing goods, through our present economy, producing services, we shall more and more become—*the first in the world's history—a knowledge economy*, with 50 percent or more of our work force involved in the production of information." (Italics added.)

If this is indeed the wave of the future—and I suspect it is—the most important questions become quite clear: What kind of knowledge and to be used for what? Or put another way: What will such a development mean to society not only in goods and services but in the quality of human lives?

The full results of the knowledge revolution made possible by EDP (electronic data processing) are now so numerous that it would be impossible even to name them all, let alone analyze them in this introduction and in the selections to follow. The most important, however, which are drastically transforming man's way of life come readily to mind. First of all, the computer is transforming the character of modern warfare, making possible new weapons of both offense and defense. In science as a whole the computer is deeply involved and now indispensable. Its importance, however, should be emphasized, not only for such highly mathematical sciences as nuclear physics and astronomy, but for all the life

[1] From remarks by Thomas J. Watson, Jr., to the National Conference of Editorial Writers in Milwaukee, Wis., October 8, 1965.

sciences as well—for biology, medicine, zoology, and so forth—and also for the social sciences such as psychology, sociology, and economics. Indeed it is hard to find any branch of scholarship today, including most of the humanities, where data processing is not being successfully used. One recent application which I find surprises and sometimes shocks my readers is the use of the computer in analyzing stylistic differences in literary manuscripts, as a means of discovering whether a literary production is authentic or an imitation of the author to whom it has been attributed.

Following the established pattern of this book we shall focus on the effects of the new information technologies primarily on industrial organizations and through them on people inside and outside of them. First a few basic statistics on the acceleration of computer technology.

As something that does simple arithmetic better and faster, the modern computer has certain primitive ancestors, starting with the abacus, used in ancient Roman times and by the Chinese even today, and on through the cash register and various mechanical calculating devices. But until the advent of electronics, mathematical machines were relatively unimportant in the life of man.

The first electronic computer went into operation in 1946. It was called ENIAC (Electronic Numerical Integrator and Calculator), and most of what follows here on computer power has occurred since then. Twenty years later, approximately 30,000 descendants of ENIAC, worth roughly 8 billion dollars, were at work in the United States. The fastest computer among them is at least a million times speedier than a skilled arithmetician. Compared with the computer of only ten years ago today's machines are one hundred times faster, their electronic parts ten times smaller. These last two factors have led to what is perhaps the most important acceleration of all. A given task of information processing can be done one thousand times more cheaply than ten years ago. These factors of acceleration may be summarized this way: The amount of computer power available in the United States has doubled each year since 1965. According to Paul Armer, RAND computer expert, "We had 1000 times as much computing power available in 1965 as we had a decade earlier and will probably have 1000 times more in 1975."

In the selections that follow this introduction we shall explore the effects of this enormous increase in computer power first on organizations, mainly business and industrial ones, and second and more briefly, on the organization of "communications" in the modern world.

The earlier organizational uses of computer power in industry required relatively unsophisticated machines. Computers were used, for example, for payroll calculations and inventory control. Soon, however, industry found that data processing could provide instant information on the state of the market. Networks, which gave quick and accurate information, were set up between warehouses or outlying plants and the central office. Notable early users of computers were, of course, scientific laboratories, the government, and insurance companies.

As both hardware (the machines themselves) and software (programming) became more complex, reliable, and versatile, their uses in industry have multiplied, and the interactions between the human mind and the computer, closer and more productive. The selection by Martin Greenberger of MIT, which follows this introduction, puts the whole phenomenon of data processing—what we have been calling the "knowledge revolution"—into broad historical perspective, tying closely what is happening now to what happened yesterday in industrial technology. The selection then describes some of the more sophisticated present uses in industry, relating them to the new versatility of modern computers, and finally it notes both the perils and promise of the computers of the future.

Before turning to the selections, it is important to stress the new, and in some cases closer, interaction of man and machine. To illustrate, we quote certain comments by Steven Ansoon Coons,[2] of MIT, on the use of computers to help men design automobiles, ships, and buildings.

Within the past few years a way has been found to make the computer play the part of the experienced pattern-maker. The designer need only draw a few descriptive design curves; the computer immediately generates a surface that incorporates these curves, and the designer can either accept the surface or modify it by drawing additional curves.

Given this power to do what might be called mathematical sculpture, the engineer can use the computer representation of an object as the base for a variety of analytical treatments. He can perform stress analyses, predict pressures and other fluid forces on airplane and ship shapes, simulate dynamic effects such as vibration, study heat flow or do any of a number of calculations that depend partly on precise knowledge of the shape in question. . . .

Much energy and talent is being devoted to making the computer-aided design and man-machine interaction a convenient everyday reality, and as time goes on more fresh effort is being channeled into this exciting enterprise. One may hope that engineers, economists, psychologists, sociologists and other men can help to provide the appropriate human adjustments to it."

The use of the computer to do what Professor Coons calls "mathematical sculpture" is a somewhat specialized phase of the knowledge revolution, but it is cited here as one example of the newer types of possible

[2] Steven Ansoon Coons: *The Uses of Computers in Technology, Scientific American,* September, 1966, pp. 186, 188.

man-machine relationship that are emerging from an age of technological acceleration. Professor Greenberger's selection on "The Computer in Organizations," as suggested earlier, puts the whole subject of the knowledge revolution into a much broader industrial and organizational perspective.

The two selections which follow Professor Greenberger's suggest the expected impact of the new technologies in communications on the world of tomorrow. They are "Comsat and the Satellites," by Charles Silberman, and a government report entitled "Impact of New Technologies on the Telephone Industry."

BIBLIOGRAPHY

Armer, Paul: "Computer Aspects of Technological Change, Automation and Economic Progress," *The Outlook for Technological Change and Employment*, Appendix, vol I, Report of the National Commission on Technology, Automation and Economic Progress, Government Printing Office, Washington, D.C., February, 1966.

Coons, Steven Anson: "Computer Graphics and Innovative Engineering Design," *Datamation*, May, 1966.

Crowley, J. H., G. G. Harris, S. E. Miller, J. R. Pierce and J. P. Runyon: *Modern Communications*, Columbia University Press, New York, 1962.

Englebart, Douglas C.: *Augmenting Human Intellect: A Conceptual Framework*, Stanford Research Institute, Stanford, Calif., 1962.

Feigenbaum, Edward A., and Julian Feldman (eds.): *Computers and Thought*, McGraw-Hill Book Company, New York, 1963.

Grabbe, Eugene M., Simon Ramo, and Dean Wooldridge: *Handbook of Automation, Computation and Control*, John Wiley & Sons, Inc., New York, 1959.

Greenberger, Martin (ed.): *Computers and the World of the Future*, The M.I.T. Press, Cambridge, Mass., 1961.

——— (ed.): *Management and the Computers of the Future*, published jointly by The M.I.T. Press, Cambridge, Mass., and John Wiley & Sons, Inc., New York, 1962.

———, Martin M. Jones, James H. Morris, Jr., and David N. Ness: *On-Line Computation and Simulation: The OPS-3 System*, The M.I.T. Press, Cambridge, Mass., 1962.

McLuhan, Herbert Marshall: *Understanding Media: The Extensions of Man*, McGraw-Hill Book Company, New York, 1964.

——— and Quentin Fiore: *The Medium Is the Massage: An Inventory of Effects*, Random House, Inc., New York, 1967.

Mann, R. W., and S. A. Coons: "Computer-Aided Design," *McGraw-Hill Yearbook of Science and Technology*, McGraw-Hill Book Company, New York, 1965.

Minsky, M. L.: "Matter, Mind and Models," Proceedings of the IFIPS Congress, 65: vol. 1, W. A. Kalenich (ed.), Spartan Books, Washington, D.C., 1965.

Oettinger, A. G.: "A Vision of Technology and Education," *Communications of the ACM*, vol. 9, no. 7, pp. 487–490, July, 1966.

Pierce, J. R.: *Symbols, Signals and Noise: The Nature and Process of Communication,* Harper & Row, Publishers, Incorporated, New York, 1961.

————: "Communications Technology and the Future," *Daedalus,* Spring, 1965.

Sass, Margo A., and William D. Wilkinson (eds.): *Computer Augmentation and Human Reasoning,* Spartan Books, Washington, D.C., 1965.

Scientific American, September 1966 issue on "Information" ("An issue about its processing by computers"), vol. 215, no. 3.

Simon, Herbert A.: *The New Science of Management Decisions,* Harper & Row, Publishers, Incorporated, New York, 1960.

————: *The Shape of Automation for Man and Management,* Harper & Row, Publishers, Incorporated, New York, 1965.

Sutherland, I. E.: "Sketchpad, A Man-Machine Graphical Communications System," *Lincoln Laboratory Technical Report, No. 296,* Massachusetts Institute of Technology, 1963.

Wiener, Norbert: *Cybernetics: Or Control and Communication in the Animal and the Machine,* The M.I.T. Press, Cambridge, Mass., 1961.

1.   THE COMPUTER IN ORGANIZATIONS

Martin Greenberger

SYNOPSIS

In its commercial form, the digital computer has been with us for less than two decades. Yet its profound significance for the future of civilization is already well established. This is a remarkable achievement for such a technological stripling. It makes us eager to anticipate the benefits that the electronic prodigy will one day deliver to us. But it also disturbs our sense of orderly history, and causes the more cautious and thoughtful among us to recoil from too unreserved an enthusiasm for the brazen young technology.

This essay studies the past to assess trends in the computer's development and commercial application. It relates the future of the computer to the two centuries of industrialization and mechanization that led up to its christening not very many years ago. The automation of the 1960's and 1950's was born of the industrialization of the 1900's, 1800's, and late 1700's. It came about in an atmosphere of human resistance to machines which was evident in the time of the Caesars, is apparent still today, and shows no sign of fading at any time in the foreseeable future.

The psychological forces which have retarded mechanization throughout the ages are now impinging on the progress of the computer. This is one tie the modern electronic marvel has with the past. Another is the organizational forms developing within its programming and operating systems. They bear close resemblance to the forms that historically have evolved in industrial organizations of people and machines. An examination of the nature of these forms in current application areas allows us to preview and speculate on the new kinds of organizations to which the computer may be leading us.

The final part of this article is a postscript to the preceding analysis. Our technological optimism is tempered by consideration of the social and moral problems that are likely to follow upon the computer's continuing advance.

INTRODUCTION

Computers come closest to ordinary people and everyday matters in their application to commercial affairs and the administrative concerns of government. The area known popularly as commercial data processing has proven ripe and receptive to the computer's touch. As a consequence, the use of computers in business and government has climbed rapidly since the first computer produced for nonscientific use was introduced into the United States Census Bureau in 1951. Few people then could have foreseen that tens of thousands of commercial computers would be humming busily in the United States by 1968. And few today can see clearly enough through the next seventeen years to envision the place these machines will occupy in our daily lives by 1985.

History suggests that man and his inertly inclined organizations tend to resist procedural modification, regardless of how outmoded and anachronistic their current methods may be. The medieval marketplace reenacted Monday through Friday on the floor of the stock exchange vividly illustrates how long ancient practices can succeed in defying modern technology. Pre-nineteenth century mathematics still holds sway in present-day commerce, and the logarithm, dating back to the early seventeenth century, receives meager attention in many financial contexts where it has particular relevance.

Inertia is not peculiar to the nonscientist, nor is it found only in traditional occupations. The computer programmer, to cite a modern-day case, is just as loathe to change his adopted ways as the next fellow. Hanns Sachs, a student and colleague of Freud, pointed out that the Romans had a good knowledge of hydraulic pressure, and appreciated its value in lifting great weights. But they used it only for shifting scenes in the Circus and other forms of amusement. Instead of building productive machines, for which they had adequate technical and mathematical understanding, they continued to employ their dwindling supply of human slaves. The Romans had strong economic reasons to seek substitutes for manual labor. Yet more of their mills were turned by slaves than by water power.

Without attention to man's psychological structure, it is hard to understand why the Machine Age did not arrive at least 1500 years earlier than it did. Sachs attributes the postponement to a narcissistic conflict: an abhorrence of anything that threatens to devalue the human body. The body was never so glorified and ennobled as it was in the civilizations of antiquity. According to Sachs,

> *The ancient world overlooked the invention of machines not through stupidity nor through superficiality. It turned them into playthings in order to evade a repugnance.*

Other explanations of human inertia would cite man's tendency to resist the new and espouse the old, his need for security, and his fondness for familiar objects even while exploring the unfamiliar.[1] These factors have been an important component of the psyche of mankind throughout the ages, and doubtless they will continue to be.

Only during periods of war fever, duress, or agitated social change is innovation likely to conquer tradition in matters of procedure. Even then, progress can be slow. This past generation was no exception, as anyone acquainted with the halting manner in which many business computers were brought into the organization will readily acknowledge. But there is reason to believe that the next generation will put the rule of custom and inertia to its severest test. The computer, due partly to a fertile marriage with communications, and partly to an enlightened mode of use, is beginning to come of age.[2] Its double impact is now being felt by the men of affairs whose decisions will be shaping the world of the 1970's and 1980's.

The first impact of the computer is its well advertised and amply substantiated contribution to scientific and technological advance. It is well known that without the computer there would be no nuclear reactor, no commercial satellite, no space program, and possibly no jet travel. In such ways as these the computer is aiding and abetting a much-observed increase in the complexity and pace of life. The world is getting smaller and its wants are getting larger. There are new urgencies and a sense of change. Informational requirements are mounting, and the need for comprehensive analyses grows keener. A military-like preoccupation with modern methods pervades industry. These conditions invite and encourage a recasting of procedural molds.

The second impact of the computer is its welcome ability to help alleviate the same timing, volume, and computational problems that it shares in creating. But the computer can assist man meaningfully only when he is ready and willing to accept new ways. Thus, the first effect of the computer makes way for the second. In this sense, the computer paves its own path toward a deeper participation in the substance of man's activities.

The computer has not yet reached nerve tissue in most organizations, but it seems certain that it soon will. The form this will eventually take is not yet clear, but enough good developmental work is underway to permit speculation. Among those who have ventured to the crystal ball is Herbert Simon,[3] whose persuasive position is one of "technological radicalism" offset by "economic conservatism." In this essay we shall be situated a little to the right of Simon technologically, and perhaps a bit to the left of him economically. On balance we find his views very palatable—and also very stimulating.

ORGANIZATIONAL PROCESSES IN PERSPECTIVE

Division of labor, known from the worker's point of view as *specialization,* is a prominent characteristic of organizations. It appears in advanced societies, primitive cultures, certain insect colonies, and the insides of every living thing. In human civilization specialization attains its most versatile form. Emerging as an almost universal principle, it occurs in numerous contexts, from the classification of an economy into industries, to the breakdown of an industry into firms, to the patchwork of occupations and professional skills found in every community, to the differentiation of a fabrication process into tasks and movements. Most recently specialization has shown up in the context of computers. This modern-day appearance will occupy our attention after we first review earlier and more widely-known forms of specialization.

The negative side of specialization (as applied to human beings) has been portrayed eloquently by Charlie Chaplin in *Modern Times,* and also forcefully, if not so amusingly, by industrial and social psychologists. An entire human relations school has grown up in reaction to the cold time-and-motion formalism of scientific management. This school has brought psychology to the organization, but it has not reduced the importance of specialization as a way of life.

Among its strengths, specialization enables the conscientious worker to become better at his job through practice and focus. It gives rise to training programs, trade magazines, professional associations, and standard job descriptions, all of which provide valuable communication channels among companies, as well as interfaces with schools and labor markets. Work improvements are achieved through control methods and analysis which are practiced by a separate breed of specialists (eg. the industrial psychologists). These specialists, as they come into being, are typically of a higher educational, intellectual, and salary level than the man on the line. Thus, labor becomes divided vertically as well as horizontally. The vertical strata include the managers of the workers, and also the managers of the managers.

The horizontal and vertical divisions of labor are made cohesive by an organization which furnishes rules and goals to unite them in purposeful activity. The organization deals in the marketplace, negotiating for resources, and also packaging, storing, advertising, and distributing products. All of these activities along with production and control functions are differentiated in the large organization.

The organization is typically *hierarchical* in both its structure and growth pattern. Specializations are grouped. Groups of workers on one level report to superiors on a higher level, who report to their superiors on a still higher level. The hierarchical structure occurs naturally in the evolution of an organization. It is simple, flexible, general, and adaptable. In addition, it economizes on information channels, and facilitates the assignment of authority and responsibility. The form is found in all manner of things, from cellular matter to programs and list-structured information in a computer.

The hierarchical form is not without its disadvantages. With information physically dispersed around a company—along with people, supplies, inventory, and work-in-process—locating needed data can be time-consuming and grueling. Unsatisfactory communication channels can bog down an operation and create unnecesary crises. One attempted solution has been to decentralize functions and incentives through the institution of divisions and profit centers. But decentralization is a mixed blessing, since it tends to proliferate positions, duplicate activities, and create local goals that are orthogonal to organizational objectives.

An alternate solution is to streamline the organization's information system. As the development of computer and communication technology opens this second route, the issue of centralization vs. decentralization has been taking on renewed interest. Companies are now introspectively reexamining their rationale for decentralization. Some observers believe that the computer will eventually reverse the trend toward decentralization that has characterized industrial growth over the past thirty years. They cite as examples the current computer-integrating activities at International Harvester, United States Steel, Standard Oil Company of New Jersey, and General Motors, the exemplar of decentralized operations. But even if these companies are succesful in their integration efforts, the question of whether they will ever truly recentralize is very debatable. Centralization of information flow neither requires nor implies centralization of operations.

Within the company hierarchy, three distinct levels are definable conceptually. These levels, which may or may not be physically separable, are:

1. Strategic planning
2. Management control
3. Operations

In theory, the top level sets the objectives for the company, reviews and modifies these objectives as the situation warrants, determines the material and personnel required to pursue the objectives, helps to organize and allocate these resources, establishes policies that allow the lower levels an adequate measure of autonomy and self-regulation, takes remedial action when policy fails, decides on questions of organizational structure, and meets operating crises when lower levels cannot. At present, crises tend to consume a disproportionately large amount of time. Often, these crises can be attributed to a defective information system.

The middle level serves as a buffer to the top, insulating against the vibrations and oscillations of daily operations. Its function is to control the acquisition and use of resources in pursuit of company objectives within policy lines set from above. Its orientation is tactical. It is currently much more occupied with matters of operations, and with urgencies arising from below, than it should be. Again, many of these urgencies can be traced to poor information and communication.

Operations is the level at which the daily business of the company takes place. Difficulties on this level tend to filter up the hierarchy and affect the upper levels. The same may be said of amelioration of these difficulties, and improvements to operations in general, including those incident to automation.

One of the most important roles of the organization is in coordinating its differentiated elements. This includes routing information and controlling the flow of work.

The simplest form of flow control is that found on an assembly line. The automatic movement of material from one station to the next is precisely timed so that none accumulates at the stations under ordinary conditions. It is analogous to the conduct of a relay race, or the operation of a telegraph repeater without storage.

An assembly line, however, is not a valid model of the typical organization. More generally, orders and information arrive in uncertain ways, moving irregularly along variable paths through an incompletely articulated network of nodes. The job shop is a more appropriate model.

In a job shop, jobs queue at the work stations. This is partly an unavoidable result of the stochastic flow, and partly a deliberate measure to keep machines and/or people busy. Absolute efficiency master-planned from above is not feasible. *Accumulation of work* becomes an important operating principle. The alternative to it is costly over-capacity.

Even when the flow is steady through fixed steps and scheduled in advance, as it is in many large clerical operations, the practice of accumulating work is often used to keep facilities or people fully loaded and productive. Utility bills, payroll checks, and premium notices are not sent out individually, but in *batches*. Payments are not posted to the ledger as they are received; checks are not dispatched to the clearing house as they are honored; and stock certificates are not issued as sales are consummated. All of these transactions, and many more, are batched before being executed. The batching of transactions introduces a delay into the transfer and receipt of information.

The queuing of jobs in a job shop, the batching of transactions in a clerical operation, and the carrying of inventories, in general, are natural concomitants of the division of labor. The more we differentiate, the more they appear. They result from our attempts to make specialization as efficient as possible in a complex and uncertain world. There is almost always an implicit holding cost attached to these accumulations. We may regard it as a price of specialization, and it can be appreciable.

In refining tasks under specialization, an ultimate of sorts is reached when a task is mechanized. Many tasks originally fashioned for men are now performed by automatic devices. A specific instance of mechanization might result from the inspiration of a manager, an outside expert, or the worker himself. Adam Smith told of the boy who was employed to open and shut the communication between boiler and cylinder as the piston ascended and descended in one of the first fire engines. Preferring the companionship of his playmates, the boy observed that a string connecting the handle of the valve to another part of the engine would regulate the valve properly without requiring his presence. This led to a design improvement of major importance.[4]

Machines often develop as the product of a series of mechanizations of previously differentiated manual tasks. Even when a machine like the steam engine or telegraph represents a quantum jump in technology, later modifications and refinements are more typically incremental in nature. Sometimes the steps in the mechanized operation correspond exactly with the tasks they replace. The manufacture of pins is today accomplished by a single machine that turns out several hundred thousand pins per hour, while going through most of the same steps that Adam Smith observed in a labor-divided eighteenth-century operation where ten men made 48,000 pins per day.[5]

At the same time that mechanization releases the worker from his narrow niche, it may require him to retrain and readjust. Mechanization does not provide immunity against the persistent forces of specialization. They continue to impinge, as the computer operator who has been assigned to the care of magnetic tape mechanisms will testify. It is as though a recurrent cycle of natural law were taking effect. Man divides his labor into separate tasks to achieve greater productivity, then performs these tasks himself until he finds ways to mechanize them. The new jobs that emerge also are gradually differentiated, and the process repeats. The cycle has a net beneficial effect over the long term by increasing productivity.

AUTOMATION

Automation is the current phase in two centuries of expanding mechanization, and represents a movement away from the mechanization of primarily physical effort toward the mechanization of mental effort. The name arose during the 1950's upon the appearance of the commercial computer and automatic process control. To many people it represents the most recent intrusion of the machine into man's private domain, across a boundary that is constantly receding.

To Hanns Sachs, in his pre-automation analysis of 1933, contrivances like the plow and spinning wheel, which simply helped man do his job more easily and better, have always been palatable. What has been distasteful, at least until the Industrial Revolution, was the thought of machines like the steam hammer and locomotive, which did man's job alone once set in motion, and which required man only as master-mind in control. Now that we have the computer, even the man in the driver's seat is dispensable, as borne out by self-landing jetliners and completely automatic railways. The age-old man vs. machine conflict has shifted and focused onto the computer: what it should and should not be doing, and how much of our decision making and control activities we can and should delegate to it.[6] The blunders and shortcomings of no other machine attract nearly as much journalistic fervor and anecdotal attention as those of the computer.

The computer was born in the scientific laboratory and spent its childhood composing lengthy numerical tables. It made its mark in the handling of large volumes of routine calculation, and this reputation stuck for many years. It may have stuck as long as it did partly because of man's narcissistic attachment to his nonroutine ("creative") activities. In any event, an idea as complex and novel as the computer takes a while to sink into man's collective comprehension. Most people, including those who stood most to benefit from the now proven versatility of the computer, initially took a very narrow view of its prospects.

When Eckert and Mauchly formed a company to build the Univac computer for commercial application in the late 1940's, it seemed that just a few machines might take care of the routine business calculations for the entire country. Some of the engineers assigned to the project were heard to wonder aloud during their lunchtime conversation what they were doing working on equipment of such questionable potential and limited market. Executives of firms which are today prominently and busily engaged in the manufacture of computers are known to have had even graver doubts.

The Univac, like most of its successors, was a general-purpose machine. In principle, it was good for just about everything; but people speculated on whether it might possibly be good for nothing. Not the least of the problems was the uncertain reliability of computers in those days.

Under the circumstances, it is not surprising that the early commercial machines were used primarily for the most routine clerical tasks. These tasks were usually selected with an eye to the *status quo*. It was all right if a few workers were displaced; in fact, computers were (and still are) often sold on the basis of the number of workers they will supplant. What was *verboten* was structural disruption to the organization.

The first Univac for strictly business application was installed at the General Electric Appliance Division in 1954. It was set to the task of preparing the payroll. After considerable huffing and puffing, the operation finally succeeded. Payroll became a bread-and-butter application.

Other early commercial applications included billing and customer accounting for banks, insurance companies, and public utilities; also stock control in manufacturing, warehousing, and distributing operations. For the most part, these tasks were automated along lines previously established for the differentiated manual operations. Transactions on cards flowed to the computer by the trayful from keypunch, verifying, sorting, and collating machines, much as they had flowed before from one set of clerks to another. Since the computer was much faster than its co-workers and predecessors, and allowed just one point of entry at a time, transactions became batched more than ever. An additional operation was established to convert cards to magnetic tape for faster input to the computer, giving rise to what became known as the *batch tape*.

COMPUTER ROUTINES

The new machine in the organization was as subject to the forces of specialization as everyone before. The computer was set to work initially on existing tasks that were narrowly defined and routine. But it was not to be put off so easily.

Because of its general-purpose nature, and because of continuing technological improvements in its speed, capacity, and reliability, the computer was able to take on additional jobs in abundant variety. This was not defiance of the forces of specialization. The division of labor was now occurring within the machine.

Computers are constructed from transistors, diodes, magnetic cores, and most recently, monolithic integrated circuits. These are specialized elements with carefully prescribed functions which they perform with hair-trigger precision. But theirs is only one aspect of division of labor within the machine. The sequential operation of these elements is controlled by programs of instructions or logical steps. It is in the organization of programs that the most significant discrimination of specialties has been taking place.

An industrial concern grows by hiring more workers and enlarging capital plant. A computer system grows by increasing programming capability and expanding hardware facilities. The simplest and most convenient way of increasing programming capability is by the addition of routines. A routine is a set of instructions for performing some distinguishable function. As uncouth as it may seem to some, a valid and meaningful analogy exists between the computer routine and the human skill or worker.

The concept of a routine came into existence along with the first computer. It is the programmer's way of coping with complexity. The division of a program into specialized routines parallels the division of human labor into skills or tasks. In fact, in a large programming project which requires a team effort, the two are directly related. A structuring of the overall program into routines or *modules* permits the project manager to assign separate modules to separate members of his team. They are able to work in relative isolation, responsibilities are fixed, program checking is simplified, and the project can proceed along several lines simultaneously.

The modular approach is widespread. A group of us at Harvard University used it in 1957, for example, to program a demographic model of the United States economy.[7] One male programmer was appointed to the routines that simulated death and divorce, a female programmer to the routines that simulated birth and marriage (she soon became engaged), and another male to the routines for reading and writing cards and magnetic tape. When the first computer runs made it apparent that the birth routine was defective, it was easy to reach in and substitute a more valid routine in its place, a significant advantage of the modular approach.

Almost all large programming projects have been modular in structure. Among the better known are the SAGE system for continental air defense, the SABRE reservation system of American Airlines, the Project Mercury system to put a man in space, and the Project MAC time-sharing system at the Massachusetts Institute of Technology. Not all of these projects were as modular at the outset, however, as they eventually became with wisdom acquired from the sharp lessons of experience. Large programming projects are difficult and costly, as testified to by the 1800 man-years spent programming the initial SAGE system. Modularity can be a big help, although it is not a panacea by any means.

Specialization creates a need for organization. This applies to the division of programs as much as to the division of labor. As a first requirement of organization, the separate elements must be able to communicate with each other, group together, and work cooperatively. The programming profession has supplied various devices for this purpose, including the *subroutine* and the *subroutine call*. A subroutine is a routine whose function is sufficiently well defined and specific to permit it to be standardized and made generally available upon call from other routines. Conforming to standard conventions, a *closed* subroutine uses information cited by the routine that calls it, performs its function, then returns control to this routine. Since a subroutine can be called from anywhere at any time, the effort that goes into its creation is generally well repaid.

An organization must coordinate or schedule its separate elements. In a simple computer operation, the flow of control among routines is scheduled by a *main program*. The main program may be thought of as a list of work to be done. Writing the program schedules the work. Devices that facilitate the writing of programs, therefore, also provide the needed coordination among routines. The most important such device to date has been the *compiler*. The compiler allows the programmer to compose in terms of symbolically named blocks of machine instructions, instead of machine instructions themselves. The language of the compiler is of a *higher order* than the primitive language of the machine. The symbols and concepts of the higher-order language are closer to the images in which a person normally thinks.

Among the better-known compiler languages have been Fortran, Algol, and Mad for scientific computation; Cobol for commercial application; Jovial for military application; and Simscript for simulation. PL/I, a current addition to the list, combines many of the characteristics of these earlier languages with a number of useful new features.

In the use of a Fortran-type compiler, the main program directly or indirectly determines the sequence in which subroutines and named blocks of instructions are called. Simscript is different. It uses a dynamic schedule of subroutines known as an *events list*. Like a main program, the events list causes calls to subroutines whose names are on it. Unlike a main program, these names change continuously and dynamically during execution.

The concept of a main program is pleasing and easy to understand. Like an assembly line or the cycle of a washing machine, it moves one step at a time in sequence from beginning to end, then perhaps repeats.

Its steps may be single machine instructions or symbolically named blocks of instructions.

The events list is slightly more complicated. Its steps, known as events, are scheduled dynamically during execution, rather than being fixed in advance by the programmer. But even the events list has the basic simplicity of being a master list which is consulted serially, one item at a time. Not so for computer systems which keep several programs active at once to improve equipment efficiency; and still less so for systems that interact with external processes in real time.

REAL-TIME SYSTEMS

A *real-time* system keeps up with one or more external processes (events outside of the computer) as they are taking place. The Project Mercury computer, for example, guided a man into space by analyzing a continuous stream of measurements received directly from the soaring space capsule. In real-time systems, internal and external processes are active simultaneously; their interaction is asynchronous and uncertain; multiple programs cohabit memory; jobs queue as in a job shop; and control does not descend down a single main program, but is distributed. If there is a master executive, its decisions may be aborted or over-ridden at any time.

Without notice, new work may enter from an on-line terminal; information previously requested from a slow-access storage device may be announced ready for delivery; the alarm of the computer clock may ring to note the time of day; a certain periodic requirement may be in need of attention; an error or emergency condition may be sensed. Such contingencies necessitate immediate action. The routine that happens to be running at the moment cannot be expected to know what to do. Nor should this be the responsibility of the executive. Its scope of action and tolerance for complexity is as limited as that of the next program. Like the head of the company, it must delegate.

The form that contingency planning takes is another example of specialization at work within the computer. A special routine is provided for each class of contingency. When a contingency arises, the appropriate routine is called. After necessary action has been taken, normal execution is resumed from the point of interruption.

As might be surmised, under the circumstances real-time systems can have hundreds or thousands of routines and millions of instructions. Many routines are either of the:

1. Control, supervisory, executive, or monitor variety; (managers)
2. Application, operations, or user variety; (workers)

Sometimes a subset of routines within a system can perform like a division of a company. An illustration of this is our OPS system at Project MAC.[8] To the time-sharing supervisor, it is just another user's program; yet, it is actually a complete operating system with its own retinue of control routines and a wide assortment of subroutines and operational programs known as *operators*. There is an operator corresponding to each of the customary statements in higher-order languages, and also to individually tailored and arbitrarily complex compounds of these statements. This gives the user a programming capability that comes closer to his thought processes than do the statements of a higher-order language by themselves.

Lest we be misunderstood, we are not proposing a precise isomorphism between the elements of a computer system and those of a company organization. Programs and equipment are much too idiosyncratic today to make that possible. All we are suggesting is that the same kinds of organizational devices that have proven useful in human organizations are now showing up more and more in the organization of programs. There are multiple levels of control along the vertical dimension, differentiation of functions along the horizontal dimension, and a general tendency toward hierarchical forms in program evolution.

In those cases where programs and people are (or will become) interchangeable, the relationship between organizations of programs and organizations of people gets to be more than an intriguing analogy. Suppose that a company has a real-time computer system participating as a central instrument of operations. Suppose, like our OPS system, it is open-ended and able to grow easily and assume new functions. The routine it employs to store away incoming transaction data does the work of a team of file clerks. The routines it has to make this data available on demand to customer representatives, and to summarize the data in periodic reports to management, are like staff assistants. To assimilate new services and take on additional business, the company can either expand its work force by hiring employees with the requisite skills, as has been customary, or it can make equivalent extensions to its real-time programs. It can also do some of each.

In this way, the real-time system is likely to become a vital part of the company organization. In the ultimate picture, the two parallel organizations of people and programs may blend together and appear as one, just as organizations of people and machines have tended to do in the past. This conclusion is simply a projection of historical forces (e.g. differentiation and mechanization) along an axis of current trends (toward real-time systems, random access, and time sharing).

Real-time systems are already firmly entrenched in the military sphere, and they are fast gaining favor in business and industry. They seem destined eventually to win a commercial acceptance at least as broad as their batch-processing predecessors before them. Real-time systems generally have most or all of the following key attributes:

1. direct (real-time) involvement of the computer in an external process;
2. a network of remote (tele) communication terminals, each of which transmits bursts of data to the computer sporadically;
3. direct (on-line) entry of the data into the computer without any externally noticeable accumulation;
4. transaction-by-transaction, rather than batch-by-batch processing of the data;
5. arrangement of information storage internally in randomly (as opposed to serially) accessible form.

The technology for real-time systems is relatively well advanced, thanks partly to existing military applications. Terminal equipment, however, especially that providing for graphical input and output, is still too expensive. In addition, the state of the art in real-time programming is as yet at an early stage, and the present tariff schedules and modus operandi of communications companies are unrealistic for the transmission of scattered data bursts. Despite these temporary obstacles, real-time systems have been making decided inroads.

In the transportation field, several airway and railway companies have followed the lead of American Airlines and installed Sabre-type reservation systems. Soon real-time computers will be landing jetliners through heavy overcasts, scheduling railroad freight-yard activities and the movement of box cars; running and spacing high-speed passenger trains; and guiding vehicular traffic in large municipalities. These real-time systems for controlling transportation may be linked someday with each other, and with similar systems for hotels, motels, car rentals, and travel agencies, to provide integrated regional and national systems.

Real-time systems also have been gaining entry into financial circles. Banks have installed on-line systems for teller operations, demand deposit accounting, and stock transfer. Insurance companies are making centralized customer records available on-line to their agents in the field. A number of quotation services provide dial-up prices from a computer fed in real-time from the floor of the stock exchanges; and the exchanges themselves are embarked on streamlining programs that may eventually automate most floor activities. It is not overly fanciful to foresee the day when the bulk of trading and financial transactions will be carried on from office to office electrically over large computer-communication networks.[9] The implications for the future of our cities and the functioning of our economy are far-reaching.

Real-time systems are not restricted to large enterprises. Smaller companies can store their records remotely and subscribe to on-line computational services at any of a growing number of new firms being set up expressly for this purpose. The Keydata Corporation, one of the first of these so-called computer or information utilities, has clients who are wholesale liquor dealers. The client's clerk types a customer's invoice at the time of sale from a teletype terminal in the sales office. The terminal is connected to the Keydata computer by leased telephone lines. The clerk identifies the customer by number, and types in stock code and amount of the item sold. The computer fills in information from its files on date, invoice number, name and address of customer, price, and item description. It also calculates and types price extension and sum while checking for clerical errors. All in all, it types about 80% of the information of a typical invoice. By retaining information relating to the sale, it can perform inventory control and sales analyses with little additional effort.

On the industrial scene, The Lockheed Missiles and Space Company has had an Automatic Data Acquisition System in continuous operation since March of 1962. The system provides for the remote collection of data on work flow from over 200 input stations in factory locations. Remote inquiry/reply stations provide timely information to management on the location of shop and purchase orders, inventory levels, and labor charges.

The International Business Machines Corporation has a Management Information and Control System that ties together several IBM divisions through the medium of large shared tables of operating data stored on central computers. The tables are updated daily from batch tapes prepared on flexible-editing typewriter facilities situated peripherally at factories and offices around the company. The editing typewriters, controlled by their own smaller computers, belong to an IBM product line known as the Administrative Terminal System. They are supplemented by a very large number of on-line inquiry stations placed at appropriate work locations everywhere. A special inquiry language enables the user of the system to request selected items of information, as well as full reports, quickly and conveniently.

Going beyond this system, the IBM Data Processing Division is in the process of developing an Advanced Administrative System that is slated eventually to take over all information flow and control for the bulk of the company's marketing and distribution functions. Input to the system, as well as output, will be on-line through remote terminals. Salesmen and managers in IBM branch offices may some day use these terminals where today they use their pencil and pads, telephones, and automobiles. Hopefully this will make it unnecessary to fill out, shuffle, and circulate the mountain of paper forms currently in use. Paper documents may go the way of the green eye shade and the quill pen.

The Westinghouse Electric Corporation has been doing message switching for its teletype network by computer since December of 1962. Today its Telecomputer Center serves about 300 plants, field offices, warehouses, repair centers, and distributors throughout the United States and Canada. By capturing data from the messages it processes, it has been able to take over a significant amount of inventory control and order processing, and it is adding on other functions, such as production control, as quickly as feasible. The scope of timely information which the system makes available to management on the divisional and corporate levels is broadening all the time, as more operations go on-line.

Westinghouse has been working on a video display device to present financial information graphically to executives for planning and control. In 1966 the manager in charge of the operation wrote:

We have completed the programming of the initial displays for demonstration purposes and are now in the process of testing and debugging the program. Our approach here was to start with something with which our executive management is familiar—that is, a reproduction of the graphs which they use for reviewing the financial operations of the Company. We are able to display in great detail financial forecasts, actual accomplishments, and any resultant variances for any of our 65 divisions, six Groups, or the total Corporation. We can extrapolate trends based upon historical data and mathematically show control limits for each category being examined. At the present time, our inputs from the divisions are limited to the conventional monthly accounting cycle. . . . A parallel project is to get all of our operations on-line in real-time as quickly as possible. This will considerably shorten our reaction time from the generation of the data in the division to having the results displayed here in Pittsburgh. Our estimate is that it is going to take us approximately five years to accomplish this; but, at that time . . . we will be able to display performance criteria upon demand.

These selected examples illustrate real-time systems automating operations, supervising logistic flow, and facilitating customer transactions. In the process timely information can be collected and organized for the benefit of management. Since today's executive prides himself on being an alert innovator and vigorous competitor, and since others expect these qualities of him, he is propelled by his self-image plus the forces of competition into active support of these developments. This offsets the more natural inclination he might feel to dig in his heels and hold on to traditional ways.

If the manager is to take advantage of the up-to-the-minute comprehensive information being placed at his fingertips, he will have to begin to delegate some portion of his decision activity to the computer. Delegation to the computer will cause significant changes in the practice of management, and delegation will become ever more necesary because of these changes. Many of the operations research and statistical analyses now accomplished for the manager off-line in the batch-processing mode will be performed for him in real-time and in simplified form right at his on-line terminal. This does not mean that his thought processes will suddenly accelerate and enable him to keep up with unrestrained outpourings of the computer. There will have to be mutual accommodation, and certain analyses will undoubtedly continue to be done off-line. The way to gain understanding in these matters is to begin to put the manager and his staff on-line, and place analytical tools and models at their disposal. This is now being done in a preliminary and experimental way at several companies and universities.

What makes this exploratory work possible are large time-shared computers, which offer their impressive memories and information processing capabilities to many on-line users simultaneously. Although time-sharing systems customarily have not run concurrently with other real-time operations, in principle they can. In the discussion that follows, we postulate a system that time shares a large computer system for managers and their staffs at on-line terminals, while running company operations and collecting transaction information in real-time.

ON-LINE SYNTHESIS AND CONTROL

There are two ways that one can interact with the time-shared computer. The first is in the structuring of ideas and solutions to problems. For simplicity, we refer to this kind of activity as *synthesis*, even though it has decided analytical components. Synthesis includes the construction of programs and building of models. The computer is used to check the syntactic or behavioral validity of each unit as it is added, and permits an incremental approach. The OPS system takes its name from its general usefulness in *On-line Process Synthesis*.

The second form of interaction is in the execution of programs or parts of programs already synthesized. One can insert himself into the operation of a program during a preliminary or intermediate state of its construction. One can also involve himself in a computer operation as a means for incorporating judgmental and otherwise amorphous aspects of a process. Consider a decision maker, for example, who has the computer signal him on an exception or interval basis, giving him then the information necessary to make a decision. A man at an on-line terminal in the Westinghouse Treasury Office today uses the computer to display cash levels on demand and to notify him when a pre-set threshold has been reached. Tomorrow he will also use the computer to ask unstructured questions and explore how a decision he is considering will affect future cash flow.

We spoke before of a recurrent cycle which seems to govern the mechanization of human effort. In the first phase, work is differentiated; in the second phase, tasks able to be mechanized are delegated to machines. Then new jobs emerge and the phases repeat.

We now conjecture on how this cycle will manifest itself in future information systems. For simplicity, we assume a company with one integrated real-time information system and managers (or human controllers) at the consoles. The system may be built around a single centralized computer, or a distributed network of computers. Each man is responsible for monitor-controlling a separate aspect of the company's operations. In addition, he is provided with ample time and encouragement to isolate the more definable parts of his responsibility, and gradually synthesize them as new application and control programs. He runs the new programs at first experimentally with a watchful eye, and eventually incorporates them as permanent and integral components of the automatic operation. He is assisted by specialists in heuristic programming and simulation modeling.

By continual introspection and the shedding of selected parts of his function, the enterprising manager can become progresively more productive to the company. His job keeps changing, but his contribution grows larger rather than smaller. His superiors must see to it that this important fact is reflected by his income and position, since narcissistic resistance to automation in this setting is likely to be as at least as strong as ever.

Viewed from above, an intriguing interplay of centripetal and centrifugal forces can be discerned. Tasks that show the computer to comparatively best advantage are drawn inward into the body of programming; tasks that prosper more from the human touch drift outward to the men at consoles (and beyond). Many of these tasks would not be identifiable today. The environment from which they emerge will be shaped by a new kind of interaction among new kinds of organizations.

As the company expands its operations and diversifies its business, it will add new programs and people to its information system. By its basic design, the system grows easily. It is also easily modified. Additions and modifications are kept flexible (*interpretive*) until they perform satisfactorily. They may be *compiled* (consolidated into direct machine code) for a gain in running efficiency. Compiled programs may themselves be refined and made more efficient by a continuing policy of replacement and improvement. Over a period of time, the system tends to become larger in scope and better in detail.

Acquisition of new programs by the system is not unlike learning in the human being. A new program in interpretive form is similar to a response or behavior pattern that is being tried out tentatively. A compiled program resembles a habit, although it is generally not "hard to break" unless it is deeply ingrained in the system's central core.

We can carry the analogy with a human organism one step further by adapting a three-way classifiaction used by Edward Feigenbaum in a model of human memory.[10] The memory of the information system may be viewed as consisting of:

1. A *temporary* or *buffer store,* containing information received or known somewhere in the company, but not yet generally available.

2. An *active* or *short-term store,* containing information that is generally accessible to authorized persons, and is used by them in daily operations.

3. A *passive* or *long-term store,* containing information retired from the active store, and available primarily for running audits, answering questions, and conducting historical studies during non-peak hours of computer operation.

Today the temporary store of the company includes cards, drawers, vest pockets, cabinets, and tapes full of batched transaction data waiting to be processed and summarized. The data is spread around the organization, up and down the hierarchy. It may be days or weeks before some of it gets into the active store and becomes available for operations and decisions.

In the future information system, the bulk of this same data will feed directly into computer memory from terminals at the site of transaction, just as data on the flow of hundreds of thousands of inventory items currently feed into the Automatic Data Acquisition System of Lockheed from hundreds of remote terminals. There will still be an accumulation of data in the future system, just as there will still be a division of labor, but like the division of labor it will occur within the machine. A datum will wait in the input buffer of the computer but for a second or two until its personal input routine picks it up and puts it in active store. The routine will place it in one or more lists and reports, as determined by its nature, and will link it explicitly to related information already stored. Other routines will make the information in the active store flexibly and quickly accessible to persons with the need to know.

The Lockheed experience illustrates how improved information can lift the fog of needless complication and confusion that besets many companies. The manager, relieved of haunts from the past, is able to devote himself more to consideration of the future.

Management control of operations is sometimes viewed as a *feedback* system. Suppose that operations appear to be getting out of wack. Under pressure, the manager will make a decision, such as hiring more workers or purchasing more material, to correct performance. But if his information is poor, he can be as ineffectual (or perverse) as a thermostat that does not sense temperature properly.

Better information for better control is one important benefit that we might expect from automating the memory of an organization. A more profound and longer-range hope is for a system that will allow the manager to operate on a *feed-forward* rather than a feedback basis. With the help of simulation models, he will attempt to anticipate difficulties before they occur, and take preventative action. But attainment of this management Utopia will require substantial work of the intellectual kind. The requirements for an automated memory, on the other hand, do not go beyond current technology or current programming sophistication. Thus, timely information made easily accessible is likely to be the first big dividend of the automated information system. Aside from the dollars it will save, and this is already well substantiated by the experience of many companies including Lockheed and Westinghouse, it will pave the way for further automation, and give the company a new coherence and sense of unity.

POSTSCRIPT

Life with the computer is certain to be different. The organization will function more smoothly and efficiently, and it will be more productive; yet there will be no long-range massive unemployment, nor will there be the inundating overabundance of goods and services that some prophets of doom have predicted. The computer will become much easier to use, and generally more accessible to the nonspecialist; people will come to take it for granted. Job descriptions will be drastically altered. Life will indeed be different, but whether it also will be better depends on our ability to anticipate and plan.

It is self evident in this day of nuclear armaments that what may become technologically feasible may not be socially desirable. The same devastating power that makes the H-bomb so effective as a deterrent to war, far overshadowing any of its predecessors, also makes it a dire menace to the safety and security of humanity. The same impressive qualities that make the computer a prospective boon to the operation of the organization, also render it a potential threat to the privacy of the individual and his self-identity.

There has been much discussion recently of the potential problem areas associated with increasing automation and the construction of large, central files: the machine cult of impersonality; clandestine invasions of privacy by unscrupulous persons; overzealous intrusions by agents of the government; and criminal subversion for illegal gain. These hazards have received considerable attention and publicity. Congress is holding hearings, and the issues are being actively discussed by many people. It should be obvious, however, that the computer is not bad in itself, any more than atomic energy is intrinsically bad. The possible evils, as well as the possible benefits, depend on how man uses the computer, and how he chooses to weave it into his organizational structures.

Man must regard himself more closely now than ever before, as he begins to draw a blueprint of his future with the computer. We have always tended to accept too readily the "conventional wisdom" of the order of wise men, and we now seem to be creating a similar kind of mystique around the computer and its simulations. We are inclined to place too much unquestioning faith in the oversimplifications, routinizations, and quantifications of life; it is tempting to trust the simple numerical results of the computer more than we should. We often proceed too quickly to delegate our work and responsibilities to others; the computer is a glutton for work and responsibility.

It may seem strange to warn against the very things which in more positive and moderate terms we previously predicted; particularly peculiar in view of what we have said about natural resistance to machines. But collective man has a dual nature. He is bi-stable. Having accepted an innovation in procedure, albeit begrudgingly, he can then remold himself around it and adopt it as his own. Man's resistance to the unfamiliar is just the other side of his avid attachment to what he has committed himself to accept.

The scientist may not be as susceptible in this sense as the average man, but he is not immune by any means. In 1957, for example, a very simple and fast program for generating random numbers made its appearance upon the computer scene. Because of its unprecedented speed, it was adopted as a standard library subroutine by a number of large computer installations, including several of the most prestigious. Random numbers are used in enormous quantity for a wide variety of computer applications (including Monte Carlo simulation of nuclear reactions and war games). Hundreds and maybe thousands of intelligent people must have used this particular generator in the past eleven years. Recently it was found to have serious second-order serial correlation.[11] None of its users was naive enough to believe he was getting genuine random numbers, since that is not in the nature of a programmed machine; and perhaps the serial correlation did not affect the results of most. The fact remains, however, that almost all of the users were ready and happy to put their suspicions aside and accept the quick and convenient pseudo-random numbers provided by the installation under its implicit seal of approval. A few users, to their credit, did conduct their own statistical tests. That is how the aberration was eventually discovered. In post-mortem, it was easy to spot the difficulty by analysis because of the transparent quality of the generator. It would not have been as easy in a more complex generator.

The problem is older than the computer. How many of the executives who base their decisions largely on the biweekly figures of the national Nielson Television Index worry about the size of the statistical sample used to produce these figures? How many concern themselves with the fact that the sample is fixed ("continuing") and therefore subject to idio-syncracy and tampering? There is a certain magic in the statement that a program is rated third in the nation or was viewed by 29.2% of families owning television sets. How many executives know that these findings refer to 1000 families under an "area-probability design," and that these families are ones willing to have meters placed on their television sets? How many take account of the fact that a rating is determined not only by a program's own merits, but also by the size of the audience it inherits from the preceding program, the strength of its competition, the time at which it is broadcast in various regions of the country, the number of stations that run it, and the extent to which it is advertised?

The same kinds of questions could be raised about the annual finan-cial report of a corporation, the Gross National Product, figures on un-employment, and countles other sets of numbers and uses of simple formulas. As the computer makes numbers ever more a way of life, pro-ducing them by ever more complicated formulas and complex models, we must not lose our ability and desire to question. We must find ways to use the computer itself, and its on-line capabilities, to challenge and rebut. The will and power to examine critically has to be stimulated by the computer, and not stifled by it. This is an obligation that a viable society must not permit itself to shirk.

NOTES

1. Harlow's monkeys were immobilized when confronted by a totally strange situation. They ventured to investigate the unknown only when in the presence of the mother-figure. In Berlyne's experiments on human exploratory behavior, subjects showed a marked preference for stimuli which were moderately, rather than highly novel.

2. In particular, the development of time sharing is opening new possibilities. See the September, 1967, issue of the *Scientific American;* especially the article on communications by John Pierce, and the one on time sharing by Fano and Corbato. One of the first discussions of time sharing is contained in an interesting paper by John McCarthy in M. Greenberger (ed.), *Computers and the World of the Future,* The M.I.T. Press, Cambridge, Mass., 1964.

3. See, for example, Herbert Simon, *The Shape of Automation,* Harper & Row, Publishers, Incorporated, New York, 1965.

4. A better-known anecdote is the story of Thomas Edison as a young telegraph operator. His distaste for routine, and his ingenuity for finding ways of avoiding it, led to one of the early versions of the automatic telegraph repeater, and also to a

forerunner of the messenger call box. The year before he built his repeater, when Edison was sixteen, he worked as an operator on the 7 P.M. to 7 A.M. shift. In order to be able to experiment during the day and preserve his nights for sleeping, he rigged a simple mechanism to an alarm clock. It transmitted a required signal to his supervisor on the hour throughout the night. The history books do not agree on precisely what happened when the supervisor grew suspicious and dropped by to find the lad asleep during transmission of the 2 A.M. signal. Whether the outcome was an amused rebuke or a stern dismissal, it is interesting to note that Edison never patented the device.

5. Adam Smith cited this example at the beginning of the Wealth of Nations to illustrate how productive a workman could be made by division of labor.

"A workman not educated to this business (which the division of labour has rendered a distinct trade), nor acquainted with the use of the machinery employed in it (to the invention of which the same division of labour has probably given occasion), could scarce, perhaps, with his utmost industry, make one pin in a day, and certainly could not make twenty.

"But in the way in which this business is now carried on, not only the whole work is a peculiar trade, but it is divided into a number of branches, of which the greater part are likewise peculiar trades. One man draws out the wire, another straightens it, a third cuts it, a fourth points it, a fifth grinds it at the top for receiving the head; to make the head requires two or three distinct operations: to put it on, is a peculiar business, to whiten the pins is another, it is even a trade by itself to put them into the paper; and the important business of making a pin is, in this manner, divided into about eighteen distinct operations which in some manufactories, are all performed by distinct hands . . ."

6. See, for example, the views and concerns of C. P. Snow, Norbert Wiener, and Elting Morison in an interchange appearing in Computers and the World of the Future, op. cit. A paper in the same collection entitled "What Computers Should Be Doing" clearly points up the controversial aspects of the subject.

7. G. H. Orcutt, M. Greenberger, J. Korbel, and A. M. Rivlin, Microanalysis of Socioeconomic Systems: A Simulation Study, Harper & Row, Publishers, Incorporated, New York, 1961.

8. M. Greenberger, M. M. Jones, J. H. Morris, Jr., and D. N. Ness, On-Line Computation and Simulation: The OPS-3 System, The M.I.T. Press, Cambridge, Mass., 1965.

9. For two optimistic discussions of the future, see M. Greenberger, "Computers of Tomorrow," The Atlantic Monthly, May, 1964, and "Banking and the Information Utility," Computers and Automation, May, 1965.

10. Paper presented at the December, 1965, meeting of the American Association for the Advancement of Science, Berkeley, California.

11. M. Greenberger, "Method in Randomness," Communications of the ACM, March, 1965.

INTRODUCTORY NOTE

As this book goes to press, the perspectives for global communications based on the computer, on satellites in space, and on a series of breakthroughs in the science of electronics are just beginning to unfold. But it is already possible to suggest the main outiines of communications in tomorrow's world with some assurance.

"I expect that in every office, and to some extent in every home, you will have a communication facility that can be used for whatever type of communication you want," predicts John R. Pierce, executive director of research at the Bell Telephone Laboratories. "You will have the option of sending text, or speaking, or seeing, or perhaps communicating all three ways at once." [1] On such a future in communications, James J. Clerkin, Jr., who is executive vice-president of General Telephone and Electronics, makes a significant comment. "The main concern," he says, "isn't going to be technological but rather economic and social. We could provide many of these futuristic services right now if people wanted them and were willing to pay for them." [2] We shall discuss further the social motivations and implications of such a gigantic development in global communications in the final chapter of this book.

At this point we include below two brief selections: the first one on the role of Comsat and of satellites in making possible a new era of communications in the modern world; the second, a report on the impact on manpower of expected technological revolutions in the largest of contemporary communications systems, the telephone industry.

2. COMSAT AND SATELLITES

From Charles E. Silberman, "The Little Bird That Casts a Big Shadow," Fortune, *February, 1967, pp. 108, 109.*

"The benefit to mankind staggers the imagination," says Dr. Harold A. Rosen of Hughes Aircraft Co., discussing the potential of satellite communication. Dr. Rosen, the principal designer of Early Bird, speaks with the understandable enthusiasm of one who has contributed as much as anyone to the rapid development of satellite technology, but he is hardly indulging in overstatement. For the satellite, in the phrase made popular by Marshall McLuhan, the Canadian student of communication, represents another vast "extension of man," enabling him to communicate almost without regard to distance. The telegraph cable, the radio, the telephone cable, and the microwave relay each enormously extended the range of man's voice and thought, but the cost of sending a message with these technologies still varies more or less proportionately with the distance it travels. With the satellite, cost is nearly independent of distance.

Moreover, satellite technology is advancing faster than anyone except Rosen and a few other enthusiasts had expected. A single satellite now scheduled to be put in orbit next year by the Communications Satellite

---

[1] *Wall Street Journal,* January 16, 1967, p. 1.
[2] *Ibid.*

Corp. (Comsat) will provide 1,200 overseas circuits—about as many as are now available from *all* other technologies for transmision of telephone, telegraph, and data from the U.S. to the rest of the world. And this satellite is only the first of several to be launched by Comsat in the next two years on behalf of an international consortium; each satellite in this Intelsat III system will have a 1,200-circuit capacity and a five-year life expectancy. By contrast, Early Bird, orbited by Comsat in 1965 to demonstrate the feasibility of satellite transmission, has a capacity of only 240 channels and a life expectancy of a year and a half. And next-generation satellites now under development will have five times the capacity of the Intelsat III "birds"—twenty-five times the capacity of Early Bird—at only nominal increases in cost.

The implications, clearly, *do* stagger the imagination. Through satellites the nations of Africa, Asia, and Latin America will have easy access to the advanced nations—and to each other—and a capacity to use radio and television for mass education and information that otherwise would have been utterly impossible. Communication among the developed nations will be facilitated enormously, too. In the past decade international communication has been growing at more than 15 percent per year, compounded; in some regions the growth has been much faster—e.g., 33.9 percent a year between the U.S. and Puerto Rico and the Virgin Islands since the first cable was laid in 1960. And these figures may grossly understate future growth since, in communication, supply tends to create its own demand. Without an exception in recent years, the introduction of new facilities has been followed by much faster than expected growth in demand.

While the satellite's greatest impact may be felt in international telecommunication, at least for the near future its largest market may be within the U.S., which has nearly half of the world's telephones and 40 percent of its TV sets. Satellites can be used to reduce the cost of long-distance telephone and telegraph communication. They may be even more effective in bringing down the cost of data transmission. And a recent highly imaginative and enormously controversial Ford Foundation proposal has made it clear that the most fruitful immediate application of satellite technology is for distribution of network television. Satellites could substantially reduce the cost of television distribution, dramatically increase its range, and improve its coverage and quality. All of the U.S., including Hawaii, Alaska, Puerto Rico, and the Virgin Islands, might be linked by a number of new networks that could enable TV, at long last, to realize its promise.

Understandably, therefore, the satellite has evoked more interest and excitement than any other technological development of recent years, save possibly the computer. (The atom bomb, of course, is in a class by itself.) It has also evoked more opposition and controversy. By making older technologies obsolescent for some (but by no means all) purposes, the satellite threatens the position or even survival of companies whose operations are based upon those technologies.

NOTE BY THE AUTHOR

The controversies surrounding the future of communications satellites, and especially of Comsat, cast a dramatic and revealing light upon the economic and political problems of dealing with new technologies in our era. In this instance they stem from the fact that when the Communications Satellite Act of 1962 was written, certain limited assumptions were made by the lawmakers. It was taken for granted that for many years the only operable satellites would be low- or medium-altitude "random" satellites such as Bell Laboratories' Telstar. As they were impractical for domestic communications, the 1962 act envisioned them for international communications only. But technology leaped ahead of the experts and lawmakers. Since the success of the Early Bird satellite in 1965, communications engineers are agreed generally that all future satellites, like Early Bird, will be placed in orbit high enough (22,300 miles) so that their orbits will be synchronous with the rotation of the earth. In short, the satellite will be stationary relative to any point on the earth's surface. This advance in satellite technology has several important advantages. Both the satellites themselves and their ground stations will cost less than "random" satellites and their range of application will be far greater, including broad possibilities of domestic use.

Public policy and private industry are now faced with a whole range of decisions not foreseen as recently as 1962. Here are a few examples:

What kind of a domestic satellite system should be built, and for what type of communications—for voice, data, or television? Who will control the systems, and how should savings in communication or losses through obsolescence of existing systems be shared? All such questions were first highlighted by the proposal of the Ford Foundation in 1966 that the FCC authorize the creation of a new nonprofit corporation to distribute television programs via satellite. The economic and policy ramifications of this proposal are great and beyond the scope of this brief note. But as the reader will have observed many times before, here again is a technological explosion which brings obsolescence not only to older technologies but to the efforts of both industrial organizations and government to control them. The basic law regulating communications carriers was written in 1934, or as *Fortune* puts it, "technologically several millennia ago." And now it is apparent that the Communications Satellite Act of 1962 was inadequate almost by the time it was enacted.

3. IMPACT OF NEW TECHNOLOGIES ON THE TELEPHONE INDUSTRY

From "Technology and Manpower in the Telephone Industry, 1965–75," Manpower Research Bulletin, No. 13, pp. 3, 4, 5, U.S. Department of Labor, Manpower Administration, November, 1966.

Electronic solid state switching systems, communications satellites, and semiautomatic information service are several of the major innovations which will bring significant changes in telephone company operations, services provided to the public, and employment and skill requirements during the 1965–75 period.

1. *Communications satellites* will be used to make available inexpensive, long-distance, point-to-point communications. Overseas long-distance rates, particularly international rates, are expected to drop when the satellite becomes the mainstay of the overseas international communications network. By 1975, projections are that 50 percent of overseas long-distance calls will go through satellites. Manpower will be only indirectly affected. The increasing amount of telephone communications as a result of satellites will tend to swell employment, particularly of operators engaged in overseas communications.

2. *The electronic central office* (ECO) represents a significant change and the first major application of solid state electronic systems in the telephone industry. It will result in faster and more flexible switching systems, which will provide many new services to the customer. The manpower impact will fall mainly on the central office craftsmen category, whose members will need training in electronics principles to complete nonroutine repairs. Some repair and maintenance operations, however, will require less skill than at present. The number of these workers will grow at a rate slower than that of total central office craftsmen as a direct result of electronic central office technology.

3. *Traffic service position* (TSP) will replace the cord switchboard for handling person-to-person, collect, credit card, and certain other types of toll and personal assistance calls. The TSP will reduce the amount of operator worktime per call by around 25 to 30 percent. The demands of TSP on the operator are those concerning assistance to the public. Projections indicate that by 1975, about 70 percent of operator assisted toll calls will be handled by TSP, and by 1985, the conversion from switchboards will be complete. The development will tend to reduce the number of telephone operators needed in the industry in relation to the number of operator assistance calls made.

4. *Automatic intercepting* may reduce the number of calls requiring an operator's assistance or the amount of time an operator spends on each intercept call. Under one such system, the amount of operator time spent on an intercept call is reduced by a minimum of one-third.

5. *Semiautomatic information service* will enable a telephone operator to provide a requested telephone number using an electronic processor instead of a telephone directory. This technology is still in an experimental stage and by 1975, if successful, will be in only limited use.

6. *Dedicated plant,* which provides for the permanent assignment of telephone lines from a central office to each actual and potential subscriber, will tend to reduce the need for cable and telephone installers, construction workers, and central office craftsmen. Introduction was started in 1962, and industry experts expect the use of dedicated plant to accelerate during the coming decade.

7. *Automatic data processing* is expected to be used to an increasing extent by the telephone industry during the coming decade. Increases will be especially significant among functions for which computers have been used to only a limited extent. The impact will fall primarily on clerical workers, although other occupation groups will also be affected.

In addition to these seven technologies, other technologies now in the research or development stage have been widely publicized, but industry experts do not expect these to be introduced on a wide scale until sometime after 1975. Four of these are picturephone service, pulsecode modulation, laser transmission, and helical waveguide transmission. Barriers to early widespread use of these innovations include technical breakthroughs that must be made, high costs, and the lack of mass markets necessary for the economic use of the technologies. In addition, the technical possibility exists that sometime beyond 1975 a semiautomatic information system with audio response will be introduced in large cities. However, it should be emphasized that such a system is not currently planned for introduction by any telephone company.

epilogue: tomorrow on the spaceship earth

INTRODUCTION

█ N an earlier selection the British economist Barbara Ward, borrowing
█ a phrase from Buckminster Fuller, remarked, "The most rational way
█ of considering the whole human race today is to see it as the ship's
crew of a single spaceship on which all of us, with a remarkable
combination of security and vulnerability, are making our pilgrimage
through infinity." This imaginative comparison gives a cosmic scale
to the present status of the human race. We are indeed the inhabitants of one planet, circling one star—our sun—which is only one of
a multitude of many stars in many galaxies. Put into other words, in
a somewhat mixed metaphor, we are like a ship careening in a vast
and stormy ocean and had best contrive a minimum of discipline for
the crew if we hope to continue the voyage through whatever millenia
are allotted to us.

The first selection in this final chapter reduces metaphors and
images to science-based epochs of life and time spans on the earth.
The selection is by the distinguished British biologist Julian Huxley.
Man, as *homo sapiens*, late descendant of earlier and less complex
species, passed through a period of perhaps 1 million years on our
planet before he entered the brief yesterday of recorded history. He
is now in the middle of what Huxley calls "his psycho-social phase."
It is a phase in which he has begun to take evolution into his own
hands, or in Huxley's words: [1] "Man's place and role in nature is now
clear. . . . Only man is capable of further real advance, of major
new evolutionary achievement. He and he alone is now responsible
for the future of this planet and its inhabitants." It is easy in the
present confused state of the world to be pessimistic about the crew
of the spaceship. As many have pointed out, it is within the crew's
power to take the Promethean fire they have stolen from the atom

[1] Julian Huxley, "The Future of Man," *Bulletin of the Atomic Scientists,* vol. 15,
no. 10, December, 1959.

and destroy themselves and the ship. Or Man may, as the "agent of evolution of this earth," realize richer and ampler possibilities and provide "greater fulfillment for more human beings."

The question that Huxley's essay leaves unanswered is this: How in the midst of an age of bewildering accelerations, and of wars and upheavals, can we see what steps to take in setting our course and in disciplining the ship's crew—or, in basic terms, creating common goals and a common culture for the planet?

The second selection by the anthropologist Margaret Mead offers at least one answer. It is based quite frankly on the premise that science and modern technology have already laid the basis for a single planetary civilization. We know that it is possible *technically* to reach the eyes and ears of every man and woman on earth. The obstacles that prevent such intercommunication between the peoples of the world are political, not technical as they were only a decade ago. It is sensible, therefore, to ask, as Margaret Mead does: What could be the basis for beginning to build a planet-wide culture in a world divided like ours by race, language, and tradition—not to mention the burning hostilities of past and present conflicts? Margaret Mead, tackling this question in the final paper of our series, names "The Future as the Basis for Establishing a Shared Culture."

Both papers, the one by Huxley and the one by Margaret Mead, deal, as does our opening chapter, in broad perspectives of time, space, and history. But in accord with the overriding approach of this book, the final selection spells out *practically* how to begin action *today*. In short, it names the first strategic steps toward creating such a "shared culture" and moving toward a planet-wide civilization of tomorrow.

BIBLIOGRAPHY

Bell, Daniel: "The Study of the Future," *The Public Interest,* Fall, 1965, pp. 119–130.

Calder, Nigel (ed.): *The World in 1984,* vol. 1, Penguin Books, Inc., Baltimore, Md., 1965.

Colm, Gerhard: *America, 1980: Man's Work and Who Will Do It in 1980,* National Planning Association, Washington, D.C., 1965.

de Chardin, Pierre Teilhard: *The Future of Man,* trans. from the French by Norman Denny, Harper & Row, Publishers, Incorporated, New York, 1964.

————: *Man's Place in Nature,* trans. from the French by René Hague, Harper & Row, Publishers, Incorported, New York, 1966.

Diebold, John: *Beyond Automation: Managerial Problems of an Exploding Technology,* McGraw-Hill Book Company, New York, 1964.

Mesthene, Emmanuel G.: "On Understanding Change: The Harvard University Program on Technology and Society," *Technology and Culture*, Spring, 1965.
Some New Technologies and Their Promise for the Life Sciences, The Life Sciences Panel, President's Science Advisory Committee, Washington, D.C., January, 1963.
Sullivan, Walter: *We Are Not Alone*, McGraw-Hill Book Company, New York, 1964; paperback, The New American Library, Signet Books, New York, 1966.

1.   A BIOLOGIST LOOKS AT MAN'S PAST AND FUTURE

From Julian Huxley, "The Future of Man," Bulletin of the Atomic Scientists, vol. 15, no. 10, December, 1959.[1]

Science provides increased control over the forces of nature, and so gives us the means of realizing our aims in practice. But it also provides fuller understanding and a truer vision of natural reality. This is in the long run the more important, for our vision of reality helps to determine our aims.

Humanist era

By discovering how to control intra-atomic energy, science has launched us into the Atomic Era, with all its attendant hopes and fears. But by giving us fuller comprehension of nature as a whole, it has set us on the threshold of a greater and more revolutionary age, which I will call the Humanist Era. It is the era in which the evolutionary process, in the person of man, is becoming purposeful and conscious of itself.

Today, for the first time in man's long and strange history, science is revealing a comprehensive picture of the natural universe and of man's place and role in it—in a word, of his destiny.

Thanks to the patient labors of thousands of scientists—biologists and astronomers, geologists and anthropologists, historians and physicists—the universe of nature in which man lives is now revealed as a single process of evolution, vast in its scales of space and time. Man is part of this universal evolving world-stuff. He is made of the same matter, operated by the same energy, as all the stars in all the galaxies.

Most of the universe is lifeless and its portentously slow evolution has produced only simple patterns of organization and little variety. But on our earth (and doubtless on other planetary specks) conditions permitted the appearance of the self-reproducing and self-varying type of matter we call life. With this, natural selection could begin to act and the biological phase of evolution was initiated.

---

[1] This article was originally delivered as one of a series of presentations on "The Future of Science" at the Day of Science at the Brussels Exposition.

Change becomes more rapid

Through natural selection, change—though still slow by human standards —could become much more rapid, and surprising new possibilities could be realized by the world-stuff. From the uniformity and relative simplicity of submicroscopic particles, there was generated the astonishingly rich variety of life, from sea-anemones and ants to cuttlefish and lions, from bacteria and toadstools to daisies and giant trees; the astonishingly high organization of a beehive or a bird; and most astonishing of all, the emergence of mind, living matter's increasing awarenes of itself and its surroundings.

But there are restrictions on what the blind forces of natural selection can accomplish. A few million years ago, it now appears, living matter had reached the limits of purely material and physiological achievement: only the possibilities of mind remained largely unrealized.

By exploiting the possibilities of mental advance, man became the latest dominant type of life, and initiated a new phase of evolution, the human or *psychosocial* phase, which operates much faster than biological evolution, and produces new kinds of results. Man's capacity for reason and imagination, coupled with his ability to communicate his ideas by means of the verbal symbols of language, provided him with a new mechanism for evolution, in the shape of cumulative tradition. Pre-human life depended only on the transmission of material particles, the genes in the chromosomes, from one generation to the next. But man can also transmit experience and its results. With this, mind as well as matter acquired the capacity for self-reproduction. Natural selection became subordinate to psychosocial selection, and the human phase of evolution could begin.

Science has also shown man his position in evolutionary time. Life has been evolving on the earth for over two thousand million years. Man-like creatures have existed for only about one million years, and human civilization, with all its achievements, for a bare five thousand. But evolving man can reasonably expect an immensity of future time—another two thousand million or more.

The psychosocial phase of evolution is thus in its infancy: man as dominant evolutionary type is absurdly young. I may adapt a simile of Sir James Jeans: If you represent the biological past by the height of St. Paul's cathedral, then the time since the beginning of agriculture and settled life equals one postage stamp flat on its top. And, unless man destroys himself by nuclear war or other follies, he can look forward to evolving through at the least the time-equivalent of another St. Paul's.

Role of man

Man's place and role in nature is now clear. No other animal can now hope to challenge his dominant position. Only man is capable of further real advance, of major new evolutionary achievement. He and he alone is now responsible for the future of this planet and its inhabitants. In him evolution is at last becoming conscious of itself; his mind is the agency by which evolution can reach new levels of achievement. Man's destiny, we now perceive, is to be the agent of evolution of this earth, realizing richer and ampler possibilities for the evolutionary process and providing greater fulfillment for more human beings.

The revelation of fulfillment as man's most ultimate and comprehensive aim provides us with a criterion for assessing our own psychosocial evolution. Already in its brief course psychosocial evolution has produced real progress—increased expectation of life, less disease, more knowledge, better communications, increase of mechanical power and decrease of physical drudgery, more varied interest, and enrichment through creative achievement—in buildings and works of art, in music and spectacle, in discovery and ideas. But it has also produced poverty and crime and slavery and organized cruelty, and its course has been accompanied by constant exploitation, indignity, and slaughter.

In this new perspective, we see that what Père Teilhard de Chardin called the process of hominization—the better realization of man's intrinsic possibilities—has barely begun. Few human beings realize more than a tiny fraction of their capacities, or enjoy any but the most meager degree of possible satisfaction and self-fulfillment. The majority are still illiterate, undernourished and short-lived, and their existence is full of misery and indignity. Nor have human societies realized more than a fraction of their capacities. They provide inadequate opportunities for expression and enjoyment, they still produce more ugliness than beauty, more frustration than fulfillment; they can easily lead to the dehumanization of life instead of its enrichment.

Science and the future

What has all this to do with science? I would say a great deal. First let us remember that most of what we can properly call advance in psychosocial evolution has stemmed from new or better organized knowledge, whether in the form of traditional skills, sudden inventions, new scientific discoveries, technological improvements, or new insights into old problems.

Science is a particularly efficient method for obtaining, organizing, and applying knowledge. Though modern science is barely three centuries old, it has led to the most unexpected discoveries and the most spectacular practical results. Scientific method involves controlled observation of fact, rational interpretation by way of hypothesis, the publication and discussion of procedures and results, and the further checking of hypothesis against fact. The use of scientific method has proved to be the best way of obtaining fuller intellectual understanding and increased practical control, in all fields where it has been tried. It leads inevitably toward more and fuller truth, to an increasing body of more firmly established factual knowledge, and more coherent principles and ideas.

Science is often used to denote only the natural sciences; but this is a false restriction, which springs from the historical fact that scientific method could be more readily applied to simpler subjects, and so first became effectively applied in non-human fields. But it can be applied to all natural phenomena, however complex, provided that we take account of their special peculiarities and go to the trouble of devising appropriate methods for dealing with them.

Psychosocial science

Today, the time has come to apply scientific method to man and all his works. We have made a piecemeal beginning, with psychology, economics, anthropology, linguistics, social science, and so forth. But we need a comprehensive approach to the human field as a whole. We already have physical science, chemical science, and biological science: to deal with man as a natural phenomenon, we must develop psychosocial science.

The primary job of psychosocial science will be to describe and analyze the course and mechanism of psychosocial evolution in scientific terms. It will also include a science of human possibilities. What are the possibilities of man and his nature, individually and collectively? How is their realization helped or hindered by different types of psychosocial environment? How can we estimate human fulfillment; in what ways and to what extent can it be promoted by changes in psychosocial organization? In particular, such a science will involve a radical re-thinking of man's systems of education, their aims, content, and techniques.

The value of such an approach and such criteria is clear when we look at concrete problems. Two new challenges have recently appeared on the evolutionary scene—the threat of over-population and the promise of excess leisure. The population problem obstinately resists solution in terms of power-politics, economics, or religion, but the criterion of greater fulfillment immediately lights it up and indicates the general lines of the policy we should pursue in reconciling quantity with quality of human life.

The new possibilities opened up by science are exerting two effects on psychosocial evolution. Increased scientific control over the forces of nature has produced a flood of new conveniences and comforts, and has led directly to death-control and the recent alarming increase of human numbers. But the knowledge that healthier and longer life is possible, and that technology can provide higher standards of living and enjoyment, has changed the attitude of the vast underprivileged majority: they are demanding that the new possibilities shall be more abundantly realized.

Limited possibilities

The next step must be to grasp the fact that the quantitative possibilities are not unlimited. Unless present-day man controls the exploitation of natural resources, he will impoverish his descendants; unless he supplements death-control with birth-control, he will become the cancer of the planet, ruining his earthly habitation and himself with it.

The leisure problem is equally fundamental. Having to decide what we shall do with our leisure is inevitably forcing us to re-examine the purpose of human existence, and to ask what fulfillment really means. This, I repeat, involves a comprehensive survey of human possibilities and the methods of realizing them; it also implies a survey of the obstacles to their realization.

Let me summarize the new picture of human destiny from a slightly different angle.

Man is the latest dominant type of life, but he is also a very imperfect kind of being. He is equipped with a modicum of intelligence, but also with an array of conflicting passions and desires. He can be reasonable but is often extremely stupid. He has impulses to sympathy and love, but also to cruelty and hatred. He is capable of moral action but also has inevitable capacities for sin and error.

As a result, the course of psychosocial evolution has been erratic, wasteful, and full of imperfection. It is easy to take a pessimistic view of man's history in general, and of his present situation in particular, where force and fear have become magnified on a gigantic scale.

Hopeful process

But when we survey the process as a whole, it looks more hopeful. During its course, there has been progress. Progress has always been the result of the discovery, dissemination, or application of human knowledge, and human knowledge has shown a cumulative increase. Furthermore, the erratic course of past psychosocial evolution was largely due to man as a species being divided against himself, and not having discovered any single overriding aim.

There is now a dramatic change in process. The human world has become inextricably interlocked with itself; the separate parts of the psychosocial process are being forced to converge toward some sort of organized unity. We are at last able and indeed compelled to think in terms of a single aim for mankind, while our increasing knowledge is enabling us to define our aim in relation to reality instead of in terms of wish-fulfillment: our knowledge of our imperfections and limitations is helping to define the possibilities of our improvement.

This marks a critical point in history. We have discovered psychosocial evolution as a complex but natural phenomenon, to be explored and controlled like other natural phenomena. Up till now, it has operated in erratic and often undesirable fashion, with self-contradictory aims. We now see that it could be transformed into an orderly mechanism for securing desirable results.

The idea of greater fulfillment for all mankind could become a powerful motive force, capable of influencing the direction of future evolution, and of overriding the more obvious motives of immediate personal or national self-interest. But it can only do so if it and its implications are properly understood, and made comprehensible to the bulk of men, all over the world. For this we need not only an extension of science but a reorientation of education; not only more knowledge, but also a better expression and a wider dissemination of ideas.

We must not imagine that the fuller realization of possibilities will be accomplished without effort, conflict, or suffering. This is inherent in the nature of man and of the psychosocial process: but so is hope.

The individual human brain and mind is the most complicated and highly organized piece of machinery that has ever existed on this earth. So-called electronic brains can perform extraordinary tasks with superhuman rapidity: but they have to be given their instructions by men. The human organism can give instructions to itself; and can perform tasks outside the range of any inanimate machine. Though at the outset it is a feeble instrument equipped with conflicting tendencies, it can in the course of its development achieve a high degree of integration and performance.

How shall we use it?

It is up to us to make the best use of this marvellous piece of living machinery. Instead of taking it for granted, or ignorantly abusing it, we must cherish it, try to understand its development, and explore its capacities.

The collective human organism, embodied in the psychosocial process, is an equally extraordinary piece of machinery. It is the mechanism for realizing human destiny. It can discover new aims for itself, and devise new methods for realizing them; but it is still primitive and inefficient. It is up to us to improve it, as we have improved our inanimate machines.

Our ignorance about its potentialities is profound; therefore our immediate task is to understand the first principles of its operation, and think out their consequences.

Thus the new vision we owe to science is one of real though tempered optimism. It gives us a measure of significance and rational hope in a world which appeared irrational and meaningless. It shows us man's place and role in the universe. He is the earth's reservoir of evolutionary possibility; the servant of evolution, but at the same time its youthful master. His destiny is to pursue greater fulfillment through a better ordering of the psychosocial process. That is his extraordinary privilege, and also his supreme duty.

Our new vision assures us that human life could gradually be transformed from a competitive struggle against blind fate into a great collective enterprise, consciously undertaken. We see that enterprise as one for greater fulfillment through the better realization of human possibilities.

It is for us to accept this new revelation given us by science, examine it, and explore all its implications, secure in the knowledge that ideas help to determine events, that more understanding leads to more appropriate action, that scientific truth is an indispensable weapon against stupidity and wickedness and the other enemies of fulfillment, and true vision the parent of progress.

2.   FIRST STEPS TOWARD A COMMON WORLD CULTURE

From Margaret Mead, "The Future as the Basis for Establishing a Shared Culture," Daedalus, published by the American Academy of Social Sciences, Cambridge, Mass., Winter, 1965, pp. 142–154.

I would propose that we consider the future as the appropriate setting for our shared world-wide culture, for the future is least compromised by partial and discrepant views. And I would choose the near future over the far future, so as to avoid as completely as possible new confusions based on partial but avowedly totalistic projections born of the ideologies of certainty, like Marxism and Leninism, or the recurrent scientific dogmatisms about the possibilities of space travel, the state of the atmosphere, or the appearance of new mutations. But men's divergent dreams of eternity might be left undisturbed, providing they did not include some immediate apocalyptic moment for the destruction of the world.

Looking toward the future, we would start to build from the known. In many cases, of course, this would be knowledge very newly attained. What we would build on, then, would be the known attributes of the universe, our solar system, and the place of our earth within this system;

the known processes of our present knowledge, from which we shall proceed to learn more; the known treasures of man's plastic and graphic genius as a basis for experience out of which future artists may paint and carve, musicians compose, and poets speak; the known state of instrumentation, including both the kinds of instrumentation which have already been developed (for example, communication satellites) and those which are ready to be developed; the known numbers of human beings, speaking a known number of languages, and living in lands with known amounts of fertile soil, fresh water, and irreplaceable natural resources; the known forms of organizing men into functioning groups; and the known state of modern weaponry, with its known capacity to destroy all life.

These various kinds of knowledge would be viewed as beginnings, instead of as ends—as young, growing forms of knowledge, instead of as finished products to be catalogued, diagrammed, and preserved in the pages of encyclopedias. All statements would take the form: "We know that there are at least X number of stars" (or people in Asia, or developed forms of transportation, or forms of political organization). Each such statement would be phrased as a starting point—a point from which to move onward. In this sense, the great artistic productions of all civilizations could be included, not as the splendid fruit of one or another civilization, but on new terms, as points of departure for the imagination.

The frenetic, foolhardy shipping of original works of art around the world in ships and planes, however fragile they may be, can be looked upon as a precursor of this kind of change—as tales of flying saucers preceded man's first actual ventures into space. It is as if we already dimly recognized that if we are to survive, we must share all we have, at whatever cost, so that men everywhere can move toward some as yet undefined taking-off point into the future.

But if we can achieve a new kind of consciousness of what we are aiming at, we do not need actually to move these priceless objects as if they were were figures in a dream. We can, instead, take thought how, with our modern techniques, we can make the whole of an art style available, not merely single, symbolic examples, torn from their settings. Young painters and poets and musicians, dancers and architects can, today, be given access to all that is known about color and form, perspective and rhythm, technique and the development of style, the relationships of form and style and material, and the interrelationships of art forms as these have been developed in some place, at some time. We have all the necessary techniques to do this. We can photograph in color, train magnifying cameras on the inaccessible details of domes and towers, record a poet reciting his own poetry, film an artist as he paints, and use film and sound to transport people from any one part to any other part of the world to participate in the uncovering of an ancient site or the first viewing of a new dance form. We can, in fact, come out of the "manuscript stage" for all the arts, for process as well as product, and make the whole available simultaneously to a young generation so they can move ahead together and congruently into the future. Given access to the range of the world's art, young artists can see in a new light those special activities and art objects to which they themselves are immediately related, wherever they are.

Working always within the modest limits of one generation—the next twenty-five years—and without tempting the massive consequences of miscalculation, we can include the known aspects of the universe in which our continuing experimental ventures into space will be conducted and the principles, the tools, and the materials with which these ventures are beginning. Children all over the world can be given accurate, tangible models of what we now know about the solar system, models of the earth, showing how it is affected by the large scale patterning of weather, and models showing how life on earth may be affected by events in the solar system and beyond. Presented with a clear sense of the expanding limits of our knowledge, models such as these would prepare children everywhere to participate in discoveries we know must come and to anticipate new aspects of what is as yet unknown.

Within these same limits, we can bring together our existing knowledge of the world's multitudes—beginning with those who are living now and moving out toward those who will be living twenty-five years from now. The world is well mapped, and we know, within a few millions, how many people there are, where they are, and who they are. We know—or have the means of knowing—a great deal about the world's peoples. We know about the world's food supplies and can relate our knowledge to the state of those who have been well nourished and those who have been poorly fed. We know about the world's health and can relate our knowledge to the state of those who have been exposed to ancient plagues and those who are exposed to "modern" ambiguous viruses. We can picture the ways of living of those who, as children, were reared in tents, in wattle and daub houses, in houses made of mud bricks, in tenements and apartment houses, in peasant houses that have survived unchanged through hundreds of years of occupancy and in the new small houses of modern suburbs, in the anonymity of urban housing, in isolated villages, and in the crowded shacks of refugee settlements. We can define the kinds of societies, all of them contemporary, in which human loyalties are restricted to a few hundred persons, all of them known to one another, and others in which essential loyalties are expanded to include thousands or millions or even hundreds of millions of persons, only a few of them known to one another face to face. In the past we could, at best, give children some idea of the world's multitudes through books, printed words and meager illustrations. Today we have the resources to give children everywhere living experience of the whole contemporary world. And every child, everywhere in the world, can start with that knowledge and grow into its complexity. In this way, plans for population control, flood control, control of man's inroads on nature, plans for protecting human health and for developing a world food supply, and plans for sharing a world communication system can all become plans in which citizens participate in informed decisions.

None of this knowledge will in any sense be ultimate. We do not know what form knowledge itself will take twenty-five years from now, but we do know what its sources must be in present knowledge and, ordering what we now know, we can create a ground plan for the future on which all the peoples of the earth can build.

Because it must be learned by very young children and by the children of very simple parents, this body of knowledge and experience must be expressed in clear and simple terms, using every graphic device available to us and relying more on models than on words, for in many languages appropriate words are lacking. The newer and fresher the forms of presentation are, the greater will be the possibility of success, for, as in the new mathematics teaching, all teachers—those coming out of old traditions and having long experience with special conventions and those newly aware of the possibilities of formal teaching—will have to learn what they are to teach as something new. Furthermore, parents will be caught up in the process, in one sense as the pupils of their children, discovering that they can reorder their own knowledge and keep the pace, and in another sense as supplementary teachers, widening the scope of teaching and learning. Knowledge arranged for comprehensibility by a young child is knowledge accessible to all, and the task of arranging it will necessarily fall upon the clearest minds in every field of the humanities, the sciences, the arts, engineering, and politics.

There is, however, one very immediate question. How are we to meet the problem of shared contribution? How are we to ensure that this corpus is not in the end a simplified version of modern western—essentially Euro-American—scientific and philosophic thought and of art forms and processes, however widely selected, interpreted within the western tradition? Is there any endeavor which can draw on the capacities not only of those who are specially trained but also those with untapped resources—the uneducated in Euro-American countries and the adult and wise in old, exotic cultures and newly emerging ones?

A first answer can be found, I think, in activities in which every country can have a stake and persons of every age and level of sophistication can take part. One such activity would be the fashioning of a new set of communication devices—like the visual devices used by very simple peoples to construct messages or to guide travelers on their way, but now raised to the level of world-wide intelligibility.

In recent years there has been extensive discussion of the need for a systematic development of what are now called *glyphs*, that is, graphic representations, each of which stands for an idea: male, female, water, poison, danger, stop, go, etc. Hundreds of glyphs are used in different parts of the world—as road signs, for example—but too often with ambiguous or contradictory meanings as one moves from one region to another. What is needed, internationally, is a set of glyphs which does not refer to any single phonological system or to any specific cultural system of images but will, instead, form a system of visual signs with universally recognized referents. But up to the present no sustained effort has been made to explore the minimum number that would be needed or to make a selection that would carry clear and unequivocal meaning for the peoples of the world, speaking all languages, living in all climates, and exposed to very different symbol systems. A project for the exploration of glyph forms and for experimentation with the adequacy of different forms has been authorized by the United Nations Committee for International Cooperation Year (1965—the twentieth anniversary of the founding of the United Nations). This is designed as an activity in which adults and children, artists and engineers, logicians and semanticists, linguists and historians—all those, in fact, who have an interest in doing so—can take part. For the wider the range of persons and the larger the number of cultures included in this exploration, the richer and the more fully representative will be the harvest form which a selection of glyphs can be made for international use.

Since meaning is associated with each glyph as a unit and glyphs cannot be combined syntactically, they can be used by the speakers of any language. But considerable experimentation will be necessary to avoid ambiguity which may lead to confusion or the adoption of forms which are already culturally loaded. The variety of meanings which may already be associated with certain forms can be illustrated by the sign + (which, in different connections, can be the sign for addition or indicate a positive number, can stand for "north" or indicate a crossroad, and, very slightly modified, can indicate a deceased person in a genealogy, a specifically Christian derivation, or stand for the Christian sign of the cross) or the sign ○ (which, in different connections, may stand for circumference or for 360°, for the full moon, for an annual plant, for degrees of arc or temperature, for an individual, especially female, organism, and, very slightly modified, can stand for zero or, in our alphabet, the letter O).

Work on glyphs can lead to work on other forms of international communication. In an interconnected world we shall need a world language —a second language which could be learned by every people but which would in no sense replace their native tongue. Contemporary studies of natural languages have increased our understanding of the reasons why consciously constructed languages do not serve the very complex purposes of general communication. Most important is the fact that an artificial language, lacking the imprint of many different kinds of minds and differently organized capacities for response, lacks the redundancy necessary in a language all human beings can learn.

Without making any premature choice, we can state some of the criteria for such a secondary world language. It must be a natural language, chosen from among known living languages, but not from among those which are, today, politically controversial. Many nations would have to contribute to the final choice, but this choice would depend also on the outcome of systematic experiments with children's speech, machine simulation, experiments with mechanical translation, and so on. In addition, it would be essential to consider certain characteristics related to the current historical situation. Politically, it should be the language of a state too small to threaten other states. In order to allow for a rapid development of diverse written styles, it must be a language with a long tradition of use in written form. To permit rapid learning, it must be a language whose phonetic system can be easily learned by speakers of other languages, and one which can be easily rendered into a phonetic script and translated without special difficulty into existing traditional scripts. It should come from the kind of population in which there is a wide diversity of roles and occupations and among whom a large number of teachers can be found, some of whom are already familiar with one or another of the great widespread languages of the world. Using modern methods of language teaching, the task of creating a world-wide body of readers and speakers could be accomplished within five years and the language itself would change in the process of this world-wide learning.

Once a secondary world language is chosen, the body of knowledge with which we shall start the next twenty-five years can be translated into it from preliminary statements in the great languages, taking the stamp of these languages as divergent subtleties of thought, present in one language and absent in another, are channeled in and new vocabulary is created to deal with new ideas.

One important effect of a secondary world language would be to protect the more localized languages from being swamped by those few which are rapidly spreading over the world. Plans have been advanced to make possible the learning and use of any one of the five or seven most widespread languages as a second language. Fully implemented, this would divide the world community into two classes of citizens—those for whom one of these languages was a mother tongue and those for whom it was a second language—and it would exacerbate already existing problems arising from differences in the quality of communication— rapid and idiomatic among native speakers and slower, more formal, and less spontaneous among those who have learned English, French, or Russian later. In contrast, one shared second language, used on a worldwide scale, would tend to equalize the quality of world communication and, at the same time, would protect the local diversity of all other languages.

Another important aspect of a shared culture would be the articulate inclusion of the experience of those who travel to study, work, explore, or enjoy other countries. One of the most intractable elements in our present isolating cultures is the interlocking of a landscape—a landscape with mountains or a desert, jungle or tundra, rushing cataracts or slow flowing rivers, arched over by a sky in which the Dipper or the Southern Cross dominates—and a view of man. The beauty of face and movement of those who have never left their mountains or their island is partly the imprint on the human form of a complex relationship to the scale and the proportions, the seasonal rhythms and the natural style of one special part of the world. The experiences of those who have been bred to one physical environment cannot be patched together like the pieces of a patchwork quilt. But we can build on the acute and vivid experiences of those who, reared in a culture which has deeply incorporated its environment, respond intensely to some newly discovered environment—the response of the countryman to the city, the response of the city dweller to open country, the response of the immigrant to the sweep of an untouched landscape and of the traveler to a sudden vista into the past of a whole people. In the past, the visual impact of discovery was recorded retrospectively in painting and in literature. Today, films can record the more immediate response of the observer, looking with fresh eyes at the world of the nomadic Bushman or the people beneath the mountain wall of New Guinea, at the palaces in Crete or the summer palace in Peking.

We can give children a sense of movement, actually experienced or experienced only in some leap of the imagination. In the next twenty-five years we shall certainly not explore deep space, but the experience of movement can link a generation in a common sense of anticipation. As a beginning, we can give children a sense of different actual relationships to the physical environments of the whole earth, made articulate through the recorded responses of those who have moved from one environment to another. Through art, music, and film we can give children access to the ways others have experienced their own green valleys and other valleys, also green. We can develop in small children the capacity to wonder and to look through other eyes at the familiar fir trees rimming their horizon or the sea breaking on their island's shore.

In the past, these have been the experiences of those who could afford to travel and those who had access, through the arts, to the perceptions of a poet like Wordsworth in *The Prelude,* or a young scientist like Darwin on his Pacific voyage, or painters like Catlin or Gauguin. With today's technology, these need no longer be the special experiences of the priv-ileged and the educated elite. The spur to action may be the desire for literacy in the emerging nations or a new concern for the culturally deprived in older industrialized countries. And quite different styles of motivation can give urgency to the effort to bring the experience of some to bear on the experience of all.

Looking to the future, the immediacy of motivation is itself part of the experience. It may be an assertive desire to throw off a colonial past or a remorseful attempt to atone for long neglect. It may be the ecumenical spirit in which the Pope can say: "No pilgrim, no matter how far, reli-giously and geographically, may be the country from which he comes, will be any longer a stranger to this Rome. . . ."[1] It may be the belief that it is possible to remake a society, as when Martin Luther King said:

> *I have a dream today . . . I have a dream that one day every valley shall be exalted, every hill and mountain shall be made low. The rough places will be made plain, and the crooked places will be made straight. And the glory of the Lord shall be revealed, and all flesh shall see it to-gether. This is our hope. This is the faith that I go back to the South with. With this faith we will be able to hew out of the mountain of despair a stone of hope.*[2]

Or it may be the belief, expressed by U Thant, that men can work toward a world society:

> *Let us look inward for a moment on this Human Rights Day, and recog-nize that no one, no individual, no nation, and indeed no ideology has a monopoly of rightness, freedom or dignity. And let us translate this recog-nition into action so as to sustain the fullness and freedom of simple human relations leading to ever widening areas of understanding and agreement. Let us, on this day, echo the wish which Rabindranath Tagore stated in these memorable words, so that our world may be truly a world*

Where the mind is without fear and the head is held high;
Where knowledge is free;

[1] *The New York Times,* May 18, 1964.
[2] From the speech by the Rev. Martin Luther King at the March on Washington, *New York Post Magazine,* September 1, 1963, p. 5.

Where the world has not been broken up into fragments
  by narrow domestic walls;
Where words come out of the depth of truth;
Where tireless striving stretches its arms toward
  perfection. . . .[3]

There are also other ways in which experience can more consciously
be brought to bear in developing a shared understanding. All traditions,
developing slowly over centuries, are shaped by the biological nature of
man—the differences in temperament and constitution among men and
the processes of maturation, parenthood, and aging which are essential
parts of our humanity. The conscious inclusion of the whole life process
in our thinking can, in turn, alter the learning process, which in a changing world has become deeply disruptive as each elder generation has
been left behind while the next has been taught an imperfect version of
the new. One effect of this has been to alienate and undermine the faith
of parents and grandparents as they have seen their children's minds
moving away from them and as their own beliefs, unshared, have become
inflexible and distorted.

The policy in most of today's world is to educate the next—the new—
generation, setting aside the older generation in the mistaken hope that,
as older men and women are passed over, their outmoded forms of knowledge will do no harm. Instead, we pay a double price in the alienation of
the new generation from their earliest and deepest experiences as little
children and in the blocking of constructive change in the world by an
older generation who still exercise actual power—hoarding some resources and wasting others, building to an outmoded scale, voting
against measures the necessity of which is not understood, supporting
reactionary leaders, and driving an equally inflexible opposition toward
violence. Yet this lamentable outcome is unnecessary, as the generation
break itself is unnecessary.

In the past the transmission of the whole body of knowledge within a
slowly changing society has provided for continuity. Today we need to
create an educational style which will provide for continuity and open-
ness even within rapid change. Essentially this means an educational
style in which members of different generations are involved in the process of learning. One way of assuring this is through a kind of education
in which new things are taught to mothers and young children together.
The mothers, however schooled, usually are less affected by contemporary
styles of education than the fathers. In some countries they have had no
schooling; in others, girls are warned away from science and mathematics

---

[3] From the Human Rights Day Message by (then) Acting Secretary-General U
Thant, December 8, 1961 (United Nations Press Release SG/1078 HRD/11 [Decem-
ber 6, 1961]).

or even from looking at the stars. So they come to the task of rearing their small children fresher than those who have been trained to teach or to administer. Child rearing, in the past fifty years, has been presented as almost entirely a matter of molding the emotional life of the child, modulating the effects of demands for cleanliness and obedience to permit more spontaneity, and of preserving an environment in which there is good nutrition and low infection danger. At the same time, we have taken out of the hands of mothers the *education* even of young children. So we have no existing rationale in which mother, child, and teacher are related within the learning process. What we need now, in every part of the world, is a new kind of school for mothers and little children in which mothers learn to teach children what neither the mothers nor the children know.

At the same time, grandparents who, perforce, have learned a great deal about the world which has gone whirling past them and in which, however outmoded they are declared to be, they have had to maintain themselves, can be brought back into the teaching process. Where patience, experience, and wisdom are part of what must be incorporated, they have a special contribution to make. Mothers of young children, lacking a fixed relationship to the growing body of knowledge about the world, provide freshness of approach; but older people embody the experience that can be transformed into later learning. The meticulous respect for materials, coming from long experience with hand work, the exacting attention to detail, coming from work with a whole object rather than some incomplete part, and the patient acceptance of the nature of a task have a continuing relevance to work, whatever it may be. So also, the disciplined experience of working with human beings can be transformed to fit the new situations which arise when democracy replaces hierarchy and the discipline of political parties that of the clan and the tribe.

We have been living through a period in which the old have been recklessly discarded and disallowed, and this very disallowance resonates —as a way of life which has been repressed rather than transformed— in the movements of unaccountably stubborn reaction from which no civilization in our present world is exempt. Grandparents and great-grandparents—even those who are driven from their land to die in concentration camps and those who voluntarily settle themselves in modern, comfortable Golden Age clubs—live on in the conceptions of the children whose parents' lives they shaped. Given an opportunity to participate meaningfully in new knowledge, new skills, and new styles of life, the elderly can embody the changing world in such a way that their grandchildren—and all children of the youngest generation—are given a mandate to be part of the new and yet maintain human ties with the past which, however phrased, is part of our humanity. The more rapid the rate of change and the newer the corpus of knowledge which the world may come to share, the more urgently necessary it is to include the old—to transform our conception of the whole process of aging so their wisdom and experience can be assets in our new relation to the future.

Then we may ask, are such plans as these sufficiently open ended? In seeking to make equally available to the peoples of the world newly organized ways of moving into the immediate future, in a universe in which our knowledge is rapidly expanding, there is always the danger that the idea of a shared body of knowledge may be transformed into some kind of universal blueprint. In allowing this to happen we would, of course, defeat our own purpose. The danger is acute enough so that we must build a continuing wariness and questioning into the planning itself; otherwise even the best plan may result in a closed instead of an open ended system.

This means that we must be open ended in our planning as well as in our plans, recognizing that this will involve certain kinds of conscious restriction as well as conscious questioning. For example, we must insist that a world language be kept as a second language, resolutely refusing to consider it as a first language, in order to protect and assure the diversity of thought which accompanies the use of different mother tongues. We should also guard against a too early learning of the world language, so that the language of infancy—which also becomes the language of love and poetry and religion—may be protected against acquiring a too common stamp. We must insist on the inclusion of peoples from all over the world in any specific piece of planning—as in the development of an international system of glyphs—as a way of assuring a growing and an unpredictable corpus. We must be willing to forego, in large-scale planning, some kinds of apparent efficiency. If we are willing, instead, to include numerous steps and to conceive of each step somewhat differently, we are more likely, in the end, to develop new interrelationships, unforeseeable at any early stage. A more conscious inclusion of women and of the grandparental generation in learning and teaching will carry with it the extraordinary differences in existing interrelations between the minds and in the understanding of the two sexes and different age groups.

We can also take advantage of what has been learned through the use of cybernetic models, and equip this whole forward movement of culture which we are launching with a system of multiple self-corrective devices. For example, criteria could be established for reviewing the kinds of divergences that were occurring in vocabulary and conceptualizations as an idea fanned out around the world. Similarly, the rate and type of incorporation of special developments in particular parts of the world could be monitored, and cases of dilution or distortion examined and corrected. Overemphasis on one part of knowledge, on one sensory modality, on the shells men live in rather than the life they live there, on sanitation rather than beauty, on length of life rather than quality of life lived, could be listened for and watched for, and corrective measures taken speedily.

A special area of concern would be intercommunication among all those whose specializations tend to isolate them from one another, scientist from administrator, poet from statesman, citizen voter from the highly skilled specialist who must carry out his mandate using calculations which the voter cannot make, but within a system of values clearly enough stated so that both may share them. By attending to the origins of some new communication—whether a political, a technical, or an artistic innovation—the functioning of the communication process could be monitored. Special sensing organs could be established which would observe, record, and correct so that what otherwise might become a blundering, linear, and unmanageable avalanche could be shaped into a process delicately responsive to change in itself.

But always the surest guarantee of change and growth is the inclusion of living persons in every stage of an activity. Their lives, their experience, and their continuing response—even their resistances— infuse with life any plan which, if living participants are excluded, lies on the drawing board and loses its reality. Plans for the future can become old before they are lived, but the future itself is always newborn and, like any newborn thing, is open to every kind of living experience.

index of contributors

subject index